THREE MUSKETEERS   1945-46

NORTHERN TROIKA   1945-46

SOUTHERN TRIO   1944-46

SRI

The Founding Years

SRI

The Founding Years

A SIGNIFICANT STEP
AT THE
GOLDEN TIME

By

Weldon B. Gibson

Publishing Services Center   Los Altos, California

Headquarters in Stanford Village
1947-1958

Library of Congress Cataloging in Publication Data

Gibson, Weldon B   1917-
  SRI, the founding years.

  1. Stanford Research Institute.   I.   Title.
T178.S754G5   607'.20794'74   79-23783
ISBN 0-913232-80-7

Publishing Services Center titles are distributed worldwide by
William Kaufmann, Inc., One First Street, Los Altos, CA 94022

Printed in the United States of America

Table of Contents

Cover Design — The first SRI colophon, See page 102

SRI

STANFORD RESEARCH INSTITUTE

Guiding Themes
in
The Founding Years

IN CONCEPT   ----------   VISION

IN ORIGIN   ----------   INSPIRATION

IN CREATION   ----------   PERSEVERANCE

IN PURPOSE   ----------   DEDICATION

HIGHEST HONOR

ROBERT E. SWAIN — Proponent
ALVIN C. EURICH — Architect
ATHOLL MCBEAN — Founder

SRI and Stanford

Stanford Research Institute, also known as SRI, was founded in 1946 by the Trustees of Stanford University. The basic idea originated within the University in the 1920s. However, the principal Founding Years are 1939 and then 1944-1946.

The subtitle of this book, A Significant Step at the Golden Time, arises from two separate sources — a Stanford Committee report in 1945 and Dr. Donald B. Tresidder's comments at SRI's first board meeting in early 1947. Tresidder was Stanford's president and first SRI chairman.

During its first two and a half decades, SRI was, in effect, a subsidiary, nonprofit corporation of the University. By mutual agreement, the two institutions separated in 1970 but with no change in SRI's structure or purposes. Its name was changed to SRI International in 1977, but the acronym, SRI, is still widely used around the world.

This book deals with events leading to SRI's formation in 1946 and with its operations through 1948. The names Stanford Research Institute, SRI, and the Institute are used interchangeably — as they were during most of the Founding Years.

Public Service*

- *Promote* the educational purposes of Stanford University through research in the physical, life and social sciences, engineering and the mechanic arts.

- *Extend* scientific knowledge in the several pursuits and professions of life and assist Stanford University in extending learning and knowledge.

- *Apply* science in developing commerce, trade and industry and in improving the general standard of living and peace and prosperity of mankind.

- *Publish* research results deemed to be of general public interest.

---

*The essence of SRI's basic purposes. See also page 200.

Appreciation

AS THE AUTHOR OF THIS BOOK about the origins of SRI, I have an overpowering urge to begin with a note of high appreciation. It centers on SRI and my good fortune.

My professional life has been — and continues to be — a very happy one indeed. Here are the circumstances as I see them:

- A central position in SRI since its formative days
- Ample opportunities to pursue professional interests
- Participation in building an exciting and useful institution
- Living in a wonderful community and pleasant setting
- Possibilities for service to a great university
- Work in and with virtually all the nations
- Associations with able people at home and abroad
- Avenues for contributions to world economic progress.

Thus, it has been — and still is — my lot to live where I like to live, work where I want most to work, pursue professional paths that interest me greatly, and be among able and interesting people.

All this has been — and remains — a lucky set of circumstances. Perhaps, then, it is wholly understandable why I am so dedicated to SRI and in a broader way to Stanford University.

My whole professional life is wrapped up in — and with — SRI. I have seen it grow from a concept to a worldwide institution. Certainly, I am most grateful for the opportunity that came my way.

Many thousands of people have come and gone at SRI over the yeas. Very few remain from the early days; two continue from the first year; only one dates from the very beginning.

As the years go by, there may be more and more interest in SRI's origin. This is why I have attempted to present the story. The book is written largely for an "inside audience" and not particularly for the public or the profession. But, hopefully, the account — even with all its details — may be of some interest beyond SRI circles.

I am indebted to many people who have given a hand along the way. Dr. Alvin C. Eurich, vice president of Stanford University during our Founding Years, read all the chapters, added numerous facts, and helped on interpretations about events of the times. Dr. Philip Leighton and Dr. Maurice Nelles, members of early groups associated with SRI's formation, did the same on portions of the history in which they were involved. Morris M. Doyle, an SRI director and a principal author of the Institute's charter, reviewed the book in its entirety and made helpful comments.

Others involved in one way or another in SRI's emergence were consulted at various points. The list includes, for example, Donald J. Russell (a founding director), Dr. Frederick Terman (a Stanford faculty member, later University Provost, and then an SRI director), as well as William Rand and Dr. Carsten Steffens from the Institute's early staff.

Although Dr. J. E. Wallace Sterling, Stanford's president and SRI chairman for many years beginning in 1949, was not directly involved during the Founding Years, he graciously reviewed every chapter and made many suggestions.

Many others within SRI and elsewhere have been most helpful. They include my wife, Helen (the watercolors), Ronald J. Moore (the sketches), Wilbur W. Ashworth (graphic design), and my secretaries, Carolyn Mulkeen and Buelah Madsen.

For all this help in many ways, I am most grateful. They helped make the whole effort possible.

WELDON B. GIBSON

Menlo Park, California - 1979

Significant Step

"... the Stanford Research Institute has been founded to provide a center for sponsored industrial research in the West ..."

ANNUAL REPORT OF THE PRESIDENT
Stanford University
Academic Year 1946-47

Long Service

D R. WELDON B. GIBSON has been deeply involved with SRI since its beginning in 1946. No one has more percipient knowledge about SRI, or has been more committed to its welfare, than the author of this book on its founding. His commitment also includes a great and continuing dedication to Stanford University.

Although involved in the events that led to the creation of SRI, I was nevertheless astonished in reading the manuscript of this book to learn many things about which I had no knowledge. Based on firsthand involvement since the earliest days and close associations over the years with all the principals, Dr. Gibson is uniquely qualified to tell the story of SRI's formative years.

Our author — Hoot Gibson as he has long been known — joined SRI, in effect, even before it was incorporated. He has since been at the center of its operations, and has played a major role in making SRI a great international institution.

He became associate director of the Institute in 1955, its first vice president in 1959, executive vice president in 1960, and then, for a few years was also president of SRI International — the Institute's international arm until the entire organization was renamed SRI International in May 1977. He continues as executive vice president — still at the heart of SRI's worldwide operations.

This history of SRI's Founding Years ends in 1948, but the subsequent growth and success of the institution are well and widely known. Hoot's leadership role in helping build SRI to what it is today has many facets — as suggested by the following accomplishments.

- Founded and then developed its economics, management and social sciences program until 1956, by which time it had become one of the largest research groups of its kind in the world;

- Instigated and led the growth of its international activities, especially during the 1950s and 1960s, to an involvement in scores of countries around the world;

- Created and managed implementing plans that brought its first permanent buildings into being in the late 1950s and early 1960s;

- Initiated and directed the SRI-sponsored International Industrial Conferences, major gatherings of world business leaders held in San Francisco every four years since 1957;

- Conceived and developed the SRI International Associates Plan, including the elite of the international business community and many widely-appreciated, prestigious meetings, devoted to world business, on all the continents;

---

*By Morris M. Doyle. (As counsel to Stanford University, Mr. Doyle was instrumental in SRI's formation in 1946. He was elected director emeritus in 1978. See chapters on The Founding Charter and The Policymakers.)

- Organized and led — with strong backing by several fellow directors (notably S. D. Bechtel, Sr.) — a worldwide effort that resulted in construction and furnishing of SRI's Central International Building in the late 1960s;
- Generated and directed the SRI-Moscow Conference in 1974, a major international conclave of western business executives and high Soviet officials.

An interesting aspect of these activities — aside from the permanent building program — is that *no* similar large-scale initiatives had ever been undertaken by a research institute of SRI's type. More recently, at the invitation of the People's Republic of China, Dr. Gibson led an industrial research mission to that country.

In addition to the above, Hoot is international director of the Pacific Basin Economic Council, executive head of the Japan-California Association, a trustee or equivalent of three universities in the United States and abroad, chairman of an educational foundation, the holder of two foreign government awards and a member of many international professional and honor societies. He has co-authored three books on world economic geography and countless articles on international affairs. He is a director of several American and foreign companies and is an International Associate of the Hoover Institution at Stanford University. An energetic supporter of intercollegiate athletics, Hoot has been an official lineman for Stanford's home football games for almost three decades and served a term on the University's Athletic Board.

Dr. Gibson has long been known by hundreds of senior business executives, as well as by many high government officials, around the world. He has traveled extensively to virtually every country, many of them every year or two. The value and effect of these associations and friendships have been incalculable in helping build SRI's international interests, which he has always identified with the cause of free enterprise in world economic progress.

A few years ago, Lord Kearton, the chairman of a major British company, wrote what many other executives throughout the world have thought and said about Dr. Gibson:

> *"... I have the most profound admiration for what he has done for SRI
> and for International Business, and I know of no one, absolutely no one,
> who has more friends in more places round the globe ..."*

To all of his countless friends, especially those in international circles, Hoot has long been known as "Mr. SRI" — a tribute that is indeed well deserved.

Dr. Gibson has been my close and valued friend since SRI was founded, and I am delighted that he has somehow found time to prepare this book about the Founding Years. I commend it to everyone who may be interested in institutional history — or concerned with the development of research institutes, and SRI in particular. I hope and expect a second or third volume will emerge in time covering the later years of SRI's development and maturity.

MORRIS M. DOYLE

San Francisco, California - 1979

HOOVER TOWER — STANFORD
The Parent Institution

593 GERONA ROAD — STANFORD
Early Discussions about SRI in a Stanford Campus Home

CHEMISTRY BUILDING — STANFORD
Source of the SRI Idea

BOHEMIAN GROVE
The Scene of Early Decisions

Watercolors by Helen Gibson

Continued on page 191

Prologue

We must move along on the research institute idea at Stanford.

— HERBERT HOOVER - 1939

THIS HISTORY OF STANFORD RESEARCH INSTITUTE — later to be known as SRI — begins in some respects in the 1920s when a Stanford University professor conceived the idea of a research center dedicated primarily to work in chemistry, physics, and biology. Dr. Robert E. Swain soon found support for his proposed venture from the University's president, Dr. Ray Lyman Wilbur, and also from a distinguished alumnus, Herbert Hoover.

Their plans were later set aside as the Great Depression engulfed the United States and then the world. However, Swain did not give up hope and in the late 1930s began to elaborate on his vision for a research institute at the University. Then, for the second time world events interfered. The outbreak of World War II made it impossible to advance the cause.

As the War drew to a close in 1945, the man with the dream took up the cudgel once again. He interested the University's new president, Dr. Donald B. Tresidder and its vice president, Dr. Alvin C. Eurich, in the idea. Also, he sought help from two colleagues — one a fellow chemistry professor and the other a Stanford alumnus and businessman. These men, calling themselves The Three Musketeers, worked diligently on the research institute concept.

Meanwhile, beginning in mid-1944, a trio in Los Angeles led by Dr. Maurice Nelles had created and was promoting a Pacific Research Foundation aimed at serving industry's research needs. Their activities came to Stanford's attention in the summer of 1945. In due course, some of their ideas were merged with those at Stanford and with a San Francisco initiative. Thus, the Foundation in Southern California went out of existence before really getting started.

The San Francisco group was led by Atholl McBean, a well-known member of California's business community. He found a warm reception at Stanford and energetically worked towards the day when SRI was founded in the autumn of 1946. His main partner at the University was Alvin Eurich. McBean was soon to become known at the "founder" of SRI. But he always looked upon Alvin Eurich as the "architect." The legal founders were the Trustees of Stanford University.

In creating a research institute at Stanford, the Trustees had answered Herbert Hoover's clarion call of 1939. They had also brought to reality a vision of Robert E. Swain that began much earlier. Still further, they were responsive to more recent urgings by Atholl McBean in San Francisco.

Triumvirates

"Three groups of three men each — Robert Swain, Philip Leighton and Dudley Swim at Stanford; Maurice Nelles, Eugene Black and Morlan Visel of Los Angeles; and, finally, Atholl McBean, Donald Tresidder and Alvin Eurich of Northern California — are honored, as well they should be, in this journal on SRI's Founding Years."

CARSTEN STEFFENS

The three initiatives that led to SRI's formation as an independent research institute are interesting in several respects. Two arose completely independently of each other; western economic progress and assistance to industry were common denominators; all the principals agreed on the value of a Stanford-industry relationship; and everyone was in a hurry to create an institute. Furthermore, as in most human endeavors of this sort, personalities played a key role in each group. Finally, three men acting more or less as a committee in each case were leaders of each of the three movements.

The common idea on speed towards the launching of a new Stanford-affiliated industrial research institute arose partly from attitudes at the time in the American West. Many believed that the area was on the verge of a great new day in economic development. Thus, the three converging endeavors took on an atmosphere of expectant action. Events moved quickly on a countdown towards lift-off. But, as will be seen, many mid-course corrections were to be needed on the way to SRI's formation and then to an upward thrust.

The first four chapters of this book deal, in turn, with an early Stanford vision for a research center and with the three initiatives that led to SRI's founding. The Three Musketeers, The Southern Trio, and The Northern Troika are the building blocks in the story. Their collective concepts were articulated by Morris M. Doyle, counsel to Stanford University, in a charter for a nonprofit, public service research institute affiliated with Stanford.

The first meeting of SRI's board of directors was held on the Stanford Campus on January 8, 1947. The session came after about eighteen months of rather intensive work by the University Trustees, its principal officers, and a group of western business executives.

Stanford's president was chairman of the new board by virtue of his University post. As general members of the SRI corporation, the Stanford Trustees had elected its founding directors. Five of the eleven board members were also Trustees.

The chairman's keynote at the first meeting shows that he held high hopes for the success of a fledgling organization that was later to be widely known around the world. He said that its creation was "a significant step" in western economic progress. Tresidder also thought that the move to establish SRI had been made at the right time. The Three Musketeers' report in late 1945 to Stanford's top officers had been specific on the point. They said that "The Golden Time" was at hand.

This history is written from a vantage point in the late 1970s. Three or even four decades is a short time span in the history of many organizations. This is certainly true for SRI. However, only a few people who were involved at one point or another in the founding and early operations of the Institute are still active in their business and professional pursuits. As the years go by, the list grows shorter and shorter.

It is inevitable that memories grow dim on details of thirty or more years ago. Even the records of earlier days lose some meaning when viewed by those who were not a part of the scene at the time.

This situation is by no means unique with SRI. It exists in varying degrees in all organizations. One result is that, in time, an institution often acquires an early history consisting of a a mixture of facts and often-told stories of questionable accuracy. The more time that passes without an orderly marshalling of the facts and events of earlier days, the more difficult it becomes to separate truth from fancy.

On the other hand, interpreting and recording recent history of an organization runs headlong into the problem of achieving objectivity without the benefit of sufficient time perspective. And, of course, while eyewitness experience and personal participation are valuable sources of information, they can also result in interpretations imparting a certain authenticity that may not be fully justified or complete in some instances.

I have heard it said on many occasions by people in other organizations that mistakes had been made in not recording institutional history before the principals departed from the scene. The point made an impression on me in light of my association with SRI since the first days of its operation and even earlier. I reflected on the idea that, even with SRI's short life span, I may be the only person who has been associated continuously with the organization in a central capacity since its opening in late 1946 and who also knows (or knew) personally all those who were involved in creating the organization and getting it under way.

This idea of recording the early history of an organization before the principals are too far removed from the scene — or have passed on — is illustrated by experiences at Arthur D. Little, the nation's leading profit making research institute. During the 1950s, its two senior officers attempted to prepare a history of the enterprise that began prior to the turn of the 20th century. Their difficulties show up in the following comment by one of the authors.

> "We found that recollections varied somewhat ... depending presumably on the views of individuals ... I found that each of several individuals is apt to think of himself as the prime mover, and this feeling strengthens as the years go by when the part played by others begins to fade. We neglected ... a study ... covering the early days, and it is now impossible to fill in many of the gaps ..."

Over the years many people have said in my presence that they were greatly involved in SRI's creation or in its first operations. Knowing this not to be a fact in many instances, I have sometimes wondered about possible errors in my own recollection of events. Such a risk is ever present even when one has indeed been personally involved to a great extent.

There is no doubt whatsoever in my mind about the prime movers in SRI's formative years. Their activities are chronicled in this book. I saw the process at first hand in many ways and participated in parts of it.

My direct association with SRI began in late 1946 even before it had been launched. A few contacts occurred during the embryonic stage prior to World War II. Beginning in September of 1946, I was frequently in touch with Donald Tresidder, Alvin Eurich, Atholl McBean, Robert Swain, Philip Leighton, Dudley Swim, Maurice Nelles and many others mentioned in the account that follows.

My affiliations with Dr. William F. Talbot, William Rand, Dr. Carsten Steffens, and Dr. J. E. Hobson within SRI were, of course, much more frequent. They were on a day-to-day basis.

To the best of my ability, I have reflected the actions, viewpoints and words of these and other people involved in SRI's early history. In all possible cases, the written record is the prime source. In some instances, I have relied on my notes and conversations at the time. Each principal still living has been invited to refresh my memory and to add recollections and explanations. However, the interpretations are mine alone, and I bear the full responsibility.

Although the initiative in which Atholl McBean played a leading role was decisive in launching the Institute, the two earlier ones were nonetheless important. The officers and Trustees of Stanford University might not have moved as rapidly toward SRI's creation had not a University committee been urging the administration to form such an institution. Furthermore, Atholl McBean and his business associates in San Francisco, as well as University officers, might not have acted as promptly as they did in 1946 had an institute initiative in Southern California not occurred. Thus it seems clear that all three initiatives were significant.

SRI was launched with enthusiasm and high aspirations on the part of its founders only to encounter difficulties and misunderstandings among the principals during its early operations. In retrospect, some of this may have been avoided had there been a clear articulation and agreement at the outset on the goals, policies, and mission of the new organization, including its operating relationships with Stanford University. However, it is not unusual for the first step in new ventures of this type to be halting and uncertain. Suffice it to say here that in due course a path of development was selected and then pursued vigorously in a second stage following the Founding Years.

This book covers events within and about the Institute from beginning of the idea in the 1920s through 1948. By the end of 1948, SRI had been in operation a little more than two years. The first executive director, William F. Talbot, had departed; the second, J. E. Hobson, had been aboard less than ten months.

The Founding Years came to an end as a vigorous thrust got under way in 1948 under Hobson's leadership. The story of events that occurred during the next few years as SRI grew rapidly in size, scope, and impact will appear later in another volume called The Upward Surge.

Perhaps in due course more recent SRI events can be portrayed with a perspective that seems hardly possible at present.

Although the acronym SRI was not used at the very beginning of Stanford Research Institute, the organization was often known during its early history as simply "the Institute." In any event, as indicated earlier, the three names are used interchangeably in this publication.

In the 1970s the institution's official name was changed from Stanford Research Institute to SRI International following a mutually-agreeable separation from Stanford. However, this did not change the abbreviated name, SRI, in any way.

A final note about Stanford and SRI is much in order at the end of this prologue. Although no longer within the Stanford family in a legal sense, SRI has a great heritage from Stanford University. Its reason for existence remains unchanged. It must, and I feel sure always will, strive to fulfill the high purposes for which it was brought into existence. ■

An Early Vision

The University, the nation, and the world beyond
will greatly benefit in time from an industrial
research institute at Stanford.

— DR. ROBERT E. SWAIN - 1939

THE IDEA OF CREATING A SCIENTIFIC RESEARCH INSTITUTE at Stanford University first arose within the University itself in the 1920s.

The late Dr. Robert E. Swain, who was professor of chemistry, then head of the department, later vice president and acting president of the University and finally professor emeritus, began thinking about the idea in 1925. Swain was a friend of Herbert Hoover, Stanford's most distinguished alumnus, who was then Secretary of Commerce in the Coolidge administration. During several of Hoover's visits in 1926 and 1927 to his home on the Stanford Campus, he and Swain talked about the need and possibilities for some sort of research center at the University.

Only a short time earlier, Hoover had played a leading role in founding Stanford's Graduate School of Business. At two Summer Encampments of San Francisco's Bohemian Club, he and Swain stimulated each other's thinking about "a new idea for the Stanford family of institutions."

Hoover felt that with the Business School launched at the University something should be done at Stanford to stimulate greater productivity in American industry. He liked Swain's idea centered on scientific research aimed at developing new products, processes and techniques.

The Business School was the third new entity at Stanford in which Hoover had been involved. Shortly after World War I, he suggested to the Carnegie Corporation that a Food Research Institute be created at the University. The proposal was accepted. With funds provided by Carnegie, the new Institute began working on "problems of production, distribution, and consumption of foodstuffs," and soon became prominent on a worldwide basis.

Meanwhile, Hoover had given Stanford some money to house his growing collection of documents associated with The Great War and its aftermath. Soon to be known as the Hoover War Library and later as the Hoover Institution on War, Revolution, and Peace, it became a world-renowned center at the University. Its buildings bear his name and that of his wife, Lou Henry.

It is not surprising that by 1927 the Stanford faculty had a very high respect for Hoover's contributions of money and ideas to his Alma Mater. And, it is not surprising that after his initiatives on a food research institute, a library and a business school, Hoover's interests widened to include research for industry.

Hoover encouraged Swain to pursue his research institute idea and especially to take it up with Dr. Ray Lyman Wilbur, the University's president. They agreed that Wilbur might well "buy the idea" in light of his scientific background in the medical field. But, before Swain made his move, Hoover himself spoke to Wilbur and in Swain's words much later "paved the way." The Swain-Wilbur talks took place in the autumn of 1927.

After getting a "green light" from Wilbur to develop some sort of plan, Swain was eagerly looking forward to further talks with Hoover. But early in 1928 Hoover announced he would run for president. This came on the heels of President Coolidge's famous statement — "I do not choose to run —." From then onward, Hoover had no time to work with his Stanford friend on the institute idea.

He did not, however, lose interest in the concept he had helped set in motion. Several times during the 1928 campaign and even into his presidency, Hoover asked Swain how the idea was being received and urged him to keep up his good work. Many years later, Hoover said to a group at Stanford that Swain was the man with "an early vision" for a research institute at the University.

Greatly encouraged by Hoover's continuing interest, Swain did indeed keep the ball rolling. He talked to many faculty members and enlisted their support in various ways. Among them was Dr. Eliot G. Mears, professor of geography and a specialist in international economic affairs at the University's new Business School. Swain became more than ever convinced that an institute affiliated with the University would be helpful to both industry and Stanford.

Wilbur's support for his colleague did not flag in 1928 even though he was devoting a lot of attention to Hoover's campaign. He approved of Swain's contacts outside the University aimed at gaining support for the institute concept. Swain did in fact arouse interest in the idea including general commitments for financial support from several eastern firms. Among them was General Electric, already a leader in the world of industrial research.

Dr. Eliot G. Mears

"With recognition to my father-in-law who encouraged the enthusiasm of Herbert Hoover, Ray Lyman Wilbur and Robert Swain for an industrial research institute at Stanford."

WELDON B. GIBSON

Wilbur later took a leave of absence from Stanford to serve as President Hoover's Secretary of the Interior. But, before accepting the appointment in 1929, he readily acceded to Swain's urging that a University committee be asked to explore the institute concept. No one was surprised when Swain was asked to lead the effort, and he quickly seized the opportunity.

But Swain soon found himself wearing a new hat. He was appointed acting president of the University when Wilbur departed for Washington. This did not deter him from following up within the University on the institute idea. In fact, it put him in a much better position to do so. His first report on University affairs went directly to the point.

"... over a year ago President Wilbur appointed a special committee of the faculty to make a study of the question of establishing here a research center in which there would be brought together in one building those members of the faculty and other research workers who, regardless of departmental affiliations, were engaged in research which from any angle approached the general field of biology from the standpoint of chemistry and physics."

Swain later acknowledged that his committee centered on biology partly because of faculty interest especially in the biological sciences but also as a means of holding and indeed increasing Wilbur's interest when he would return to the University. All this was in line with Wilbur's professional background. But Swain and his colleagues had firmly in mind that chemistry and physics should be the basic building blocks for the new organization. First of all, of course, Swain was a chemist.

The acting president's report on the University's 1928-29 academic year made it clear that his Stanford committee wanted to move ahead on the research center. "We have given the whole project careful consideration and are all agreed with you that, properly developed, this will strike a new note in University organization and research."

Swain's use of the word "you" in referring to the absent president shows that he was already convinced of Wilbur's support. Then, he wrote that the proposal "amounts to practically bringing the research institute idea into the University on a scale and plan which takes full advantage of its best features without, at the same time, imposing upon it any hampering restrictions."

Swain and his colleagues, but particularly Swain, were thinking at the time that any new research center would be a part of the University. The "best features" they had in mind were simply that an interdisciplinary approach in scientific research had some definite advantages and that such a center could attract new funds from outside the University. They knew there would be problems in operating the center outside of the University's regular academic structure. But they felt these could be overcome as various departments and faculty members perceived the new activity as a source of financial support for their own research projects. Swain was convinced that the center should have considerable freedom of action within the University.

Although a part of the University's Annual Report, the institute proposal appeared in the form of a paper prepared by Swain's Committee on a Survey of Research at Stanford. It was addressed to Wilbur at the Department of the Interior in Washington. Following some comments on "major problems" in biology, the report prophesied that "the great advances of the future will come from bringing more closely together highly trained workers in physics, biology, and chemistry ..."

The Stanford committee pointed out that "this is precisely the main purpose which this project (a research center) will serve." Avoiding needless duplication of equipment was mentioned as one benefit to the University. The report went on to say that "the gap between chemistry and physics is rapidly being bridged as the two sciences overlap in many important fields of research." The group also emphasized that a new "center for research" at Stanford could become "a productive meeting place for workers" in chemistry, physics, and biology.

Apparently, Swain was quite convinced that some sort of research institute could and would be created at Stanford. In 1928, he offered a chemistry faculty appointment to Dr. Philip A. Leighton. One of the inducements he laid before Leighton was "the prospect of an interdisciplinary research institute" at the University. In any event, Leighton accepted and later joined in promoting the institute idea.

Swain was not unmindful that within academic circles around the country there was mounting concern about the rise of independent research institutes — some devoted to basic investigations and others to applied pursuits. Many university presidents and faculty members looked upon them as a threat to both university research and education. They were afraid that funds might be drained away from academic and basic research programs.

Some writers during the late 1920s and early 1930s were predicting that the new institutes would attract faculties away from universities, move too much research to the realm of business away from universities and, in general, work to the detriment of the nation's academic institutions.

These fears did not unduly trouble Swain and his colleagues because they viewed them as being largely in the social sciences. This was undoubtedly true. Nevertheless, there was a concerted attack on the research institute principle. One social scientist, for example, wrote in 1928 — "What stirs misgivings is the swift multiplication of extra-academic agencies devoted wholly to research of a high order, often well endowed, manned by competent staffs and directed by men of vision, able to select research projects at will and concentrate upon them for any requisite period of time."

Although these alarms were most often sounded about such independent organizations as the Rockefeller Institute, the Institute for Government Research and the Carnegie Institute, the social scientists did indeed raise some basic questions — and they were being heard. "Is this a sort of thing with which universities can successfully compete? Does it portend their gradual conversion into mere training schools? Is it ... in the interest of the highest and most fruitful scholarly achievement?"

One reason Swain and his associates were not too concerned about these voices around the country was their view that the Stanford institute should be part and parcel of the University, and thus not a threat from the outside. Furthermore, neither Swain nor anyone else at Stanford had any desire whatsoever to create an "extra-academic" institute even though it might directly serve industry to some extent. Even so, the basic questions were to arise later within Stanford when the institute idea came again to the forefront.

It appeared to many in the Stanford family as the 1920s drew to a close that a new institute was about to appear on the scene. But Wilbur's absence and the "crash of '29" soon put a damper on prospects. The developing economic crisis in the country — later to spread around the world — made it virtually impossible to attract interest and support from outside the University. The whole idea soon went into "limbo" and was "put on the shelf" as Swain later described the situation.

But, again, Swain did not give up on his idea. He continued to talk with his Univer-

Dr. Robert E. Swain
The Man With an Early Vision

Herbert Hoover — The Chief
Early Support for Swain's Vision

sity associates about the concept and took every opportunity to promote interest outside Stanford. Proceeding slowly to "spread the word," he realized nevertheless that time and events had overtaken his initiative.

Even so, Swain did not despair that the time would come when the institute idea could be brought to fruition. For a while after Wilbur's return to the University following Hoover's defeat by Franklin Roosevelt, Swain thought something might soon be done to advance the cause. Wilbur, on the other hand, was quite pessimistic that anything useful could be initiated in the depths of the Great Depression.

Wilbur had ample reason to be discouraged about raising money for a research institute. During the early 1930s, the University lost two large gift prospects simply because it could not raise matching funds. Well over $3 million was lost when $2 million could not be found to meet donor conditions.

Some Stanford alumni were to say later that the University's inability to raise money was Wilbur's fault. Fearful that he was trying to change Stanford to a graduate school, alumni leaders held back at times on fund-raising help to Wilbur. One said much later, "We turned him down cold on one of his gift-matching projects."

Swain acknowledged many years later that his idea on a Stanford research institute changed considerably as time went by. Although from the beginning service to industry

Dr. Ray Lyman Wilbur
President, Stanford University
A Green Light for the Vision

Credit: Stanford University Archives

was a factor in his mind, the first motivation was basic research in chemistry, physics, and biology. Gradually, however, he saw a great need for industry-oriented work supported by a strong fundamental research program at Stanford. Hoover's influence on this shift in thinking was significant in the late 1920s and early 30s. Later on, however, Swain's contacts with business were more decisive.

Aside from the economic crisis, Swain gradually became fearful of another problem. He felt that the New Deal was mounting a sustained attack on the patent system. It seemed to him and some of his University colleagues that the presidential effort might succeed in abolishing or greatly modifying patent protection on inventions and new products. He thought this would greatly reduce incentives for industry to sustain research particularly on a contract basis in outside organizations.

Although Swain laid aside his promotional efforts aimed at creating a new research center, he continued to debate with all and sundry on a philosophical base for the idea. Being a keen student of science history and a distinguished scientist himself, Swain kept advancing a theme that "the application of science for useful purposes" is a noble cause in improving the lot of mankind.

He pointed out to audiences large and small that this basic idea was not new and indeed that it had arisen four centuries earlier during the Age of Commerce and Discovery. Francis Bacon believed that the world's attention should be turned from a medieval emphasis on deductive reasoning to the Kingdom of Man and to human society and its many problems. He had contended, as Swain was to emphasize, that this could best be done through the applied sciences and that the chief task for mankind was to make the world a better place for human habitation.

The scientists of the 16th century were indeed greatly concerned about a discouraging tone in the idea that "an increase of knowledge is an increase in sorrow." Harvey, Kepler, Galileo, Descartes, Boyle, Newton, Locke, Spinoza, and others argued for a more robust confidence in what science might achieve in the betterment of man's life. Herbert Spencer later put the idea in a pithy sentence, "Science is for Life, not Life for Science."

Bacon believed that one of the main objectives of research should be to create a "rich storehouse for the glory of the Creator and the relief of man's estate." This dedication led him to create Salomon's House, a foundation devoted in his words to "enlarging the bounds of human empire." Thus, perhaps, we find the conceptual forerunner of present-day institutes and research foundations, partly if not wholly in the pattern Swain visualized for Stanford.

As Swain was to emphasize on several occasions, even Einstein in his quest for new knowledge often expressed concern about "the great unsolved problems" of human endeavor. He often emphasized that these problems must be the final interest of all technical pursuits. During the 1930s, Einstein counseled an audience at Cal Tech in Pasadena, California, to "never forget this in the midst of your diagrams and equations."

Lofty as these expressions may be, they were placed in modern focus in the late 1930s by an Englishman, J. Arthur Thompson. He wrote about "bringing the light of science to bear on man's problems all along the line, on health of mind as well as of body, on education as well as on agriculture, on ethical development as well as on industry, on eugenics as well as on utopias." Thompson's perspective certainly involved many of the concepts Swain had in mind at the time.

All this might seem to argue that the practice of science for beneficial purposes is a panacea for mankind's problems. However, many scientists over the years have pointed to the difficulties as well as to the potentials of highly directed research. One of Swain's Stanford colleagues in the 1920s, Dr. Truman Kelley, observed that "organized and professional research can be overdone, and moneys devoted to it can be poorly spent." Needless to say, this was not what Swain had in mind, but he was fully aware of possible pitfalls along the way.

A GREEN LIGHT

Dr. Ray Lyman Wilbur, Stanford's president in the 1920s and 30s, was often cryptic in responding to proposals placed before him. In 1939, he said, "Swain wants to start an institute; I told him to go ahead." Swain was hoping the president might lead the way. But Wilbur merely added, "I don't want to get in his way."

During his period "in the wilderness" in the 1930s, Swain thought about what had happened on his favorite subject in the eastern part of the United States. The idea that useful results within business and industry could accrue from an organized approach in scientific research had arisen around the turn of the century. Swain was intrigued by what had been done.

A research firm known as Arthur D. Little was already operating in Massachusetts. A few American companies — notable among them being General Electric — began to create laboratories aimed directly at generating products and devices for the future. Their leaders came to believe that results such as those achieved by Bell and Edison could be brought into being on an ascending scale by organizing specifically for the purpose.

These people and companies maintained that groups of scientists working in a favorable environment with modern scientific paraphernalia could direct their efforts to a desired result and thus greatly increase the odds for success.

This whole idea was helped along the way in 1915 when one of the nation's philanthropists created the Mellon Institute in Pittsburgh. The Mellon concept involved an institution independent of universities, the principal sources of new knowledge, as well as of industry, the principal user of scientific information.

Teams of scientists and engineers at Mellon, and in Arthur D. Little, were available under commission, so to speak, to pursue research objectives placed before them by the business world. Thus, the contract research business as we know it today came into being on a small scale.

In due course, Battelle Memorial Institute and Armour Research Foundation (now known as IITRE) were created by benefactors who believed strongly in the potential contributions of an independent contract research organization. All of these first institutes developed slowly during the years leading up to 1941 when their attention was turned to national defense.

These and similar research centers were on Swain's mind as he awaited a new and more propitious time to advance his idea for a Stanford institute. He knew not when this could come, but as war clouds gathered on the horizon in the late 1930s he began to think that the time might come sooner rather than later.

Swain thus began to to "talk up" the idea again in late 1938 and during 1939. Also, he felt that the nation's economic situation had improved sufficiently to justify renewed contacts with the business world. He began to inquire about possible targets. His good friend and Stanford associate, Paul E. Holden, professor of industrial management at the University's Business School, brought him in touch with a Stanford alumnus, Dudley Swim, who was soon to become involved in one of the initiatives that led through other avenues to fulfillment of Swain's dream.

In the meantime, Swain had worked in close harmony with one of his colleagues, Philip Leighton, in the Stanford chemistry department. They began talking about gaining firsthand information by visiting some of the eastern-U.S. research centers. They also brought Dr. J. W. McBain, a fellow chemistry professor, into their orbit.

Even though Swain actively promoted his institute idea, especially during the late 1930s, he turned mostly to his professional field. Apparently, he did not fully visualize the potentials in other disciplines. Dr. Frederick Terman, later Stanford's Provost but then on the engineering faculty, was not aware of Swain's interest. But he was familiar with Swain's industrially-oriented work in chemistry especially on sulphur dioxide affluents. Terman remarked many years later, "It is not surprising that this experience led Swain to a research institute proposal."

Dr. J. E. Wallace Sterling, appointed president of the University and chairman of SRI in 1949, had long been aware of Swain's early vision for a Stanford institute. He later wrote that "major credit" should go to Swain especially in view of his "quality of persistence, never flamboyant, always quiet, but ever present."

Sterling heard directly from Swain in the late 1940s about the earlier sessions with Wilbur, Leighton, Mears, and Swim. Years later, he said, "These talks bespoke (Swain's)

interest in having science applied for the benefit of mankind, an interest which would certainly square with his vision about a research institute."

At one point, probably in early 1939, Swain spoke with Wilbur about seeking financial support from the U.S. Government for the institute plan at Stanford. Wilbur advised Swain to do what he thought best but said, "I cannot and will not deal with that man in the White House." Swain was not suggesting that he contact Roosevelt but was encouraged by another "green light" from the University's president.

Swain's interest in outside financial support for a University research institute turned again to industry. He brought his project to the attention of Harry Reynolds who was head of the newly created Stanford Associates, an alumni fund raising organization for the University. Reynolds introduced him to his banker brother in New York and this led again to some discussions with General Electric. However, once more, events were to overtake a promising prospect for action. War clouds were thickening in Europe.

According to Swain's later accounts, some questions were raised during the 1930s on whether or not an industrial research institute within Stanford was consistent with the University's educational purposes. He and Wilbur had talked about this much earlier.

They were convinced that an institute was quite in line with the Stanford Founding Grant including, among other things, a mission "to promote the public welfare ... (and) to render the greatest possible service to mankind." Also, they pointed to the founders' desire that "experimentation and research in the advancement of useful knowledge" as well as its "dissemination and practical application" should be embraced by the University.

Both Swain and Wilbur realized, of course, that in time University lawyers should deal with the matter (which, of course, they subsequently did), but the two men were already satisfied that the path was reasonably clear.

Even with a renewed feeling that something might be done as the 1930s drew to a close, Swain was by no means sanguine about the prospects. He knew that many years would be needed to accomplish his goal. But he stepped up his enthusiasm about the ultimate value of such an endeavor.

So it was in early 1939 at a small gathering in the home of Eliot Mears on the Stanford Campus that Swain gave voice to his views on the institute idea. "The University, the nation, and the world beyond will greatly benefit in time from an industrial research institute at Stanford." Hoover, Wilbur, Mears, and McBain heard his remarks and urged him to persevere.

Dr. Robert E. Swain

"... as well it should, this book gives special honor to Bert Swain. SRI stands today as testimony to his early vision."

PHILIP A. LEIGHTON

Swain lived to see the "object of his eye" in full operation under University auspices. On several occasions, he was honored by the new organization for his early vision and promotion of its concept, especially within the University. He was greatly pleased when his son, Robert, Jr., an American Cyanamid executive at the time, became a director of SRI after it was well under way.

Few men in Stanford's history have given greater service to the University than Robert E. Swain. A graduate in the class of 1899, almost all of his professional life was spent at Stanford. He was well-liked by the faculty and highly respected on the campus and elsewhere for his contributions in the field of chemistry. Some, however, looked upon him as being a conservative administrator and a "firm supporter of the status quo."

This certainly was not the case in Swain's continuing promotion of a research institute at Stanford. Nor was he unduly conservative as acting president in Wilbur's absence. The reason he did not get more done between 1929 and 1933 on the institute idea arose from the economic collapse rather than from any conservatism on his part. He had the idea and the energy, but the University did not have the wherewithal.

Swain was born on January 5, 1875. He entered Stanford in 1894 and later earned his doctoral degree at Yale. His faculty tenure at Stanford began in 1912 and for more than two decades later on he was executive head of the Chemistry Department. Swain pursued a wide range of professional interests outside the University and at various times was a consultant to the Departments of Justice and Agriculture and to several companies.

Bob Swain, as he was widely known around Stanford and in his profession, travelled frequently both in the United States and abroad. He was sometimes called the "Pullman Professor of Chemistry" because of his long train trips.

Herbert Hoover was to say many years later that "Robert Swain was the first man to visualize the concept of SRI and it is to his everlasting credit that others were able in time to bring the idea into being."

This accolade by Hoover was not the first he gave to Swain on the research institute idea. In the early summer of 1940, Hoover made an informal appearance at a graduation dinner for Stanford's Business School class. Following some comments on the state of the nation, he gave the new MBAs some direct advice — "Buy all the real estate you can, and buy it on the San Francisco Peninsula."

Hoover said the basis for his advice was that in time the Stanford influence including "the new research institute" would attract more and more people and more and more business interest to a broad area around the University. He went on to say that "land values on the Peninsula are sure to rise for a long time to come — more so than elsewhere in California." He could hardly have been more prescient.

As a member of the GSB Class of 1940, I heard Hoover's advice on real estate. But, alas, I and others did not have the means to profit from his remarks. I did note what he had to say about a research institute and assumed it would shortly emerge on the Stanford scene. But the spread of World War II was soon to intervene.

It was at this dinner that Hoover spoke of "an early vision" by Swain on the research institute concept for Stanford. Swain was not present, but as a graduate student living in the home of Dr. Eliot Mears (later my father-in-law), I had come to know Swain and on several occasions heard him hold forth on why Stanford should create an industrial research institute. Within a few days after Hoover's remarks I had the pleasure of telling Swain what the nation's ex-president had said.

There was not the slightest inkling in my mind in the spring of 1940 nor in earlier conversations with Swain that it would be my good fortune to join the new Stanford institute at its very outset some years later. But over the years after this came to pass, I spoke often with Swain and repeatedly gave him the honor he deserved for a vision that eventually led to SRI's formation. We could — and we should — have done more.

On at least two occasions in the late 1930s, I was present when Wilbur, Swain, and my future father-in-law talked about a Stanford research institute. The idea seemed a bit remote to me at the time. In fact, it was Swain who reminded me in 1950 about my chance presence at one of their talks in late 1939. Eliot Mears invited me to join the late-afternoon session with Hoover, Wilbur, and Swain because he thought "it might be interesting." Little did he or I suspect that another chance happening in 1946 would bring me into SRI even before it was incorporated. In any event, the institute proposal passed from my mind. Even in 1946 when my wife brought the SRI idea to my attention I did not associate it at the time with the earlier Swain initiative.

Some seventeen years after Swain's death, Philip Leighton, a Stanford colleague for more than three decades, gave high credit to his co-worker on the SRI idea. "He was the moving force within the University, and was delighted to see the later success of his vision." Then Leighton went on to say, "I only wish Bert were able to read what has been written, as I can imagine how deep his satisfaction would be to know that his years of effort are ... remembered."

Swain was known as "Bert" to some of his closest friends. Shortly before his death on May 31, 1961, I had a welcome opportunity to tell him that his name would never be forgotten in the annals of SRI. He was our instigator in concept. He would indeed be gratified to see the present-day results of his early vision. ∎

The Three Musketeers

Now is the golden time to start (a Stanford institute).

— A STANFORD COMMITTEE - 1945

ROBERT SWAIN, PHILIP LEIGHTON, AND DUDLEY SWIM had three abiding interests in common — Stanford University, San Francisco's Bohemian Club and creating a research institute at Stanford. In July of 1939, they headed for the Club's summer encampment in the redwoods north of the Golden Gate, having agreed to spend some hours talking about a possible institute at the University.

By this time, the three men had more or less come to feel that the emphasis in any new research center should be on industrial problems rather than on basic studies. Swim's interest was almost totally along this time, and he had considerable impact on his cohorts' thinking.

In the relaxed setting of the Grove, the trio talked about the needs and potentials for an industrial research organization in the West and the mutual benefits of a Stanford affiliation. Their enthusiasm grew from day to day as they agreed to start doing something about the idea. They met again at Stanford soon after the encampment and talked by telephone several times. Swim's home was in Carmel (California) but, being retired at a young age, he often spent time on the Stanford Campus.

During the autumn, Swain and Leighton discussed the institute idea with Dr. Ray Lyman Wilbur, Stanford's president. They told him about the recent "committee meeting" in the redwoods. Wilbur liked what he heard and shortly afterwards brought the idea to the University Trustees. One of the Trustees, ex-president Herbert Hoover, felt that the initiative should be moved along as rapidly as possible.

As portrayed in the opening chapter, the Stanford institute idea was not news to Wilbur and Hoover. Swain had been promoting the concept with them since the 1920s.

On at least one occasion in late 1939 and again in 1940, Wilbur, Leighton, and Swain met with a committee of Trustees. Their idea got a good reception, and they resolved to keep the ball rolling in spite of the war in Europe and its implications for the United States. In the meantime, Leighton succeeded Swain as head of the University's Chemistry Department and in his new role continued the talks with Wilbur on the possibility of creating a Stanford-affiliated research institute.

Both Swain and Leighton — feeling they had a new "green light" from Wilbur and the Stanford Trustees — tried throughout 1940 to generate wider support for their idea. But matters remained in a "talking stage"; the war threat was growing ominous. By 1941, Swain had reached retirement age and with Wilbur's pending retirement in mind he made it clear to Leighton that the project was his to pursue.

DR. ROBERT E. SWAIN
A Musketeer

H. DUDLEY SWIM
A Musketeer

During early 1941, Leighton outlined the plan to Dr. George Harrison, professor of physics at MIT. Leighton approached Harrison, a Stanford graduate, partly because it appeared he might be Stanford's next president. Harrison made a practical suggestion on how to advance the cause — get one or two research contracts and start an institute around them. He urged Leighton to get in touch with the newly-created National Defense Research Committee in Washington.

Early in autumn, an opportunity arose to follow up on Harrison's advice. Leighton attended an NDRC meeting in Washington and returned to Stanford with a list of possible research projects. One was later started in the University's Chemistry Department with an understanding that the contract would be transferred to the research institute as soon as it was formed.

Leighton thought this would surely take place within a year. But, alas, Pearl Harbor brought America into World War II. Leighton soon went to the Army's Dugway Proving Ground in Utah; the research contract followed him there in short order. Thus, the institute idea went "on the shelf" for the second time in a decade.

Leighton had one more talk with Dudley Swim about the institute before all was laid away for the duration. The meeting was in New York shortly before Swim joined the Navy. They again went over plans for organizing and financing the new institution. Leighton later recalled Swim's view that the institute should be a Stanford subsidiary with its own board of directors. But before anything further could be done, Leighton was called into the Army.

The Great Depression had blocked the first institute movement at Stanford; World War II did the same thing in 1941. Leighton was, of course, greatly disappointed. More than two decades later he wrote — "there is little doubt that if the war had not interfered the Stanford Research Institute would have come into being in 1942 or 1943 ..." This may well have been the case, but it would have been an institute more or less "on paper" in a small Stanford building with some military contracts and a few faculty members doing double duty. Leighton certainly would have been its first executive officer — probably in addition to his Chemistry Department post.

Dr. Philip Leighton
A Musketeer

Had an institute been created in 1942, it might have played a key role in the University's war effort. A Committee on University Services was formed to monitor Stanford's involvement in research and training for the U.S. Government. Dr. Paul R. Hanna was the committee's executive director. An office was set up in Washington. Contracts began to multiply; projects ranged all the way from aircraft manufacturing studies to further development work on penicillin.

Stanford facilities — dormitories, classrooms, and laboratories — were used to capacity during the war. New academic centers were created (e.g., anthropology and geography); new departments were organized and some new faculty appointments were made. In essence, the University — along with many others — became a large applied research and training center. This situation made it even more feasible for the Trustees, administrators and faculty at the end of the war to embrace the idea of a separate research center at the University.

Even with all of Stanford's wartime involvement, it had no major military-sponsored programs in the physical sciences and engineering similar to those at Harvard, MIT, Chicago, Cal Tech, and Berkeley. One reason for this is simply that one by one many key faculty members took up posts elsewhere before anything substantial could be created at home. Had there been a major wartime laboratory at Stanford, it might well have hastened the day for SRI.

Swain again entered the institute picture in a changed post-war national and Stanford environment. In the summer of 1945, he went again to the Bohemian Grove

Encampement and while there had a long talk with Dr. Donald B. Tresidder, who had been Stanford's president since January 21, 1943. The institute idea was not new to Tresidder; he had been president of the University's Board of Trustees when Wilbur and Hoover were urging that something be done.

The Swain-Tresidder talk was followed a day later by a larger forum at the Sempervirens Camp in the Grove. Tresidder, Swain, Swim, and Leighton were there — also Eliot G. Mears, Pearce Mitchell, and Paul Holden from Stanford. The so-called Stanford Camp was indeed a good place for a quiet mid-morning discussion. Tresidder listened carefully as Swain and Swim outlined three possibilities — a University-owned institute, cooperation with a privately-owned venture, and an entirely independent organization. He favored the first approach and encouraged Swim to "put his thoughts on paper."

Less than a month later, while vacationing at Sun Valley in Idaho, Swim summarized his views in a letter to Tresidder. He felt that Stanford should move promptly so as to take advantage of the post-war research and excess profits tax situations, and also to meet new needs in the West, before the University found itself in a "me too" rather than a leadership position. His proposal on auspices was quite specific — "a wholly-owned subsidiary of the University" with "its own separate and distinct board of trustees or directors."

Swim was not clear on whether the new corporation should be nonprofit or a regular company. For a name he suggested "Stanford Industrial Institute" or "Stanford Research Institute" with a preference for the former, thus showing his strong business motivation. This appears to be the first use in writing of the exact words that were soon to be given to a new Stanford organization. Anyhow, Swim wanted to be involved; he volunteered his services on a committee "to act on behalf of the University."

Some were to say later that Swim had a profit or self-serving motive in mind. In retrospect, this seems unfair. He was a man of considerable means growing out of stock market investments in the depression and was looking for new and interesting things to do. But he always insisted that his only motivation was to help Stanford; there is no evidence to the contrary and quite a lot to support what he was saying.

Tresidder was much interested in Swim's letter and telephoned him in early September (1945). He invited elaboration on the proposal. Swim immediately sent a paper to Tresidder with copies to Swain and Leighton in which he emphasized that the institute idea had "great potentialities." Again, he offered to help — "it would be a pleasure ... to be of assistance ... (in) bringing about its realization."

Swim's memo, which he said summarized thinking developed over the years with Swain and Leighton, begins with a purpose for the proposed institute — "to provide industry on the Pacific Coast and in other Far Western states with technical and research facilities as is done for Eastern industry by such organizations as Arthur D. Little ... and the Mellon Institute." He suggested that the new institute should operate in two major ways — "(1) consulting, and (2) research and patent development for its own account."

After pointing to institutes in other parts of the country including the recently-created Midwest Research Institute in Kansas City, Swim outlined the scope for a Stanford entity. He suggested chemistry, physics, engineering, management consulting and

Stanford Campmates — Sempervirens — Circa 1940

Bohemian Grove

Front Row — *left*, Al Roth, comptroller; *right*, Pearce Mitchell, registrar.
Back Row — *left*, Paul Davies, fund raising; *center*, Paul Holden, Business School;
right, Eliot Mears, Business School.

economics, as well as industrial styling and design. He thought the food and mineral industries were prime potentials for research. In light of later developments at SRI in industrial economics and the management sciences, Swim's recommendations are most interesting. No other technically-based institute had yet entered these fields in a substantial way. New ground was about to be ploughed.

Swim laid out a broad path for "economic facilities" in a Stanford institute. They would "appraise the economic potentialities of any project." He suggested that the institute "might be retained by a municipality to appraise its potentialities and to recommend the direction of its business development ..." He also thought it could make "economic surveys of the Western States for the purpose of formulating a basic picture of resources, markets, etc..." Then he sketched a noble objective — "In short, the Institute could provide the economic statesmanship and vision for the future development of the West."

It is clear that Swim (and thus Swain and Leighton) were thinking primarily about the western states. They were echoing a regional objective — a popular note at the time. They did not fully appreciate the problems in such a narrow course nor did they really comprehend the far greater needs and opportunities across the country and around the world.

Swim's proposal emphasized that the institute should be predicated on "a benefit to Stanford University." He repeated the three alternatives discussed at the Bohemian Grove and mentioned Tresidder's preference for a University-owned entity. He said that, if the institute should become taxable at some point, the impact on the University might be minimized by "some royalty arrangement" between the two institutions.

Turning to organization of the new enterprise, Swim suggested a chairman and research director along with a small staff and modest facilities "in some presently unused or otherwise available building in close proximity to the University." This was the first time anyone had ever brought up the possibility of an off-campus location.

Swim proposed a "cautious and conservative financial policy" for the institute. He thought an initial investment of $10,000 plus $25,000 for operating expenses would be sufficient with a gradual buildup as projects were obtained. Even in 1945 dollars, this was a modest beginning. It is a good thing that the actual start a year later was far less cautious.

Following through on organization, Swim mentioned five possible divisions for the institute — technical and scientific, legal, economic, industrial styling and design, and business services. He thought the legal division could work with the Stanford Law School in providing case material in patent law.

Three possible names were placed before Tresidder — Stanford Research Institute, Stanford Industrial Institute, and Industrial Research Institute. As before, Swim felt the word "industrial" was essential. But he was not unmindful that the Stanford name had enormous value.

Swim then came to his punch line. He suggested that the University Trustees approve the project in principle, an organizing committee be set up, and a survey be made of a few research institutes in the eastern part of the country. Then he implied that the Swim-Swain-Leighton group would be glad to be "commissioned as the organizers" along with the president of the University.

Some have said over the years that Tresidder "tried to kill" the institute idea and that others "pushed it through" over his objections. But the record shows the contrary. Only nine days after Swim's proposal was written, Tresidder was on the move. He urged an eastern trip by Swim and Leighton. He thought Leighton could "cover the research angles, faculty relationships, and details of university administration" while Swim could look into "financing, tax angles, experience with patents, infringements, and so forth." Leighton was still a colonel in the Army but his release was expected shortly.

Tresidder found that Swim and Leighton, and later Swain, were willing to form a survey committee. He asked the trio "to act in behalf of the University in exploring the advisability of establishing an Industrial Research Institute at Stanford." Tresidder wanted to be in a position after their eastern trip "to formulate a specific plan for such an institute at Stanford." He could hardly have moved faster or more to the point.

One of the reasons Tresidder wanted to do something about a research institute arose from his situation in the University. For various reasons he was being criticized by many faculty members. Thus, he was reluctant to bring the faculty into the picture on the institute. The president gave the impression to some — and indeed said as much on one occasion — that by organizing and operating a separate research institute he could "show the faculty a new way to get some things done." Whatever his motivations might have been, he did not hold back.

By this time (September 1945), Atholl McBean, a San Francisco business executive, had been in touch with Tresidder and Alvin Eurich (Stanford's vice president) on a similar institute idea that had grown, at least in part, out of a Pacific Research Foundation initiative in Southern California. For some time, the Swim and McBean efforts went along independently of each other except for Tresidder's and Eurich's involvement in both. The two Stanford officers wanted to see which one offered the most promise and whether or not the two could be combined.

The Swim-Swain-Leighton group, calling themselves "The Three Musketeers" at Swim's suggestion, lost no time in setting up an eastern trip. They visited a dozen research centers in the east and midwest during a two-week period immediately after Thanksgiving in 1945. Some of the people they met were later to be consulted by others about the formation of SRI. One of them, Dr. J. E. Hobson, was to become the second head of SRI in a little more than two years.

The Musketeers met with Dr. Earl P. Stevenson and Ray Stevens, the top officers of Arthur D. Little in Cambridge, Massachusetts, and then with Nathaniel Sage, director of MIT's Division of Industrial Cooperation. Swain and Leighton went to see Dr. R. E. Swain (a father-son meeting) at American Cyanamid and then visited Air Reduction and U.S. Industrial Chemicals. Swim and Leighton sought advice from Dr. E. R. (Eddie) Weidlein, director of The Mellon Institute in Pittsburgh, and Dr. Clyde Williams, chief executive of Battelle Memorial Institute in Ohio. They also saw the chairman of the chemistry department at nearby OSU and the head of the University's Research Foundation.

Leighton made several visits alone, including Indiana Steel Products and International Minerals and Chemicals (IMC). Then, much to the points at hand, he had long sessions with Hobson at Armour Research Foundation (now IITRE) followed by meetings with Dr. Harold Vagtborg, director, and Dr. George E. Ziegler, chief scientist, at the newly-formed Midwest Research Institute.

The call on Williams at Battelle was the first of many contacts he was to have with others on the West Coast who soon became involved in the Stanford institute idea. While serving as head of the National Research Council's War Metallurgy Committee during World War II, Williams had looked into the possibility of creating a research institute in California. He was much involved in the aircraft industry and had many contacts with the state's metallurgical and other manufacturing companies. Some of his business friends suggested that Battelle open a branch in Southern California.

Williams was enthusiastic about the idea and soon was in contact with Dr. Maurice Nelles at Lockheed, who later would enter the Stanford picture through his own research foundation initiative. Nelles encouraged Williams to move ahead on a Battelle plan. Williams was an energetic man and went to work on the idea. His plan included financial support by several West Coast companies, and he got promises for a few research contracts. But, much to his disappointment, the plan was "turned down cold" by Battelle's Board. The Pacific Coast was "too far away" in the view of several directors. All this occurred in the winter of 1944-45.

Several times during later years, Williams said that the Battelle decision was "a very bad one indeed." He felt keenly that Battelle had "missed the boat" on the West Coast.

But, in late 1945 beginning with Leighton's visit, and for years thereafter, he supported the Stanford initiative in every way he could. SRI owes him a vote of thanks for all he did by way of advice and being "a friend and promoter" of the California initiative. It was the start of a good relationship between SRI and Battelle that continues to this day.

Leighton's contact with a research engineer, W. E. McKibben, at Indiana Steel was to have an interesting connection with SRI in the years to come. McKibben had known E. Finley Carter during their earlier days at General Electric, and they had kept in touch with each other. In the meantime, Carter had taken an executive post at Sylvania. McKibben mentioned the Leighton visit to his friend merely as a matter of general interest. Carter had more than a general interest. He looked into the situation and watched it closely. Ten years later, he joined SRI after coming into direct contact with it as a client. Following Hobson's resignation in the mid-1950s, he became SRI's third executive director.

The Musketeers were back on the Stanford Campus by mid-December. Things began to move rapidly. They met in San Francisco with Frank F. Walker, the University's comptroller and financial vice president, and with Morris M. Doyle, Stanford's legal counsel. On December 21, they delivered a report to Tresidder. Its title went directly to the point — "Stanford Research Institute."

The late-1945 meeting in San Francisco was not Frank Walker's first or last association with early events in SRI's history. Almost two decades later he recalled "the conversations with my old friends, Dud Swim, Bert Swain, and Phil Leighton." Walker, Swim, and Leighton were campmates at the Bohemian Grove. In Walker's words — "We 'romanced' about the institute at considerable length during our leisure time under the redwoods. Bert Swain used to visit our camp very frequently, and of course joined in the discussions."

From Walker's recollections and from the record, it is clear that Swim, more than Leighton or Swain, had become by mid-1945 the leader of the Musketeers. This came about, in part, because of Swain's earlier retirement at Stanford.

In developing the committee's recommendation to Tresidder, the three men were specific; Stanford Research Institute should be created and it should be a separate corporation. They urged prompt filing of legal papers.

The Musketeers felt that the word "industrial" in the name would be limiting, so they called for the word "Stanford" instead. Their reasons were twofold — "in order that the University might directly receive credit for the undertaking and derive prestige therefrom" and so "the Institute may have full advantage of the prestige and 'acceptance' that goes with the name." The concept of mutual benefit in their reasoning is clear.

The committee thought that a separate corporation was necessary for tax and administrative reasons and so as to segregate more easily various industrial research activities from the University's teaching work. Also — and quite important — the Musketeers said that a separate entity would permit carrying out work on a confidential basis with industry.

The group urged that the new institute be nonprofit with a self-perpetuating board of directors separate from the Stanford Trustees but with the University's chief financial officer as a member of the board. Complete control over the institute by Stanford was visualized in the form of a management contract between the two institutions. This was one approach, but it was hardly an arrangement to attract top-flight directors for a new institute.

The Musketeers' plan included an interesting financial arrangement. The group thought "... the Institute would pay, say, 50% of its annual earnings, after the first three years of operation, to the University ..." This was to be in return for "the use of the name 'Stanford' ... sponsorship by the University, and ... use of the University's facilities." Had this scheme been adopted, it most certainly would have severely restricted SRI's early development. But, some return to Stanford was certainly justified under the circumstances

Working capital for the institute was to come from bank credit and other borrowings. Swim said he would be willing to act as guarantor on bank credit or lend money directly to the organization. The Musketeers — and also Frank Walker — knew that Stanford was in no position to divert funds to the institute.

The idea of patent income had intrigued the Stanford committee from the outset. Various possibilities were discussed, leading to a recommendation that "a Western Development Corporation" be created to hold and manage patents. Morris Doyle, however, felt that the institute should hold its own patents.

Three action points were then laid before Stanford's president. The first was immediate incorporation; the trio offered to be "incorporating directors" on a "pro tem" basis. Then, they suggested Henry B. Hass, chairman of Purdue's chemistry department, as a possible executive director. Finally, they submitted a draft press release urging that it be sent out by January 1, 1946, so that Stanford's leadership position could be preserved.

Why were Swim and his colleagues in such a hurry? The New Year was only ten days away. The clue is in the word "leadership." Swim was aware of an initiative under way by Atholl McBean with Tresidder and Eurich and was afraid it might lead to an institute outside the University or to one under "other auspices" within Stanford. McBean knew of the Musketeer plan in general but was not interested in joining forces with Swim. The two men were not on close terms.

Tresidder was dealing primarily with the University committee while Eurich, Stanford's vice president, was working closely with McBean. Tresidder knew that eventually one of the groups would drop out of the picture, and he thought it would be the Stanford committee. His reasoning was obvious; McBean was promising financial support by western business. But this is a story for a later chapter.

An appendix to the Swim-Swain-Leighton report gives more information about their study. They agreed that the institute's objectives should be to serve industry, speed up industrial and technological development, help on regional growth, support basic research, train people, improve relationships between Stanford and business, widen viewpoints and experiences of the faculty, provide student fellowships and add to faculty salaries. The latter point, especially, was expected to attract faculty interest to their proposal.

The group marshalled several arguments on why a research institute should be created in the West. They pointed to "the remarkable success of similar ventures in the East," emphasized that no such center existed in the West even though "the opportunity is ample," and said that "both government and industry are more research-minded than ever before." The trio was enthusiastic about the Pacific Coast being "unique both in the opportunity ... and in the prospects for future growth." Then, they told Tresidder — "It is the unanimous opinion of the key men in eastern research institutes that, properly handled, it cannot fail."

All this was followed by even more reasons why Stanford should sponsor the new western research institute. They said it had "educational functions," could be "a source of income" and would "improve contacts and relations between the University and industry." There were more arguments along this line such as attracting "large government contracts" and placing Stanford in a leading position on "industrial and regional development of the Pacific Coast." They went on to say that Stanford's physical location and standing were "favorable factors" — a point that needed no elaboration.

Somewhat in the form of a peroration, the committee returned to an urgency theme. "Research has come of age ... the new emphasis on research, particularly organized interrelated projects, must be recognized and a mechanism developed to meet and take advantage of this emphasis. The university that does not do this will be left on the shelf." In retrospect, this rush to judgment was overdone but is understandable from the setting. The basic reasoning was on target. But, of course, Stanford's future by no means depended on creating an SRI.

The Three Musketeers did not overlook a few reasons why Stanford might not want to sponsor the institute. They recognized an inherent conflict of interest by stressing an institute's primary goal of serving industry and applying knowledge while a university must advance knowledge through basic research and education. They were blunt in saying "these two primary interests cannot be mixed without loss to both ... Is the gain worth the loss?"

The group went on to say that "scores of second- and third-rate colleges and universities are planning research institutes" and predicted that "many of these ventures will fail." They wondered in writing if this might create a situation "which is best avoided by remaining out of the field, or should the field be entered with such strength and aggressiveness as to ensure leadership and success?"

Swim, Swain, and Leighton were quick to answer their own question and did so with an admonition and a plea. "Now is the golden time to start, before industry has been able to get the men for its contemplated research expansion and before the National Research Foundation is implemented." The plea was simple and direct — "Positive decisions should be reached and action taken without delay ..." Then they tried to give Tresidder a basis for acting right away. "One research contract is available. This is all that is needed to start."

In retrospect, this report to the president of Stanford University by a committee of two faculty members and one alumnus from the business world is quite remarkable. In implementation, SRI was affiliated directly with the University rather than being somewhat remote legally as suggested by the committee. On other points, however, the committee's recommendations were adopted in most respects by the University Trustees and to a great extent have guided SRI's operations over the years.

Tresidder was quick to thank the three-man committee for its "excellent report." He told them he had to discuss all phases with the Board of Trustees and hence could not announce the new organization immediately. He promised to keep them informed and recognized "the need to 'lead the parade' if we can." Tresidder was waiting for further developments from the separate McBean-Eurich-Tresidder group before acting on the Swim-Swain-Leighton proposal.

The time had come by early February of 1946 to bring the two efforts into focus. Tresidder wrote to Swim at his first home in Twin Falls, Idaho. He told of a visit by Dr. Henry Heald (president of Illinois Institute of Technology) in line with "plans I had previously discussed with you." This indicates that Tresidder had told Swim earlier about McBean's interest in a research institute affiliated with Stanford. Swim said many years later that this discussion was "in very general terms — no specifics."

The letter to Swim mentions a meeting with Heald by a group of San Francisco industrialists headed by McBean and says that Heald had recommended against plans for setting up a separate Pacific Research Foundation (a Los Angeles proposal) and had gone on to urge the industrialists to ask Stanford to form an institute.

Tresidder's letter of February 12 gave Swim a summary of the situation at the moment.

> "I had lunch with Mr. McBean last Thursday. He is now engaged in seeing whether or not such an initial sum ($500,000) can be raised. Meanwhile, Mr. Eurich is in the East, and will interview two promising prospects for director of such an institute.
>
> "Henry Heald's recommendations to the industrialists followed the ideas of Leighton, Swain, and yourself except that he did not believe the institute should be entirely divorced from Stanford and suggested that the trustees of the Institute be drawn from the existing University Board of Trustees.
>
> "I am presenting the Heald report to the Board of Trustees ... and will ask for action along the lines of that recommendation."

Tresidder's account of Heald's recommendations appears to be somewhat in error. The University committee had not recommended an institute "entirely divorced" from the University. Furthermore, Heald's report did not confine membership in the board of directors to University Trustees.

Apparently, Tresidder was overly concerned that somehow an institute outside the University and particularly away from the president's involvement might get started. Some faculty members at the University had this image of his attitude.

The main significance of Tresidder's letter is that it brought all three institute initiatives into one effort. He thanked Swim for the "spade work" his group had done and expressed the hope that money would soon be available to get the project started. Also, he said "it is the hope of the Atholl McBean group that the men sponsoring the Pacific Research Institute can be induced to join our movement." Tresidder was referring to Dr. Maurice Nelles, Morlan A. Visel, and Ernest Black, and to the Pacific Research Foundation. In any event, Tresidder and Eurich began concentrating their attention on the moving force led by McBean.

There was, however, at least one further discussion between Swim and Eurich on the institute plan. Swim wired Eurich from Twin Falls (Idaho) in late February with an indirect question and an offer of help. "If you desire that Leighton, Swain, and I carry on organizing research institute, kindly advise return night letter ... Can make California March 3 to 6 inclusive. Available monthly later." Eurich replied immediately saying, "Eager to have you here March 4 or 5. Want to get organization set up soon."

Obviously, Swim was anxious to be involved. Eurich wanted to retain his interest even though McBean was now the key influence.

Swim did visit the University in early March and was brought up-to-date on the McBean-Eurich-Tresidder plan. The meeting was held by Eurich with Swim, Swain, and Leighton present. The group more or less agreed on several points growing out of the earlier Musketeers' report and subsequent conversations. They agreed definitely on the name "Stanford Research Institute." They decided that the University-Institute relationship should be either (1) the University as sole member (or owner), or (2) the University to appoint all board members and have power to dissolve the entity and to veto any action by the board of directors.

They also decided that the University should own all buildings "assigned" to the institute and that SRI should pay a rental for buildings and other facilities. They adopted a statement on financial obligations to Stanford.

> "The University shall receive a royalty of 50% of the net earnings of
> the Institute payable annually and commencing after the third year
> of operations. This royalty is to compensate the University for the
> use of the Stanford name and sponsorship, of the library and incidental
> use of laboratories and other facilities maintained by the University for
> educational and research purposes."

The notes of their meeting end with a firm statement on financial liability. "The Institute will be financed primarily by research projects undertaken for industry. It is at no time to be a financial liability to the University."

Eurich thanked the committee for all the three men had done. The meeting ended with general agreement that there was little more for the group to do for the time being, particularly since the University was planning to ask counsel to prepare proposed articles of incorporation for the new institute. Eurich told his associates that Morris Doyle would handle the matter.

Many years later Dudley Swim recalled two interesting aspects of the March 1946 meetings at Stanford. One involved a conversation with Eurich while they were en

A Redwood Grove Meeting

route from the Eurich home to the campus to see Tresidder. Eurich asked Swim if he favored direct involvement of the President's Office in the proposed research institute. Swim said his reply was an unqualified "no" based on comments he had received from directors of several university-affiliated research organizations in the eastern part of the country.

Swim felt this reply was a great disappointment to Eurich and that the latter knew Tresidder would not look with favor on such an approach. Swim later wrote about the meeting with Tresidder in these words: "It was evident that this feature of our report was not very warmly received in the President's office at Stanford."

His assessment was quite correct. Neither Tresidder nor Eurich had any thought of setting up a Stanford institute and then simply standing aside.

This brings up again an impression Swim portrayed, based perhaps on his exuberant personality. Tresidder, Eurich, and others came to feel that, in effect, Swim wanted to be the "chairman" of the institute. Whether they were right or wrong, the situation was awkward. Furthermore, they thought Swim might offer some financial support. However, this would have clouded similar possibilities with McBean. There is no question that Swim wanted to have some post in the proposed institute. He expected at least to be one of the directors, if not the chairman. He said as much in private conversations during the 1960s. As for financial support, he was not interested in being a donor without active involvement in the endeavor. Several times in later years, Swim told me that he had some sort of tacit quid pro quo understanding in mind but that things did not work out along these lines. In any event, it is unlikely that McBean, Tresidder and Swim could have worked together easily. Eurich, at least, was well aware of the situation.

The second part of Swim's recollections of the March 6 (1946) meeting at Stanford is direct and to the point: "... the curtain was pulled down and we heard or knew nothing more for quite an interval." His feelings were hurt; he felt pushed aside. In any event, Tresidder and Eurich cast their lot with McBean. Both felt they had done everything they should have done in bringing the work of The Three Musketeers — and especially Swim's involvement — to an end.

A sidelight of Swim's political and economic stance is pertinent. He was an ultra conservative and often spoke of "breast beating" and "do-gooder" liberals. This did not endear him to the main body of the Stanford faculty. Nor did he aspire to be a part of the so-called Business Establishment. Swim spent a lot of time with his family and on personal interests. He had an image as a "loner" in business life and had no real ties to McBean and his San Francisco friends.

Swim was outspoken on his conservative beliefs, perhaps best illustrated by a comment he made in later years during a visit to SRI and to the Gibson home. Upon being given directions to a room — "upstairs and turn left" — he replied, "You know very well I can never do that."

While Tresidder and Swim were controversial in many ways, Swain and Leighton certainly were not. But essentially all were working within the Stanford structure, leaving to others the very necessary dealings with the business commumty. This role on the institute idea was carried primarily by Eurich, especially with McBean, the key actor in the play. This is all the more interesting in that Eurich's professional background was in education, not business or the physical sciences. He was truly the connecting link between Stanford and business on the institute idea.

In April 1946, Earl Stevenson of Arthur D. Little visited Stanford at Tresidder's invitation. He met with Tresidder, Swain, and Leighton on Saturday, April 5, to discuss the institute plan. He found uncertainty at the University on whether the institute should be a profit-making or a nonprofit corporation. It was natural that Stanford should seek Stevenson's view, particularly in light of Arthur D. Little's profit-making status contrasted with the nonprofit character of Mellon, Battelle, and Armour. Stevenson urged that SRI should be a profit-making organization.

Stevenson's reasoning ran along these lines. He thought able people could more easily be attracted to a profit-making institution. Presumably, he was thinking of people with industrial research interests. His contention was that profit gives a business rather than an academic "slant" to an enterprise. He went on to say that the handling of inventions presents income tax problems in a nonprofit institute. He concluded by stating that "the management of this kind of enterprise hardly seems to me to be a desirable responsibility of the board of trustees — better an independent enterprise under a business board, with the position of the University (being) that of a major stockholder with appropriate representation on the board of directors."

As will be seen later, University counsel did not subscribe to Stevenson's views and SRI was soon to be set up as a nonprofit corporation.

Some eighteen years later, Stevenson recalled his impressions of the mid-1940s at Stanford. He thought the University Trustees wanted a profit-making organization but that Tresidder was much opposed to the idea. His impression on the latter point was certainly correct. Tresidder saw no place in the Stanford structure for a profit-making enterprise, and he did not welcome Stevenson's strong advice. Leighton remembers the conversations as being "brusque, cold, and short."

Stevenson and his associates at Arthur D. Little continued to feel over the years that SRI might better have been created as a regular profit-making organization. They expressed this view on several occasions. Some twenty years after SRI was formed, Ray Stevens of ADL outlined his views.

> *"I confess to sharing, and having shared the view that Stanford (Research Institute) could well have started as a private enterprise operation still with close ties to the University. The group of advisors was heavily weighted from the nonprofit institute area, and they have been able and successful missionaries in propagating their faith. Further, I will also confess that I have told many people that we here would have found in any research organizations far more serious competitors had they been profit-oriented organizations. I still feel this to be true, but it may not be. It may be that the differences are less great than they once were, particularly with respect to a considerable portion of activity that is sponsored directly or indirectly by the government."*

It might have been feasible for SRI to be a profit-making company affiliated with Stanford in some way but with an entirely different name. But the University and the western business leaders wanted both a University tie and the Stanford name. This practically guaranteed that SRI would be a nonprofit organization.

During the events from early March through December of 1946, Eurich occasionally sought advice from Swain and Leighton in their capacities as faculty members. Swain was helpful, but as a professor emeritus he did not wish to involve himself too deeply in University matters. Leighton, on the other hand, continued his great interest in the project and promoted the idea whenever and wherever he had an opportunity. He prepared a short description of the basic concept and used it in speeches before various business and industrial groups.

"Despite the success of these institutes and foundations in the East, there is as yet no similar organization on the Pacific Coast. Some of us at Stanford began investigating the situation as far back as 1940. We had to find answers to a number of questions, such as:

> *"Does the opportunity exist?*
>
> *"Should such an institute be connected with a university?*
>
> *"If so, should it be a separate corporation, or a division of the University?*
>
> *"If a separate corporation, should it be tax-paying or nonprofit?*
>
> *"Should it have its own staff and facilities, or should it use the facilities at the University?*
>
> *"To what extent should it emphasize pure research?*
>
> *"To what extent should it point toward contract research, to what extent should it seek patents of its own?"*

Leighton said that the Musketeers had sought answers to these questions on the premise that the purpose of any new institute should be to "serve industry" and that if it cannot be useful to industry it had no "reason to exist." Then, he answered his own questions.

Dr. J. W. McBain

Professor of Chemistry
Stanford University

Consultant to The Three Musketeers

*"The answers we have found are: the opportunity for a research
institute on the Pacific Coast does exist, it should be connected with a
university, and Stanford is favored because of its location and because it
is privately endowed. It should be a separately incorporated tax-free
institute, with its own staff and facilities, and it should place emphasis
first on contract research, second on pure research, last on seeking
patents of its own. A relation should be established with the University
by which faculty men may be retained as consultants and by which
students, where desirable, can take their thesis work in the institute."*

These words are direct and to the point. Leighton also reported that "an organization of this type has been approved by the Stanford Board of Trustees." He said, "It is
planned to start on a small scale and grow as the work comes in." His outline mentions
that Mellon, Armour, and Purdue Research Foundation started with just one research
contract. Then he said, "We intend to do the same, and we already have the contract."

Leighton had indeed arranged a contract to start SRI. It was with the Chemical
Corps of the U.S. Army. He recounted years later with a smile how this contract entered
SRI's history. During the committee trip through the East in late 1945, it occurred to
him that their report would be more persuasive if the group had a research project in
hand. Leighton got a commitment letter from the Chemical Corps and showed it to
Tresidder. Tresidder saw the 30% overhead recovery rate and said, "I think we should
keep this contract at the University." Over the years the contract and its successors
provided more than $1.0 million of overhead recovery to the University. However, the
absence of the contract at SRI did not hold back the new institute's development.

The final remarks in Leighton's paper set up a key goal for the proposed
organization.

*"... it is our hope that the Stanford Research Institute will have a
regional as well as an industrial significance, that it may undertake
work leading to development and use of Pacific Coast resources, and that
it may thereby play a leading part in the growth of the West."*

Leighton and his colleagues had no way of knowing that SRI would make considerable progress toward this goal and that it would become an organization of national and international significance. The record is clear, however, that The Three Musketeers played a key role in bringing SRI into existence. Although two other initiatives were involved, many of the concepts of the Swim-Swain-Leighton committee found their way into SRI's formation. They prepared the base within Stanford on which the McBean-sponsored institute was developed.

Although contacts between Tresidder and Eurich on the one hand and the Swim-Swain-Leighton group on the other more or less came to an end in early spring of 1946. Eurich did keep Swain and Leighton abreast of events. Leighton in particular continued to promote the whole idea.

My first contacts with Swim, Swain, and Leighton were in the late 1930s. I saw them on occasion in 1945 and several times in 1946 — always one at a time. Thus, I was aware of their interests but gave little thought to the matter — and indeed forgot about it as the months went by. But many times after 1947 I had long talks with each of the Musketeers. Meanwhile, Athol McBean was the dominant man in SRI's early years. The Stanford committee faded into a silent background. Only a few people were aware of its contributions.

In 1956, SRI published a brief account of its early history beginning with the Stanford committee. I was the author and soon ran into some turbulence. Although McBean was front and center in the story and properly so, he felt it implied far too much about the Musketeers' role. He let his views be known in no uncertain terms. I then had two conversations with Eurich who had left Stanford in 1948. He was quite clear on events; McBean was the "founding father" but the Musketeers had made an important contribution in helping lay the groundwork at Stanford.

This was my view from the beginning. Furthermore, the record speaks for itself. In partial recognition of his contributions, Swim was later appointed to an SRI Advisory Committee, which pleased him very much indeed. But even so, some personality differences among Swim, McBean, and others continued to blur the picture. In light of this situation, little more was said by any of the principals about the Musketeer events of 1945 and 1946 leading to SRI's formation.

Recognizing the place of The Three Musketeers in SRI's early history in no way detracts from the key roles played by McBean, Tresidder, and Eurich. The result adds to the credit for all of them.

Swim, Swain, and Leighton articulated an idea, and it was a good one indeed. Eurich, McBean, and Tresidder made things happen, and they did so with dispatch. But "in betwixt the meantimes" — to borrow a humorist's line — there was an assist from Southern California. Another three-man committee was at work. But, this is another chapter in the origin of SRI.* ∎

---

*As is evident in the next two chapters, there was some overlap in the three initiatives that led to SRI's formation. Thus, there is some duplication among these three chapters. This is intentional so as to make each story complete.

The Southern Trio

The time for a western research institute has arrived.

— MAURICE NELLES - 1945

ONE DAY IN MID-JULY 1944, the staff assistant to the director of research at Lockheed Aircraft Corporation was busily at work in his office in Burbank, California, when a laboratory expediter, Morlan A. Visel, asked to see him for a few minutes. Dr. Maurice Nelles had joined Lockheed in early 1940; Visel arrived in 1942. Although the two men had vastly different backgrounds, they shared an interest in the future of the aircraft industry.

Nelles and Visel had a long talk during which Visel advanced an idea that later became one of three initiatives leading to the formation of SRI. In due course, Ernest L. Black, Visel's supervisor, who was in charge of planning, shop work and procurement in Lockheed's research laboratory, joined forces with the two men.

The varying backgrounds of Nelles, Black and Visel are interesting. Nelles, an electrical and aeronautical engineer, received two degrees from the University of South Dakota and a Ph.D. from Harvard. His first industrial position was as a research scientist for Allied Chemical and Dye Corporation. He came to California in 1934 and was employed in a similar position by Union Oil Company. This was followed by a research post with Riverside Portland Cement Company. Following a tour of duty with the U.S. Navy and just prior to World War II, Nelles joined Lockheed as a research engineer. He helped equip and staff the company's engineering research laboratory.

At the time of Visel's visit, Nelles also was serving part-time on a "dollar-a-year" basis as deputy director of the office of production research and development in the War Production Board. In this capacity, he was responsible for many government contracts with Battelle Memorial Institute, Armour Research Foundation, and various universities and industrial organizations. This experience led Nelles to believe that a research institute was needed in the western part of the United States.

During World War II, Nelles was at various times a member of at least ten committees of the National Advisory Committee for Aeronautics and served on several committees of the National Research Council. Also, he was Lockheed's representative to the Industrial Research Institute and had been the company's spokesman on various engineering and manufacturing councils.

Morlan Visel was the son of a California business executive and financier who, upon his death, left a considerable estate to his son. He was much interested in racing cars and power boats but had no special ambitions in business. Following United States entry into

World War II, Visel joined Lockheed so as to contribute directly to the war effort. His superior at Lockheed, Ernest Black (who, in turn, worked for Nelles), was a graduate electrical engineer with a flair for salesmanship. He had been employed earlier by Vega Aircraft Corporation. When Vega was absorbed by Lockheed in the late 1930s, Black was given a post in the engineering laboratory where he later met Visel.

Visel's proposal in July 1944 was simple and straightforward. He had a plan to use some of his own financial resources, Nelles' scientific and technical talents, and Black's promotional ability in a new venture. He wanted to create a research laboratory where the three men could work on whatever might interest them.

Nelles told Visel that he personally would not care for such a limited activity and suggested to his visitor that even he probably would soon tire of the venture, even though it might well be successful. Nelles went on, however, to predict that, with some financial support to develop a plan, it would be possible to interest a few California businessmen in sponsoring a nonprofit research organization similar to Battelle in Ohio.

He explained to Visel how Battelle and Armour operated and speculated on possibilities for a contract research center of their type in the western part of the United States. Nelles told his colleague that industrial leaders in the West would have to be "sold" on the need for such a new institute. Then, he suggested that Visel might be interested in financing the exploratory stages leading possibly to an independent, nonprofit, applied research organization in California. The meeting broke up on this note.

A few days later Visel telephoned Nelles and announced Black's enthusiastic response to the institute idea. And, he indicated a willingness to finance what he called the "education phase" of the proposed project. As events subsequently developed, Visel invested about $20,000 in the project. This is how he played his role as a member of The Southern Trio that contributed to SRI's formation in late 1946. However, he was more or less a silent partner.

One of the first things Nelles and Black did was to articulate the need and a plan for a research institute in the West as they visualized the situation at the time. The result was a document on need, objectives, organization and methods for the proposed institution.

The "need" section of the Nelles-Black paper is summarized in one sentence: "... there is no independent research laboratory in the West to which industry can turn for the solution of its research problems." Several objectives were outlined for a Pacific Research Foundation (PRF). They wanted it to "bring together various interests in the West" that might help in expanding industrial research.

Nelles and Black thought the Foundation should provide "a staff of competent technical personnel" who would be available to "all who need their services." They wanted the new center to have "laboratory facilities" and to "promote research activities in the West." Also, they said the Foundation would carry out research "for groups of companies and associates" and for "Government."

The document also called for a nonprofit organization with a governing body including representatives from both industry and academic institutions.

About a year after Visel made his proposal, Nelles got in touch with Stanford University. He wrote to Samuel Morris, believing that he was still dean of engineering at the University; his letter explained the goals and aims of the PRF. The reply was from Dr. Hugh Skilling, who was acting dean at the time; Morris had resigned to become general manager and chief engineer in the Department of Water and Power of Los Angeles

County. Skilling told Nelles he had discussed the matter with Dr. Frederick Terman who was about to become Stanford's dean of engineering.

Although Terman was just returning from wartime service at MIT's Radiation Laboratories, he was a member of a well-known Stanford family and had been on the University's engineering faculty for many years before World II — in fact, since his graduation from Stanford. He was later to become Provost of the University and vice chairman of the SRI board of directors.

Skilling agreed that the proposed research center on the Pacific Coast would be of great interest to all people involved in engineering research and education. He assured Nelles that the PRF and Stanford's School of Engineering could be "mutually helpful" and thus would "strengthen each other." Nelles felt this response was quite affirmative and quickly passed the news to Black and Visel.

Black pointed out many years later that Skilling's reply shows that Stanford learned about the Pacific Research Foundation prior to the time Tresidder, Stanford's president, became interested in two similar initiatives, one by a committee within the University and one that came from San Francisco. This may be true in a broad sense, but neither Terman nor Skilling mentioned the PRF to Tresidder or Eurich in mid-1945 or later.

Nelles and his two colleagues talked many times during the last half of 1944 and the first part of 1945 about plans for a new research foundation. Each sought opinions and suggestions from associates and friends. They moved with dispatch after the exchange with Skilling. On August 23, 1945, the Pacific Research Foundation was formed with offices at 417 Hill Street in Los Angeles. The location was known as the Subway Terminal Building. Black resigned from Lockheed and became the one and only PRF employee.

The basic purposes spelled out in the Foundation's Articles were general and wide-ranging. It was to engage in "scientific investigations and research" aimed at creating "new or improved devices, techniques, and methods." The basic idea was that the results should be useful in the "arts" of production, industry, agriculture, transportation, communications, and construction. The Foundation was expected to "develop, acquire, and exploit inventions" and was called upon to do the same on "new and useful ideas, theories and thoughts." Finally, the founders wanted the research center to publish "periodicals, magazines, newspapers, books, and brochures."

Although the PRF was to grant scholarships and assist institutions of higher learning, it is clear that applied research for industry was the main objective. This was emphasized in a PRF brochure published soon after its formation. "The Foundation is being created by and for the industries of the West... On-the-spot facilities for research and experimental engineering will be available to both large and small industries..."

Nelles and his associates felt that the Foundation's program should be developed only after full consultation with business, research and educational leaders throughout the West. The first brochure emphasized the point. "It is desired that this organization be the product of the crystallized judgment of all in the West who are interested in its formation." To this end, Black was asked to travel throughout the area to seek advice and suggestions.

The people consulted by Black included many of the West's business leaders in the mid-1940s, as well as chief executives of several of the nation's contract research organizations and presidents of major universities (other than Stanford) in California. Among others, he contacted Fred B. Ortman (president of Gladding, McBean & Co.), Lee

DR. MAURICE NELLES
Leader of The Southern Trio

DeForest (president of Lee DeForest Laboratories), Paul Davies (president of Food Machinery Mfg. Co.), Clyde Williams (director of Battelle Memorial Institute), Harold Vagtborg (director of Midwest Research Institute), Jesse Hobson (director of Armour Research Foundation), and Fred Lindvall (professor of electrical engineering at the California Institute of Technology).

During Black's travels up and down California on the research institute idea, the possibility of university sponsorship was explored with Dr. Robert Millikan, president of Cal Tech, and with Dr. Robert Gordon Sproul, president of the University of California. Millikan felt that with heavy orientation of the new organization to applied research and development, Cal Tech sponsorship would not be appropriate. Sproul said that University of California auspices would not be feasible because the concept of granting proprietary rights (growing out of research projects) to private parties was inconsistent with the principles upon which a tax-supported university must operate.

Nelles heard in the summer of 1945 that Governor Warren of California had appointed an Advisory Committee on Coordination of Research Facilities. Hence, early in June he wrote to the Governor about the proposed Pacific Research Foundation. The reply was from Alexander Heron, director of the State Reconstruction and Re-employment Commission.

Heron knew of the PRF plan and told Nelles it was highly desirable to enlist the interest of his Commission in the project. Stuart Walsh, one of Heron's associates, told Ernest Black in late July that the "R & R Commission" would be glad to hear about the PRF at a meeting in Los Angeles in early August. He said Governor Warren was expected to attend.

In the meantime, Walsh heard the full story from Nelles, Black and Visel and was quite impressed. He suggested to Black that emphasis in the upcoming presentation be given to recent institute initiatives in Kansas and Alabama and to "the qualifications of Dr. Nelles." Heron later made arrangements for Nelles and Black to make the same presentation to the Citizens Advisory Committee on Research Facilities. This occurred on October 10, 1945. Along with other members of the committee, Henry J. Kaiser and Robert E. Gross (head of the Lockheed Aircraft Corporation) heard the Nelles-Black explanation. Among other things, Nelles told the group that "a great need for a western research institute is at hand."

Several western newspapers and magazines carried stories in August and September 1945, about plans for a new nonprofit research institute on the West Coast. The publicity arose from a presentation on August 6 to Governor Warren by Perry Helser of Gladding, McBean & Co. and Ernest Black. Black was quoted as saying (prior to the meeting with Warren) that "discussions have been held with about 100 different industrialists." He went on to say, "We're putting all their ideas together into a concrete plan."

Black viewed himself as the catalyst and said the industrialists would implement the plan. He felt that "if they don't, all kinds of little research laboratories will be springing up and none of them will be able to give the proper results." He was quoted as saying the new organization would be set up in Los Angeles or San Francisco and that Portland and Seattle interests favored a San Francisco location.

A newspaper story on Black's announcements was sent by a Los Angeles attorney, Frank Belcher, to Donald Tresidder at Stanford. Belcher added a note suggesting it might be possible to "put our foot in the door" to good advantage.

This note and clipping soon came to Alvin Eurich's attention. He was indeed interested and in late August asked both Belcher and L. H. Roseberry of Los Angeles for more information. He thought the Pacific Research Foundation had implications for Stanford and said it might be advisable to approach its backers to discuss possible relationships.

Roseberry was affiliated with the Security Trust National Bank in Los Angeles. Both he and Belcher were active on Stanford affairs in Southern California. Both were glad to be asked for help by the University. Belcher reported that some of the major companies in Southern California viewed the new foundation as "a promotional venture." Roseberry had a visit with Black and later told the University he found no "widespread demand amongst industry for the project." However, Roseberry urged Black to call on Eurich at Stanford.

The news from Belcher and Roseberry reached Eurich at Stanford at about the same time Tresidder received Dudley Swim's outline of his ideas on a new research institute and shortly before Atholl McBean of San Francisco was to enter the picture directly through Eurich. Thus, the three initiatives were soon to center on Stanford's president

THE SOUTHERN TRIO

Dr. Maurice Nelles
Ernest L. Black
Morlan A. Visel

A Los Angeles Initiative

and vice president. Eurich did not know that the Southern California effort had already come to McBean's attention.

Shortly after hearing from Belcher and Roseberry, Eurich asked his Stanford associate, David S. Jacobson, to look into the matter. Jacobson got in touch with Paul Holden, professor of industrial management in the University's Graduate School of Business. Holden, in turn, called on Atholl McBean, a San Francisco business executive and civic leader. He did this because of friendship with McBean on Business School matters. A report on the McBean contact soon reached Eurich through Jacobson.

McBean knew little about the PRF but said one of his Gladding, McBean associates in Southern California was active in the project. He had heard that some Southern California business people wanted to see such an activity established at the University of Southern California. McBean told Holden that some one-and-a-half years earlier he had indicated to Stanford a desire to see industry and the University work together more closely. Having had no response, McBean said he was "just sitting tight" but proposed that he and Holden look further into the PRF initiative. Holden, however, made plans to introduce McBean to Alvin Eurich.

Jacobson did not rely alone on Paul Holden for information about the PRF initiative. He went directly to the principals. The day before writing to Eurich about the Holden-McBean discussions, Jacobson wrote (on September 11) to the Pacific Research Foundation asking for information about the new institution and in particular sought a copy of its publication on "Science for Industry." Black's response was a visit to Stanford in mid-October.

Upon finding Eurich away from his office, Black called on Jacobson and explained plans for the Foundation. Shortly thereafter, he told Roseberry that Jacobson was "well pleased" with the plans and had promised to discuss them with both Tresidder and Eurich.

McBean and Eurich first met each other in early autumn of 1945 at Holden's home in Palo Alto. Holden invited about a dozen people to join the two guests of honor. He "tipped off" Eurich to McBean's interests and urged him to talk at some length with the San Francisco business executive. The introduction took place as planned and touched off a long and fruitful relationship between the two men. SRI was one beneficiary of this association.

Meanwhile, the Nelles-Visel-Black contingent had come to the conclusion that there was indeed a latent interest among California business leaders in the research foundation idea. They arranged a dinner meeting in Los Angeles in September and invited a few people who had shown considerable interest. Their objective was to start making definite plans for the project. With this in mind, they developed an ambitious scheme for discussion with their guests.

> "The Foundation is to be financed by an endowment created by
> contributions from the western industries... It is felt that at least
> $5,000,000 should be provided to start the operation of the Foundation.
> The first 75 companies ... will be members of the Foundation.."

In preparing for the Los Angeles meeting, Nelles and Black wrote three more documents on the PRF. One dealt with a need for the new institution based on contacts with about 350 business executives responsible for placing research projects in outside research organizations. The second was a review of the national research situation including the role of contract research for both industry and government. The third was a description of purposes and methods of operation for the foundation.

Although the PRF proponents had contacted a great many executives, the number they mentioned as being responsible for research contracts is misleading. There simply were not that many people in the West actually awarding industrial research contracts. Nevertheless, they had circulated widely within western business circles.

A Nelles-Black paper on reasons why industrial executives placed research contracts in independent laboratories is interesting. They summarized their survey of 350 contacts in these terms.

Reasons for External Research Projects

Percent*	
24	Special type of problem — facilities not available
24	Company facilities being fully utilized
23	Need for highly-specialized, expensive equipment
18	Availability of specially-trained personnel
17	Desire to confirm internal research results
9	Opportunity to speed up programs
6	Possibilities of joining with other sponsors

*Percentage of contacts giving particular reasons.

The percentages show the distribution of their 350 so-called executive contacts who explained their reasons for contract research. Some, of course, gave Nelles and Black more than one reason why they used outside research organizations

The Nelles paper on the national research situation explained circumstances that seemed to favor creation of a new contract research organization. Among other things, he said:

> "The 'contract' method of research is now on a firm basis and a
> precedent has been set for conducting research on one problem in several
> laboratories. It now seems apparent that it will be expedient for
> companies to contract for research work in outside laboratories...
> On the basis of this probability the Pacific Research Foundation
> has been established."

The document prepared by Nelles and Black on operating methods for the Foundation included essential policies and procedures then being used by such organizations as Armour and Battelle. They mentioned, for example, research under contract with clients, granting of proprietary rights to clients, nondiscrimination in selecting clients and self-sufficiency in financial operations. They also restated the Foundation's purpose.

"The purpose of the Pacific Research Foundation, broadly, is to provide scientific research to the end that new and improved products shall be created; to provide research facilities to existing business establishments which do not have the equipment and specialized personnel to undertake the solution of their own technological problems; and to afford facilities to those industries which, although having well-equipped laboratories of their own, find it advantageous from time to time to have certain types of work done in an atmosphere removed from all direct contact with their own production problems; and for groups of companies to cooperatively sponsor mutual problems; and to stimulate basic and applied research in the universities of the West."

In retrospect, and in light of subsequent developments at SRI, this statement was a good expression of practical purpose. It was most helpful to Nelles and Black in explaining their ideas to business executives.

Black also had worked up a timetable for initiating the new operation. He hoped the first meeting of a board of trustees could be held by November 30, 1945, and that a director would be selected by December 1. His plan called for an investment of almost $2.0 million in buildings, staff and equipment, and for initial operations by mid-1946 at which time research investigations could be started. (Building costs were estimated at $7 per square foot, an interesting figure indeed by later standards.)

Black and his associates thought the investment by the end of 1946 should be in the order of $2.7 million and that after one more year and $300,000 in additional funds the organization could be self-supporting, except for further new equipment and buildings. The Nelles-Black-Visel group thought the Foundation should develop research programs in chemistry, metallurgy, bacteriology, electronics, ceramics, petroleum, mining, mechanics and structures.

The PRF group also prepared two alternative plans on a more modest scale. One called for an investment of $933,900 in 1946 and a buildup of staff to 40 persons. This plan envisioned that the Foundation would take over buildings and grounds at the vacant Pasadena Junior College Campus. The second plan called for a first-year investment of $301,000 and a staff of fifteen people.

Fred Ortman of Gladding, McBean & Co. attended the autumn-1945 dinner in Los Angeles and, among other things, suggested that a meeting be arranged with Atholl McBean in San Francisco. McBean already knew about Ortman's involvement (along with his associate, Perry Helser) on the PRF idea. Ortman thought McBean might well be interested in the idea and that his business affiliations would enable him to explore the matter with a few senior executives, particularly in the San Francisco area.

At the time, McBean was chairman of the board of directors of Gladding, McBean & Co. (a manufacturer of ceramics) and a director of several companies, including Standard Oil Company of California, Fireman's Fund Insurance Company, Pacific Mutual

Life Insurance Company, Pacific Telephone and Telegraph Company, and the Crocker First National Bank. He was also the chief executive of Newhall Land and Farming Company and a man of considerable energy and financial means.

Many years later, Ortman reflected on his suggestion about contacting McBean. "I knew that sooner rather than later Atholl's interest and involvement would have to be generated if the research institute idea was to get anywhere within California business circles." Furthermore, Ortman knew very well that he could move only so far on any such idea without McBean's support.

A meeting for Black with McBean was soon arranged by Ortman; it took place on November 6, 1945. Black explained the PRF plan and received a quick response; McBean was enthusiastic. This did not surprise Ortman who later said, "I knew the proposal would fascinate him."

It was then and there that Atholl McBean did his first great service for SRI. He told Black of his long-time interest in research and how he had employed the first graduate of Ohio State University in ceramics engineering. He was referring to Fred Ortman. According to later accounts by Black, McBean also told of his efforts (which were considerable) on civic programs leading to the two San Francisco bridges in the mid-1930s and to the City's World's Fair in 1939.

McBean was 66 years of age at the time of his first meeting with Black in 1945. He told his visitor that he welcomed another worthwhile idea to which he could devote his energies and enthusiasm.

On two occasions in later years during discussions on possible SRI retirement policies and plans, McBean said that age was not necessarily a factor in productivity, especially for new ideas, and that he had "founded SRI" after reaching age 65. He was impatient with fixed retirement-age plans and certainly would have been a strong supporter of the higher-age policy adopted by the Congress in 1978.

McBean expressed the view that the new research institute could best be operated within the framework of an existing nonprofit institution, preferably a university. He apparently felt at the time that business

ERNEST L. BLACK
A PRF Promoter

would hesitate to contribute substantial funds to an organization not affiliated with a tax-exempt educational institution. In any event, McBean often said in later years that this was "a fact without doubt." He informed Black of his long interest in and association with Stanford, his father-in-law's membership on the University's first Board of Trustees, and his own appointment as a consulting professor in the Graduate School of Business.

Before the day of their first meeting was over, McBean and Black had travelled to Stanford where they met with Eurich, vice president for academic affairs. Tresidder did not participate in this meeting. However, McBean and Tresidder met now and then during the next few months on the new idea. This sort of quick action — seeing Eurich the day he first met Black — was characteristic of McBean. He simply said to Black, "Now, we'll go down to Stanford" — then picked up the phone and called Paul Holden.

The meeting with Eurich was arranged by Holden who participated in the discussions. Following a two-hour session, McBean became convinced of Stanford's interest in the research institute idea and of Eurich's willingness to take some action. He proposed that someone be asked to study the situation, including such things as need, location, and scope. Also, he offered to pay the costs. Eurich suggested Dr. Henry Heald of the Illinois Institute of Technology and McBean agreed. Holden urged that economics research be included in the charter for the proposed institute; Eurich and McBean agreed. Apparently, Black had little to say at the November 6 session.

One of McBean's motivations in moving so quickly toward Stanford was recalled years later by D. J. Russell of Southern Pacific, one of SRI's founding directors. "He was most apprehensive that establishment of a Southern California organization would be detrimental to the interest of the San Francisco area." McBean's business interests were statewide and more, but he was first and foremost a Northern California man.

The McBean-Eurich meeting took place a mere five days following Tresidder's appointment of Swim, Swain, and Leighton as a University Committee "to formulate a specific plan" for a research institute at Stanford. This step was not discussed with McBean on November 6 except in very general terms — "We have a group looking into the idea and how it can best be organized at Stanford."

FRED ORTMAN
Connecting Link Between The Southern Trio and The Northern Troika

Holden promptly followed up the Stanford meeting with a letter to McBean in which he said, "Your visit takes the first real tangible step towards appraising this whole project in a way which will determine its practicability in the future."

Black quickly reported to Nelles on the meeting at Stanford. According to Nelles, Black said there was general agreement on organizing an institute within the University framework but with a separate board of directors, including some (but not all) of the Stanford Trustees.

Nelles had several meetings with McBean and others in the San Francisco area during the next several weeks. In addition, Black and McBean had a long session in San Francisco on November 14 during which they attempted to outline a plan of action for the Pacific Research Foundation. Their thoughts were put in writing and signed by both men.

The Black-McBean Plan

"1. *That no consideration should be given at this time to the purchase of a building.*

"2. *That present endeavors should be confined to the selection of a man qualified to determine the necessity for establishing a Research Foundation.*

"3. *That, if a Foundation is determined necessary, steps be taken immediately to formulate:*

　　a. *A program for its organization.*

　　b. *A plan of operation for the first year.*

"4. *That Mr. Alvin Eurich, Academic Vice President of Stanford University, be invited to undertake the selection and employment of a man qualified to determine the necessity for establishing a Foundation with the understanding*

　　a. *That Mr. Eurich's participation is purely in the interest of industry and does not commit the Foundation to a tie-in with Stanford University, and*

　　b. *That Mr. Eurich would select an appointee to make the investigation but would not actually employ him until he had informed Mr. Black or Mr. McBean of extent of funds required to finance the preliminary investigation and had allowed sufficient time to raise the funds necessary to permit the work to proceed promptly and without interruption."*

This paper suggests, of course, that McBean was thinking of some sort of affiliation between the PRF and Stanford University. However, as time went by, he apparently forgot about his thoughts of November 1945. McBean said many times in later years that he never intended in any way to bring the Foundation plan into Stanford. He always emphasized that the whole idea of the talks with Eurich was to develop SRI at Stanford entirely independent of the PRF proposal. Nevertheless, Nelles and Black clearly understood that McBean wanted to merge the two possibilities.

This belief prompted Nelles to seek a private talk with McBean the evening of November 27, 1945, just thirteen days after the Black-McBean plan had been created. Nelles was anxious to be more specific on the linkage between Stanford and the PRF. Apparently, Nelles thought the two men had a meeting of minds during their evening get-together in McBean's home. In any event, he immediately sent along a written plan to his host.

The PRF and Stanford

"1. *The Pacific Research Foundation ... would be taken over by Stanford University and operated as such ...*

"2. *The name, Pacific Research Foundation, would continue to be used ...*

"3. *The Board of Trustees of the Foundation will consist of those making substantial contributions to the Foundation and the following:*

- *The President of Stanford University*
- *The President of the University of California*
- *The President of California Institute of Technology*
- *The President of The University of Southern California*
- *The Provost of the University of California at Los Angeles*
- *Mr. Morlan A. Visel*
- *Three regents of Stanford University*

"4. *The Executive and Finance Committees would each have one member from Stanford University, preferably the President. The other members shall be from industry.*

"5. *The Pacific Research Foundation could be separated from Stanford University by a majority vote of the Board of Trustees of The ... Foundation or the Board of Regents of Stanford University.*

"6. *The Foundation shall not incur debts or make commitments beyond its tangible assets.*

"7. *No attempt will be made by Stanford University to utilize the Foundation as part of its educational efforts...*

"8. *Funds transferred from the ... Foundation to Stanford University for use of buildings, equipment, and grounds shall be made only in accordance with contracts."*

Nelles ended his proposal by saying he wanted to establish "an outstanding industrial research organization" rather than an education adjunct. He thought the latter would not be satisfactory to Stanford (at least to Tresidder and Eurich) nor to industry.

It seems clear that by late November Nelles was fearful the PRF idea might be more or less absorbed by Stanford, perhaps with an emphasis on education rather than on service to industry. Thus, he was lining up with McBean whose thoughts were centered on industrial research. But both men misjudged to some extent what Tresidder and Eurich had in mind. Neither wanted an institute within Stanford's educational structure. They were thinking about an independent organization in the Stanford family of institutions.

On January 24, 1946, Nelles and Black attended a meeting in San Francisco arranged by McBean. Fourteen local business executives were present. Nelles later described his presentation on the institute idea in these terms:

> *"Mr. McBean, Mr. Black, and I had several meetings, the most important one being in Mr. McBean's conference room (in San Francisco). He had invited many, if not most, of the key industrial executives of San Francisco to explain ... the plans ... and ask their support. I gave the principal talk, and Mr. McBean and Dr. Eurich agreed my outline was what they felt should be done and a start should be made. From there on Dr. Eurich carried the ball."*

Others who attended the January meeting said later that two "principal" talks were given, one of them being by Dr. Henry Heald, president of the Illinois Institute of Technology. Nelles does mention in his recollections the services of Heald at this meeting and subsequently to McBean and Eurich. In fact, the session was arranged to hear a report by Heald rather than by Nelles.

The PRF sponsors on the one hand and McBean and Eurich on the other brought their discussions to an end soon after the January meeting in San Francisco. In Nelles' view this occurred on not altogether a cordial note. In later years, he said that Eurich "chose to not utilize Mr. Black's or my experience in any way." He went on to say that "when I was in the Bay Area I called on him in his office and had the chilliest minutes I have ever had in my life."

Neither McBean nor Eurich, however, recalled any note or restraint towards Nelles (or Black) who, according to all accounts, wanted only to stimulate creation of a research institute by some organization somewhere in the western part of the United States. In fact, Nelles himself said later that McBean called on him for suggestions in late 1947 and early 1948 when SRI was seeking its second director.

Eurich apparently felt by early 1946 that McBean was the real source of the research institute proposal. Therefore, quite properly in his view, Stanford began looking to McBean rather than to Nelles and Black for implementing assistance. Eurich later made it clear that in no way did he overlook or undervalue the early contributions by Nelles and his associates and that he always had a high respect and regard for their initiative and foresight. But, it is McBean to whom Eurich gives prime credit. And it was McBean who was offering financial support. This was all-important to Stanford.

During the autumn of 1945, a separate Stanford initiative on a research institute was being considered by Tresidder, Eurich, and the University Trustees. As indicated in the preceding chapter, The Three Musketeers had made their report. This is one reason why the approach by McBean received such immediate and favorable attention. The necessary groundwork had been laid; the McBean and University initiatives were soon merged.

With industry (through McBean) and the University involved in joint consideration of the institute idea, it is understandable that Nelles and Black were not encouraged to proceed further with their plans. Many years later, Nelles learned for the first time about the Swain-Swim-Leighton initiative.

Nelles did say later that during the autumn of 1945, while discussions were under way with McBean and others, several people were helpful with advice and suggestions on the university-affiliated institute idea. He mentioned specifically Dr. Harold Vagtborg (director of Midwest Research Institute in Kansas City), Dr. Clyde Williams (president of Battelle Memorial Institute in Columbus, Ohio), and Maurice Holland (an industrial research consultant in New York). This shows that Nelles was still involved, if not at the center of events.

Following the January (1946) meeting in San Francisco, Heald acknowledged in a letter to McBean the contributions by Nelles and Black. He said Black had developed a "considerable interest among many industry executives" in the institute idea. Then, he proposed that the PRF and Stanford interests be merged. "I think it would be desirable if the Foundation at Stanford be established in such a manner as to make it clear to industry that it is the same general program which has been advanced by the Pacific Research Foundation."

There is no indication that any particular effort was made to associate what later became SRI with the program that had been developed by Nelles, Black and Visel. However, a definite association between the McBean and University initiatives was promoted. In retrospect, this seems entirely reasonable and what might have been expected. As events unfolded, there was little, if any, need for the PRF plan in the McBean-Stanford initiative. However, some connection between the PRF idea and SRI was widely perceived on the Pacific Coast for several years after SRI's formation.

Early in February 1946, Black sent copies of Heald's paper to several California business executives and civic leaders. Some of them raised questions about the Foundation-Stanford relationship. One state official who had been interested in the Foundation asked Black where the report "leaves you and Maurice Nelles." He went on to say that "Stanford would seem to know a good thing when it sees one, and should be in a position to insure the proper auspices for the kind of project that you have envisioned."

Black then wrote to McBean saying, "We here in Los Angeles are completely in the dark concerning the thinking of Stanford University in this matter." He also said that before a campaign could be launched to raise funds for the Foundation "all details of the Corporation should be completed in order that the donors will have a positive knowledge of the organization that we are creating." McBean quickly advised Black that the University Trustees had approved the plan "in principle." He did not elaborate on "the plan" because it did not include the PRF. This was, in effect, the beginning of the end between the Pacific Research Foundation and the McBean-Stanford effort.

In early March, Black wrote to some 150 business leaders in Southern California about the PRF and Stanford. This letter, in effect, signalled the end of the Foundation even though this was not apparent to those who received it.

> *"The Board of Regents of Stanford University met Thursday, February 21, to consider the proposal that the University accept the responsibility of establishing an industrial research foundation at Palo Alto in cooperation with the Pacific Research Foundation.*
>
> *"The Board approved the general plan and accepted this responsibility.*
>
> *"The final incorporation of the Pacific Research Foundation with Stanford University will not be completed until after the Director has been selected."*

Black and his associates were still expecting some sort of close coordination or amalgamation of their plans with those under way at Stanford. In practice this did not occur. The PRF was out of the picture. Black later said — "our only regret is that we were not permitted to carry on our work at Stanford Research Institute as we had been led to believe we would."

The early-March date of Black's letters is interesting in light of events at Stanford. The last meeting of The Three Musketeers was being held at this time; Eurich was telling the group that University counsel would shortly prepare articles of incorporation for a Stanford institute. He did not, however, associate this effort in any way with the PRF.

Black sent a copy of the Foundation's form letter to McBean. He also nominated several men for executive director of the pending organization. Then he brought some financial matters to McBean's attention. Referring to conversations with several business executives in Southern California, he said: "They will be glad to make their gifts to Stanford if they have a letter of assurance from Stanford that the money will be spent to finance a research foundation and that the immediate expenses of the Pacific Research Foundation will be paid from this fund." He told McBean that the Foundation's current debt was about $1700.

McBean replied promptly saying he had just met with Tresidder and Eurich and found them "most anxious to get started" but he had taken the position that finding a director and preparing a definite program were necessary first steps before soliciting funds. His letter had two items of advice to Black. He said time would be needed to establish an institute and then — "I would be unwilling to make any commitment or have Stanford University committed to the Pacific Research Foundation until we are assured that it can be organized on a going basis."

The word "it" in McBean's letter led Black (and also Nelles) to believe he was referring to the PRF. In fact, he had SRI at Stanford in mind. McBean said several times in later years that he was giving a "hint" to Black while keeping all possibilities open in case "things did not work out at Stanford."

The second point in McBean's letter referred to Black's future. He advised Black to stay in an independent position pending selection of a director lest he jeopardize his own future.

Finally, McBean wrote to Nelles, agreeing that progress had been slow but that selecting a director demanded time and utmost care. He said firmly that he was unwilling to solicit funds until a director had been selected for the proposed institute. The signal was intended to put the PRF on "the back burner."

Soon thereafter, Nelles and Black realized they would not be involved in eventual formation of a research institute under Stanford auspices. Nelles asked his friend, Stuart Walsh, to check on the matter. Walsh replied in early April, "I have looked into the status of PRF and have found it is indeed unsatisfactory." He was referring to possible incorporation of the Foundation into Stanford's operation. Walsh went on to say that "authentic sources have confirmed your own misgivings." One of these sources was McBean; another was Paul Holden.

There was little contact between Stanford and the PRF during the summer of 1946. Meanwhile, the University and McBean were busily at work on the project. Toward the end of the summer, McBean brought Nelles up to date on the matter. "... we have not moved as rapidly as anticipated, but now that we have selected a Director, we are confident that we will have a program ready for presentation to Industry by Fall." He also told Nelles that Clyde Williams of Battelle had shown "enthusiasm in the project by coming to the coast to review its establishment..."

McBean's letter informed Nelles that Dr. William F. Talbot had been appointed director of the new institute (which had not yet been created in a legal sense) and that he would arrive in September. The letter was couched in terms of "advance notice because of your keen interest in the Institute." In effect, this was notice to Nelles and his associates that a complete separation had been made between the Stanford-McBean initiative and the Pacific Research Foundation. This was, of course, disappointing news to Nelles, Black and Visel.

Although not involved in subsequent deliberations with McBean and the University Trustees, Nelles and his two colleagues saw in late 1946 that Stanford had in fact created SRI. They soon ended their immediate interest in the matter and, in Nelles' words, "the Pacific Research Foundation was abandoned for the purpose of the organization had been achieved."

Nelles and his associates felt they might well have been consulted to some extent in eventual formation of the new institute. They thought the PRF had been one important initiative, yet they had no part in the final action. Vagtborg of Midwest Research Institute later wrote that he knew of their "disappointment in not becoming associated with the final development" of SRI.

The Nelles-Black-Visel initiative to Ortman and then to McBean was certainly one impetus in the formation of SRI. However, it was not the only one. McBean also played an independent role in stimulating the University to action. Furthermore, a movement toward the same general goal had been under way in the University for some time when the PRF idea reached Northern California. However, McBean was not aware of Stanford's Three Musketeers until November of 1945 and even then gave little attention to their work.

Nelles and his PRF colleagues did not know about the Swim-Swain-Leighton initiative within Stanford. In 1964, Black commented on the situation. "... at no time did any of the Stanford people or Mr. Atholl McBean ever mention to me that Stanford had ever considered establishing a Research Institute before or after our presentation to them of the Pacific Research Foundation." At the same time, Black summarized his views on the role of the PRF and of the McBean initiative in founding SRI.

> *"... it was basically the efforts of the Pacific Research Foundation which made this dream come true. The real catalyst in this drama was Atholl McBean who recognized the Pacific Research Foundation as a gold nugget and proceeded with the craftsmanship of a Florentine goldsmith to mould it into the wonderful organization that is today known as the Stanford Research Institute."*

This is certainly an understandable attitude on Black's part. The PRF was incorporated first, and the Southern Californians did aggressively promote an institute idea. There is no doubt about McBean being the catalyst for SRI. But after mid-November of 1945 he moved away from the PRF and began working exclusively with Stanford.

McBean may have forgotten later — or decided to forget — about how much he was involved with Nelles and Black. In any event, he always talked exclusively about work with his friend, Alvin Eurich, in bringing SRI into existence. The simple fact is that neither McBean nor Eurich saw any reason to involve the PRF further.

Having been well acquainted with both Nelles and Black and long associated with McBean, I have always been struck by their varying recollections of what happened — not on the basic thrust and result but on the sequence of events and details. SRI probably would have been founded in time without the PRF initiative. But there is no question that McBean and, in turn, Eurich were galvanized into action on November 6, 1945, when McBean (with Black in tow) made a sudden visit to Stanford. Tresidder was away but Eurich more than "filled the bill" in McBean's view.

As is the case for The Three Musketeers, the men of The Southern Trio have never been given full credit for what they did. Once SRI was created, Nelles, Black and Visel went their separate ways; their contributions were generally overlooked during the years that followed. However, I continued to maintain close contacts with Nelles while recognizing the PRF's early role in SRI's history.

Nelles always emphasized that one of his early motivations in life was to "help start organizations" and then "drop out of the picture." He did both in this instance. Nelles was the Trio's leader but he put Black in the forefront.

The PRF was one — but only one — reason SRI was founded. Nelles was right in saying in 1945 — "The time for a western research institute has arrived." ■

Fred B. Ortman to Atholl McBean — 1945

> *"I think you should get acquainted with the PRF people; their idea looks pretty good to me."*

The Northern Troika

*The organization of Stanford Research Institute
seems to me a significant step in the development
of our industrial resources on the Pacific Coast.*

— Donald B. Tresidder - 1947

ALL ACCOUNTS AGREE THAT ATHOLL McBEAN OF SAN FRANCISCO first entered the picture in the history of Stanford Research Institute when in October 1945, his Los Angeles associate, Fred Ortman, arranged for him to meet with Ernest Black of the Pacific Research Foundation. Following the meeting, McBean immediately moved into action; from that day he was intimately involved in advancing the SRI idea. The significance of his early activities was later described by Alvin Eurich in a letter to McBean.

> *"I recall clearly the day you came to me with the idea of establishing a
> research institute... When you made the proposal I indicated that the
> University was interested in the general idea... You indicated a
> willingness to make funds available to employ outside expert opinion.
> With these resources available, I arranged for Dr. Heald to come from
> Chicago to meet with us and representatives from industry in order
> to give us advice on how to set up an Institute."*

This letter was written in response to McBean's request to Eurich to indicate his understanding of what took place in late 1945. McBean had read a short SRI article about The Three Musketeers. He felt it gave an impression that this University group was the originator of SRI.

The article did not say this was the case but McBean was sensitive on the point. He did not know what the committee had done and sometimes felt that whatever it was the whole effort was not crucial to the real founding.

It is entirely understandable why McBean felt this way even though the Musketeers did make a key contribution within Stanford. In effect, they paved the way and made McBean's task somewhat easier in dealing with the University.

In later years, questions would be raised as to what Dr. Henry Heald was asked to do — and what he actually did. Nelles said he made a survey of research needs in the West. He recalled having a long visit with Heald. However, Eurich later reported that Heald "did not make a survey of the region's research needs and resources," but rather his advice was sought on how best to organize and operate a university-affiliated institute.

The record shows that Heald "was asked to conduct a survey to determine the need for an institute." He came to the conclusion that an institute was needed by industry. The same account shows that "Dr. Clyde Williams of Battelle Memorial Institute, after visiting the Pacific region, supported Dr. Heald's recommendations."

Eurich had first met Heald when the two men were serving during World War II on an advisory committee appointed by the Secretary of the Navy, Frank Knox. Eurich was impressed by what Heald had done in building the Illinois Institute of Technology and indirectly the Armour Research Foundation. Thus, it was natural that Eurich turned to Heald for advice on a research institute idea.

Some thirty years later Eurich wrote that the word "survey" had a different meaning in the context of early SRI events. He said that Heald was not called upon to make a "formal survey" but rather was asked to talk with leading western executives and university presidents to get "a feel for the need." Nevertheless, Black and several others thought his work was indeed a rather complete survey, and Eurich himself often used the word at the time.

During the autumn of 1945, McBean had several discussions with Eurich and Tresidder at Stanford and with his friends in the business community. He was full of enthusiasm about the institute idea. Late in the year he reported to the University on what he believed to be favorable indications that a research institute was needed in the West and said he hoped it would be brought into being by Stanford. He offered to round up initial funds for such an organization. His activities during this period were indeed significant. Eurich later wrote to McBean on the point, "Without your initiative and early support I don't think the Institute would have been established at Stanford."

An early SRI record emphasizes McBean's late-1945 and early-1946 initiatives with Stanford. "He (McBean)... approached the Administration to express the interest of industrialists in the western area in a research institute and (inquired) whether the University would consider organizing one." McBean said later that he brought the suggestion to the University, agreed to raise funds through industry, and discussed the matter on several occasions with Tresidder and Eurich.

Following the first contacts in the autumn of 1945 between McBean and Eurich on the one hand and by McBean with Nelles and Black from Southern California on the other, several exchanges occurred between McBean and the latter through March of the following year. McBean informed Nelles in November that Heald's visit to California had been authorized. He told Nelles that selecting a director for the institute should be left to a six-man committee to be selected by Eurich in consultation with Nelles and Black. He thought the committee should include three people from the "South" and three from the "North."

Then, in early December, McBean indicated to Nelles that Black would be asked to serve as secretary during the forthcoming San Francisco meeting to which Heald had been invited. McBean went on to say that his only personal interest was to represent industry and that he thought a new research institute would be of "tremendous value to Pacific Coast manufacturers." One letter suggested that he (McBean) be reimbursed for Heald's expenses if the Pacific Research Foundation should later be established.

Nelles and Black met with Eurich at Stanford in mid-November 1945. Upon hearing from Eurich in person and later from McBean by letter that arrangements were being made for Heald to visit the West Coast to advise on the new institute, Nelles sent

information on the PRF to Heald. He told Heald that he, Eurich, and Black agreed that "an unbiased expert from the East" should be employed. Then, Nelles promised "full personal cooperation" on Heald's study.

One day later, Black wrote to Eurich saying that in anticipation of Heald's visit to California, he planned to send information once each week to more than a hundred business executives "in an effort to fully acquaint each of them with the proposed plans of the Pacific Research Foundation."

All this suggests that both McBean and The Southern Trio were hedging their bets. McBean wanted to be reimbursed if the PRF should emerge from Heald's work. Nelles and Black wanted Heald and others to know that the PRF was on the way.

Arrangements for Heald's visit to the West Coast were completed by McBean and Eurich before the end of November. Eurich sent Heald some background information.

> *"We want your help on broad policies... Dr. Nelles and Mr. Black*
> *have been promoting the Pacific Research Foundation ... They originally*
> *thought they could get together five million dollars from industry... It*
> *has since become apparent that they set their sights too high. The*
> *business executives who have been backing them now feel that they*
> *need a more practical proposal."*

Eurich told Heald that Nelles and Black favored an independent review of the situation by one or more directors of existing research institutes but that he (Eurich) had the support of "the financial backers" in inviting Heald. Eurich suggested four objectives for Heald's study.

- A quick survey of research facilities available at California's five largest universities;
- A survey of major research facilities available in industry;
- A determination of how present facilities might best be used to meet industry's needs;
- Recommendations for organization of a research institute.

On the last point, Eurich suggested four possibilities. One was an institute wholly independent of both industry and educational institutions such as the Pacific Research

Foundation. The second was a similar institute but without laboratories, thus depending on facilities in other organizations. His third avenue was an institute affiliated with one educational institution using facilities in several institutions. Finally, he mentioned an institute affiliated with one educational institution but with its own staff and equipment.

Eurich asked Heald to meet with McBean ("one of the financial backers") and with Nelles and Black. Also, he suggested visits to several universities and companies following which a meeting would be arranged with a "committee of business executives."

In the meantime, Clyde Williams of Battelle had heard of Heald's pending study and saw to it that "he got an outline of the picture I had presented to the Battelle Board." Williams was referring to his earlier proposal on a Battelle branch in Southern California.

McBean decided in late November of 1945 to make another move on the SRI idea. He organized a luncheon in San Francisco for December 6 and invited R. G. Follis and C. A. Davidson of the Standard Oil Company of California as well as Eurich. He thought a plan prepared by Nelles would be "most helpful" in their tasks.* Also, he had a list of California business executives who might be interested in the institute idea. The list had been prepared by Fred Ortman and Ernest Black. Immediately following the meeting, McBean informed Nelles, Black, and Ortman — and also Eurich — that a "very satisfactory discussion" had taken place and went on to say, "I am confident that all details will be worked out to our mutual satisfaction."

Nothing more was said to Nelles and Black about what was discussed at the December 6 luncheon. Eurich and McBean had begun to feel that the institute should be established at Stanford independently of the Pacific Research Foundation. However,

*See *The PRF and Stanford* in the preceding chapter.

Dr. Donald B. Tresidder
President, Stanford University
The First Chairman of the Board

Dr. Alvin C. Eurich
Vice President, Stanford University
The Architect for SRI

Black thought the group had agreed that an affiliation between the Foundation and Stanford was both feasible and desirable. Apparently, he received this impression from McBean. Furthermore, Eurich more or less confirmed the idea to Black. "I am sure that if we all work together on this project we can provide for the west a research institute that will be of major service to industry." Eurich did not say just how the two groups might work together.

Nelles and Black soon came to feel uneasy about the developing relationship with Stanford. Black wrote early in 1946 that the University had "offered to let us use their facilities until such a time as we are able to build our own buildings and get our equipment." He then made an even more specific statement by saying Stanford had accepted the plan outlined earlier by Nelles to McBean and Eurich.*

This version of events was wishful thinking. Both Nelles and Black were, in fact, worried about a drift away from the PRF. Black wrote to Harold Vagtborg at Midwest Research Institute in Kansas City and expressed some concern about the Foundation's relationship with Stanford.

> *"Dr. Alvin C. Eurich ... is an ex-classmate of Dr. Henry T. Heald and it was this pressure that forced us to obtain his services to come to California to study our plan ... and recommend to the industrialists who are backing the Foundation the most workable and expedient plan to get operations started as soon as possible.*
>
> *"Mr. McBean was responsible for raising money to sponsor such projects as the San Francisco World Fair ... and a number of other similar projects. He pledged the president of Stanford University that he would raise a million dollars for the Pacific Research Foundation if Dr. Heald recommended it. He has been raising money for similar things for the past 30 years and I have confidence that he can do it for us too. Our greatest problem now is to keep Stanford University from getting a stranglehold on the policy making group."*

The opening statement in Black's letter about Eurich and Heald having been classmates is incorrect. Eurich later called it "a glaring error." In any event, the letter shows clearly that Nelles and Black were greatly disappointed with the way they saw things moving toward Stanford and away from the PRF.

Black worked vigorously during January and early February of 1946 on the forthcoming visit by Henry Heald. Among other things, he sent information about the planned survey to 101 California business executives. He told McBean he had been sending "a constant flow of informative literature" to these people about the PRF. These letters worried Eurich who let his feelings be known to McBean. Black then promised McBean that no more letters would be mailed without clearing with him or with Stanford.

THE NORTHERN TROIKA

Atholl McBean
Dr. Alvin C. Eurich
Dr. Donald B. Tresidder

---

*See preceeding chapter on *The Southern Trio*

McBean began making plans early in 1946 to hear a report by Heald on the institute idea and to acquaint senior executives in the San Francisco business community with the developing program. He and Eurich arranged for Heald to be in San Francisco on January 24. Also, he invited Nelles and Black to join the discussions with Heald. Invitations for the meeting were sent to a long list of business executives.

THE McBEAN INVITATION

"Leaders of industry on the Pacific Coast have for some time considered the advisability of establishing an organization for industrial research similar to the Mellon or Battelle Institute. Due to the capital expenditure involved, the idea was deemed impracticable and it is the present thought to form an Industrial Research Department as an adjunct to Stanford University of some other California educational institution, which could be accomplished at modest cost. Stanford University has indicated an interest in the project.

"In an effort to determine the need for such a Department, Dr. Henry Townley Heald, President of the Illinois Institute of Technology, has just completed a survey and will present his conclusions at a meeting to be held at 3:00 o'clock ... at my office. It is hoped that you will find it convenient to be present at this meeting. All of the expenses of Dr. Heald's survey have been underwritten and no request will be made for finances."

The first paragraph of McBean's letter shows that he and others had decided not to back the PRF as it had been formed by Nelles and his associates in Southern California. But, somehow, The Southern Trio thought the Foundation would, in fact, be brought within the Stanford orbit.

The references in McBean's invitation to a research department at Stanford and to "some other California educational institution" are interesting, particularly in light of discussions already under way with Stanford about an independent research institute. McBean later said on several occasions that his letter was worded so as to leave matters open as much as possible. He was confident the group would look favorably on the plan as it would be unfolded at the meeting. Also, he once said that the letter was written so as to bring "even a partisan of the University of California" to the meeting.

The list of business people who attended McBean's meeting is impressive — V. S. Andrus (Southern Pacific), A. H. Brawner (W. P. Fuller & Co.), Homer Bunker, Fred Ortman, and C. W. Planje (Gladding, McBean & Co.), G. A. Davidson and R. G. Follis (Standard Oil Company of California), and A. W. Eames (California Packing Corporation). R. A. Hornby (Pacific Lighting Corporation), Edgar Jessup (Marchant), A. B. Layton (Crown Zellerbach), G. Schel (Shell Oil Company), R. H. Shainwald (Paraffine Companies), and Roland Tognazzini (Union Sugar) also were present.

According to later recollections by many of those present at the January 24, 1946, meeting, there was general agreement on the points made by both Heald and Nelles. These included general recognition of a need for a research institute that would provide direct service to industry, the desirability of affiliating it with a university, and a consensus that Stanford should be encouraged to proceed with such a plan.

One recollection of the meeting in McBean's office points to another initiative on a research institute in the West. Upon returning to his office at the Crown Zellerbach Corporation, Alfred Layton discussed the session with his associate, Alexander Heron, who was then a vice president of the company. Heron had been commissioned by Governor Earl Warren to head a statewide effort known as "Post-War Planning in California." He told Layton that his report to the Governor had pointed to a need in California for a research institute and that he had recommended its "establishment under appropriate auspices." Nothing happened in Sacramento on this proposal.

McBean's first gift for the research institute was sent to Stanford in late January 1946. Tresidder thanked him for the $2,000 check and confirmed an understanding between the two men that acceptance of the money did not involve a definite commitment on Stanford's part. McBean's gift was made in connection with the Heald arrangement.

Immediately upon returning to Chicago, Heald put his thoughts about a research institute in writing and sent a memorandum to McBean. His paper is important because later on it had considerable influence with the Stanford Board of Trustees. He was quite specific about need.

A Well-Established Need

"The need for a first-class research organization to serve Pacific Coast industry seems to be well established. The rapid growth of industrial development to its present substantial volume plus the prospect of a continued increase creates a substantial demand for such services. Such an organization can be of real value in assisting in the industrial development of the area... Industrialists with whom I talked seemed to be in substantial agreement that their companies could and would use such an organization.

"Representatives of the principal universities displayed interest in the proposal and seemed willing to cooperate.

"Research organizations such as Mellon Institute, Battelle, Armour, Midwest, and Southern are performing important services for industry in other parts of the country. No comparable facilities now exist on the Pacific Coast."

Heald was in California for only about a week — from January 16 to January 25. During his stay, he talked with many leaders in business, education and the professions.

He was particularly interested in the type of organization that would best serve western needs and the type of sponsors one could expect. His report goes on:

SERVICE TO INDUSTRY

"The Pacific Coast area will be best served by a research organization which is equipped to provide a direct service to industry in the solution of specific scientific and engineering problems appropriate to the region. This organization should have a first-class staff engaged primarily in industrial research and should be provided with adequate space and equipment to carry on its program.

"Such an organization should provide patent protection to the sponsors of projects, should accept only one project in a specific field, and should have sponsored research as its primary responsibility...

"An effective research foundation or institute can expect to undertake projects sponsored by:

   "(a) Individual companies for the solution of specific company problems.

   "(b) Groups of companies acting through associations which are interested in problems of common interest.

   "(c) Federal governmental agencies such as the Army and Navy. A substantial amount of continuing research will be done in this field.

   "(d) State or local governmental agencies interested in work of public interest of a regional character."

As events subsequently unfolded on SRI, the basic plan outlined by Heald was followed in all major respects. He also dealt with the ways in which a research institute should be organized. He believed there were two alternatives open to business and educational leaders on the West Coast. One was for a private university to establish a nonprofit entity with sufficient separation from the educational operation to insure adequate services to sponsors or clients. The second was to create a separate nonprofit organization having no formal connection with an institution of higher learning.

Heald pointed out — as he did at the meeting on January 24 — that both plans could be effective. He mentioned Armour in the first category and Mellon and Battelle in the second. He minimized the affiliation idea by saying that "sponsors of projects are not interested in the type of organization as long as the organization permits diligent attention to their problems."

Heald went on to tell McBean that, after discussing the matter with industrialists, educators, and research people, he had arrived at some definite conclusions for the

ATHOLL MCBEAN
The Founder

Driving Force — Man of the Hour

PAUL E. HOLDEN
Professor of Industrial Management
Stanford University-GSB

Introduced Atholl McBean of San Francisco
to Dr. Alvin C. Eurich at Stanford

Pacific Coast activity. At this point he was specific on a University affiliation. In direct language, he made several points:

OPERATIONS

"The Foundation should be expected to pay its way from project income after it is well in operation and should bear proper costs of University facilities used by it.

"It would seem desirable, too, for the Foundation to have an advisory committee including representatives of other universities as well as industrial organizations.

"It should be possible ... to begin operations promptly, increasing ... staff and facilities as the demand for ... services grows. The actual size and the nature of facilities ... can only be determined as its program grows and develops."

McBean's Office — Harrison Street — San Francisco

In various ways, Heald was even-handed as between the Los Angeles and San Francisco movements. He used the word "foundation" and thus retained Nelles' support but otherwise lined up with McBean and Stanford.

As mentioned earlier and as will be seen later, most of Heald's recommendations on operations were adopted in organizing SRI. His report also made some specific points on implementing the basic plan.

A STANFORD AFFILIATION

"... it is strongly recommended that a research foundation ... be developed on the Pacific Coast ... located at and operated in close affiliation with Stanford University.

"... industrialists interested in the establishment of a research organization (should) ask Stanford University to organize it, provide the University with moral support for the project, and arrange to provide an initial gift of $500,000 to be used to finance operations, space, and equipment for the foundation.

"... the Foundation (should) be organized as a separate corporation with trustees including several members of the Stanford Board as well as others interested in the Foundation. The President of Stanford, or some other chief administrative officer of the University, should be president of the Foundation ..."

Even at this early date a future executive director of SRI (yet-to-be-formed) had some influence on the Heald report received by McBean and his associates. Dr. Jesse E. Hobson was then director of Armour Research Foundation. Several times in the mid-1950s, while he was at SRI, Hobson said Heald had consulted him in preparing the report to McBean and that he had offered several suggestions which were included in the final document.

Heald ended his letter to McBean with a prediction — "You will soon have a first-class research organization that will be of great service to Pacific Coast industries and soon take an important place nationally." He offered to elaborate on his suggestions and recommendations if the need should arise.

R. Gwin Follis

Chairman of the Board
Standard Oil Company of California

Atholl McBean's Cohort on SRI

As might be expected, McBean was delighted with Heald's oral report on January 24 and with his written comments. He quickly passed the document on to Eurich and Tresidder and urged the University to proceed along the lines set down by Heald. There is no question about McBean's attitude; he was in a hurry to do something.

Action by the Board of Trustees was not long delayed. At a meeting on February 21, 1946, the Trustees agreed in principle that there should be a Stanford Research Institute. The Board also decided that a chief executive should be found and that Stanford would underwrite the cost of getting the organization started.

The Trustees were depending on McBean to raise this money as a gift to the University. In April, Dr. J. W. McBain, professor of chemistry at Stanford, urged Tresidder to move as soon as possible on the institute; he had heard that the School of Engineering at the University of California was considering a similar idea. Dr. Robert Gordon Sproul, the University's president, later said that this was "never in the cards." But, McBean thought something might be done at either Berkeley or USC in Los Angeles.

Shortly after the Trustees made their decision on a research institute, Eurich telephoned Williams in Ohio. He wanted to find out if Battelle's chief executive might be attracted to the West Coast as the first director. Williams' subsequent account of the conversation is most interesting.

> *"This was a most challenging opportunity, and on many occasions I regret that I did not accept. Alvin Eurich's approach to this was most 'unique' for a Californian. He telephoned one morning from Palo Alto and his first words were, 'How's the weather?' And I reported, 'It is snowing so hard by my window that I cannot see out.' He replied, 'The sun is shining. The flowers are in bloom and everything is rosy here. Will you take the job?'"*

In later years this approach was to be used many times — directly and indirectly —by many at SRI when attempting to attract persons in the East and Midwest to join us. However, Eurich was not successful with Williams who was too committed to Battelle. Starting anew in California was not too appealing.

In early March of 1946, Tresidder sent copies of Heald's report on the institute plan to Ira S. Lillick, a University Trustee. He also forwarded the paper prepared by Swim, Swain and Leighton within the University. He asked Lillick for comments. His reply endorsed the basic idea but sounded a warning.

"I hope ... the subject can be approached with such care ... that we have sufficient financial support by contributions from industrialists that we may not find ... that we shall be left later with a research institute that will call upon us for expenditures that we will have difficulty in meeting."

Lillick had no way of knowing that within three and a half years his words would be highly prophetic to his fellow Trustees at Stanford. The Trustees did indeed find themselves in a difficult situation.

During the next few months, McBean continued his energetic activities on the institute idea. He met and talked frequently with Eurich and Tresidder and gradually generated more enthusiasm among many of his business friends, several of whom he saw often in San Francisco's Pacific Union Club. He was active on plans for the new organization and also worked with Eurich in the search for an executive director.

Over the years that followed SRI's formation, the Pacific Union Club was often the scene of key decisions affecting the organization. McBean would gather some of his friends for luncheon and then take up SRI matters. In fact, almost all crucial items over the years would be handled around a luncheon table in the Teak Room at the PU Club — a place where meetings are not held but (in McBean's words) where "one gentleman invites other gentlemen for luncheon following which matters of common interest can be discussed."

Some time during the spring of 1946, Stanford received encouraging news from the Office of Naval Research on the proposed institute. Nelles and Black had visited ONR in Washington, D.C. in 1945, seeking interest in the Pacific Research Foundation. They were told that the Navy was interested in a new research facility on the West Coast. Shortly thereafter, ONR established an office in San Francisco and in due course its representatives called on Tresidder. They had heard about plans for a research institute affiliated with the University. Tresidder was given encouragement on the idea and unofficial pledges for support once the organization had been started. Ralph A. Krause of ONR participated in some of these meetings. Later, he became director of research at SRI.

In June 1946, Williams of Battelle visited San Francisco at McBean's invitation. He traveled down to the McBean summer home in Woodside where a long discussion ensued during which Eurich was present. Also, Williams visited Stanford, talked again with Eurich, met Tresidder for the first time, and reviewed the institute idea with a few of Eurich's associates.

Soon after returning to Ohio, Williams wrote to Eurich with great enthusiasm for the institute initiative: "I believe that you should establish an operating organization immediately, put the research you have on a businesslike basis, and go after more research now when Government contracts are relatively easy to acquire."

Eurich and Williams had discussed the possibility of somehow tying the new institute administratively into the research programs of University departments. Eurich hoped this might expand opportunities as well as financial potentials for research within the University structure. Williams supported the idea.

"I suggest that you set up this research on a financial basis that would return to the organization sufficient overhead charges to enable you to establish a strong managerial and supervisory organization. You could confine the type of projects obtained to those for which space is already available or could be readily available, as, for example, in chemistry. The management could soon thereafter implement some of the other departments, particularly metallurgy... The same thing could gradually be done in physics, engineering, and other fields."

It is clear from this message to Eurich that Williams was thinking in terms of a very close relationship between research programs at Stanford and those in the new institute. However, his own research institute experience had not involved a university affiliation. Thus, he did not go to the heart of the matter. His proposal sounded quite simple, but its implementation would have created all sorts of problems within the University.

Both SRI and Stanford might have been better served if more attention had been given at the time to operating connections between the two organizations. In many respects, the question was simply left to the future. This led more and more people at Stanford to believe that Tresidder and Eurich wanted few, if any, connections with the

faculty. Some felt, however, that both University officers wanted a close connection. Later, they thought that the first executive director at SRI was heading a movement in the opposite direction.

There is no clear-cut answer to the question in actual fact. Eurich wanted both a "separate" operation and a close "working connection" with University departments. Tresidder definitely wanted a separate institute with very few faculty involvements. McBean's interest was simply to arrange Stanford auspices for SRI.

DR. CLYDE WILLIAMS
President, Battelle Memorial Institute
Adviser to The Northern Troika

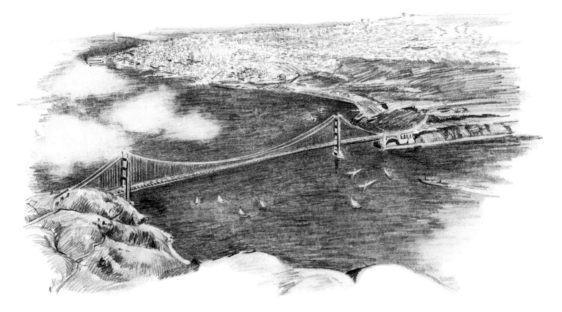

One result of this situation is that faculty leaders were not brought directly into the decision. The first SRI executive gradually grew restive under Tresidder's direct guidance in great detail. The early SRI staff was given little to go by on the University tie and in any case the group was too busy getting something under way to worry about the situation. Matters were allowed to drift at the very beginning.

The problem of finding a suitable executive director for the new institute was discussed at length during the Williams-Eurich meetings in mid-1946. Williams later wrote to Eurich in response to the latter's inquiry about Philip Leighton, professor of chemistry at Stanford: "The selection of a Director for the new institute .. is a difficult job... I believe that Dr. Leighton ... is excellently fitted to head up the organization, and that if provided with an assistant with a pleasing personality and a flare for sales work, he would be in a fine position to carry on the management job."

Leighton was not particularly interested in leaving his academic post at the University. He had recently been appointed dean of physical sciences. In any event, a search continued outside the Stanford community. During mid-summer discussions with Williams at Stanford and in San Francisco, the name of Dr. William F. Talbot of the Sun Chemical Company came up; he had been nominated during an earlier Stanford visit by Earl Stevenson, president of Arthur D. Little. Williams did not know Talbot but was asked by McBean to check on the situation.

Williams' letter to Eurich — in which the search for an executive director is mentioned — also commented on money needed for a new research institute: "... you would have to secure on the order of $50,000 a year for the first couple of years... After one or two years of operation, sufficient progress should have been made and the Research Institute's prestige should be at the point to warrant the raising of a foundation on the order of $3,000,000."

SRI did in fact receive $3.0 million in gifts in due course but the target was not reached for almost twenty years. One reason it was not reached sooner is simply that no special effort was made from the mid-1950s onward to seek gifts. There was one exception in the late 1960s when an International Building was being developed.

Both McBean and Eurich wanted to know how Williams thought he might be able to help in establishing the new organization and whether or not he could spend some time on the project. Williams made one specific suggestion to Eurich: "... I shall be very happy to act as an adviser or consultant, and to make available for this purpose also the members of the Battelle administrative staff ... we should be glad to explain ... our methods of operation ... we also would be very pleased to cooperate ... in securing of research projects and overall planning of your activities... I should expect to go out once a year... The main value from our cooperation, I believe, would result from frequent visits of your representatives to Battelle... I want you to know that all of us at Battelle are anxious to help you... I was extremely pleased with Dr. Tresidder and feel that you are most fortunate to have such a strong ally in Atholl McBean ..."

Clyde Williams was later to point out that he offered his assistance (and provided it) without charging a fee because "I wanted to see the new institute prosper." He was never called upon for visits "once a year." Nevertheless, Williams provided more help and guidance to SRI in its very early years than has ever been formally recognized. A salute to his guiding hand is much in order.

The idea of an existing research institute assisting another during a formative period certainly was not new in 1946 or even two decades earlier. Gordon Battelle, the founder of Battelle Memorial Institute, was a client of Arthur D. Little, Inc. in Cambridge, Massachusetts. He arranged for a group to visit ADL and get help during Battelle's formative days. Advice was gladly provided and as one senior ADL executive later said, "We helped many research organizations get under way." he went on to observe that "the contract research field seems almost unique in the willingness of one laboratory to help even a potential competitor get started." His comment ended on a note about SRI — "Stanford has done its share."

This brings up another point. In the formative years — but less so as time passed — SRI was often referred to, particularly by people outside the American West, as simply "Stanford." But the setting was almost always in a research institute context. Even the Institute's full name was soon shortened in general use to the initials "SRI."

In later years, we often received requests for assistance from groups interested in starting research institutes in various parts of the nation and around the world. Remembering the excellent attitude displayed by Earl Stevenson, Ray Stevens, Clyde Williams, Henry Heald, Jesse Hobson, Harold Vagtborg, and others in SRI's formative period, we always attempted to follow a similar policy in helping with advice and suggestions.

Late in July 1946, William Talbot visited Battelle and met Clyde Williams. The meeting was set up by McBean. Williams promptly wrote to McBean: "Dr. Talbot was here the other day, and I called Dr. Eurich immediately after he left, and strongly recommended him to employ Dr. Talbot. I was very much impressed by him as were also the members of my immediate staff here. I think you are fortunate in finding a man so well qualified for the work at this particular time."

McBean had written to Williams in early July, 1946, about some ideas on financing the proposed institute and asked for comments. Among other things, McBean thought that Stanford should loan the institute $1.0 million at 2.5% interest. He also mentioned with some disappointment the conclusions by Williams, Eurich and Tresidder that research facilities at Stanford would not be particularly helpful to a new research institute. McBean asked Williams to "write me very frankly because that is the manner in which I like to approach problems."

In his letter to McBean about Talbot, some direct reactions on financing were indeed presented by Williams.*

Then, Williams summarized his view on progress being made by McBean, Eurich and other in making plans for the proposed institute. His advice was encouraging: "I

---

*See page 65.

feel that the plan you have for adequately financing operations for the first three years and obtaining funds for a million dollar plant are splendid and will insure the success of the enterprise. I believe that Dr. Talbot will secure the confidence of industry and you will move ahead at a good pace. In fact, I think thus far you and the boys are doing all right."

During the first several months of 1946, McBean also was keeping in close touch with a research institute initiative in Portland, Oregon. An organization by the name of Research Institute of the Pacific Northwest had been formed and was considering various program possibilities. Several of McBean's friends were associated with the venture. Paul B. McKee, E. C. Sammons, David B. Simpson, Marshall Dana, and Vernon R. Churchill — all prominent in the Oregon business community — were members of a policy committee for the institute. They were convinced that more industrial research facilities were needed in the Pacific Northwest. At the same time, they conceded that there were great opportunities for service by a "truly coast-wide organization."

A Stanford Loan

"I approve most heartily of your suggestion to borrow $1,000,000 from the Trustees of Stanford. This is really a modest request in consideration of the great good the Institute, if properly financed, will be to Stanford. As to repayment of this loan ... I would adjust my charges for research work so that after a substantial volume of business is developed, say, $500,000 to $1,000,000 ... you would be able ... to make a profit of the order of 5%... If donations from industry for buildings prove disappointing, this profit could be used to repay the loan or for expansion.

"It seems to me, however, that with the start the Institute would be given by a million dollar plant on a long-time loan at low interest rate from Stanford, and a $200,000 or $300,000 fund for operations during the first three years, that industrialists will come across with at least $1,000,000 and over the next few years with perhaps as much as $3,000,000. I would be disposed not to use the first million dollars or even the first two or three million dollars to pay off the loan ..."

Clyde Williams' letter to Atholl McBean, mid-1946.

Key Decisions at The Bohemian Grove

This message reached McBean through Homer W. Bunker, one of his Gladding, McBean associates. Bunker told McBean on March 18 that "the Pacific Northwest group is now willing to mark time, pending the outcome of our efforts to perfect a coast-wide organization."

McBean had several contacts with the Portland group and kept them informed on the Stanford initiative. Although he did not discourage the northern contingent, he hoped their efforts could be brought into the Stanford program. Finally, in August, McBean wrote to Vernon Churchill of The Oregon Journal.

> "... we have not moved as rapidly as anticipated but ... we are confident that we will have a program ready for presentation to industry by fall.
>
> "Dr. Clyde Williams, Director of Battelle Memorial Institute, has evidenced his enthusiasm ...
>
> "Immediately after his arrival, sometime before the end of September, Dr. Talbot will ... develop a program which we will present to Industry shortly thereafter."

This news marked the end of the Pacific Northwest initiative for a research institute. Paul B. McKee, then president of both Pacific Power and Light Co. and Portland Gas and Coke Company, and a Stanford graduate, later became a founding board member of SRI.

Early in August 1946, McBean got in touch with Eurich on a specific proposal for organizing an SRI. He mentioned a meeting with Gwin Follis of Standard Oil Company of California who viewed the initiative with enthusiasm and joined McBean in a commitment.

A GIFT PROMISE

"If Stanford University will immediately employ Dr. Talbot, we will agree to use our best efforts in raising, as a gift to Stanford from Industry, $100,000 a year for three years. Should we be unable to raise sufficient funds to warrant establishment of this Institute as programmed, Standard Oil Company of California and Gladding, McBean & Co. will underwrite Dr. Talbot's salary for three years in a total sum of $50,000."

McBean had asked Eurich two days earlier to arrange a Stanford loan of $1.0 million to the proposed research institute. But, he had second thoughts about Trustee reaction to such an approach and thus dropped the idea in his gift commitment.

The financing proposal from McBean also included a general appeal to Eurich and the University — "I hope that you will be able to convince the Trustees of the necessity for getting behind this project in order that we may proceed as quickly as possible." Again, he showed a desire for speed in creating the institute.

Stanford acted quickly on McBean's plan. The Talbot appointment was formalized within a month, following which Eurich advised Heald of progress on his earlier recommendations and thanked him for "all the help that you gave us in getting this under way." Tresidder wrote to the University Trustees soon thereafter recommending that steps be taken to organize SRI.

A PROPOSED PURPOSE

"The major purpose of this Institute would be to provide, equip, and maintain laboratories, experimental and other facilities for general and specific scientific and industrial research and to make such facilities available to Stanford University and other institutions and organizations, public or private, for the conduct of research and investigation."

Even before this recommendation to the Trustees had been made, Eurich wrote to McBean confirming their understandings and saying that the action point had been reached. Then he gave special appreciation and recognition to his friend: "Again, I want to say how grateful we are for your efforts in behalf of the Institute. I am sure that as it develops, you will be proud of the exceedingly important part you played in getting it set up ... you have done a fine thing for industry and for Stanford." Eurich was even more prescient than his words indicate. As time went by, McBean's pride in SRI was immense indeed.

It is, of course, apparent that during much of 1946 McBean was leaving no stones unturned in his drive for a Stanford institute. He was acting almost as a University officer or Trustee — writing letters, making telephone calls, arranging meetings, seeking a director, raising money, advising Tresidder and Eurich, dealing with Nelles and Black, and so on. His mind was made up, and he wanted to move quickly. He could hardly understand why even a few weeks were needed for Trustee decisions.

All this involvement could have created problems and misunderstandings with the University and its Trustees had it not been for the close relationship nurtured during the year between McBean and Eurich. They were acting in close consort and with high respect for each other. It was precisely during these days that McBean gained the image of "SRI's Founder", while Eurich took on the mantle of "Architect."

By early autumn 1946, plans for creating SRI had reached the final stage. University attorneys were drafting the necessary documents. On September 27, Tresidder announced "establishment" of the new organization as "an important new factor in the development of industrialization in the Pacific West." The news item went on to say that "all research problems ... are within the scope of the new institute" and that "in this respect it differs from similar institutions in other parts of the United States that restrict their operations to research in the natural sciences."

In retrospect, it is significant that this announcement emphasized (at least by implication) the social sciences. In due course, SRI was to become one of the largest private research organizations in the world in the fields of industrial economics and management sciences. However, even SRI with its wide spectrum never has attempted to embrace "all research problems" within its scope.

In making his announcement, Tresidder was careful to mention the western nature of the new institute. He said that leading industrialists of Southern and Central California and of the Pacific Northwest had cooperated in organizing the new entity rather than creating separate and smaller institutes in various localities. The release said that the new institute would draw upon Stanford faculty and laboratories but would have its own staff and facilities. Talbot's appointment as executive director also was announced on September 27.

On October 24, 1946, three San Francisco attorneys filed Articles of Incorporation for the new nonprofit research corporation. Then, at its regular December meeting, the University Trustees (meeting as SRI General Members) adopted Articles of Incorporation and By-laws and accepted resignations of the three "incorporating" directors. Eleven new board members were then elected. They were Donald Tresidder, Charles Blyth, John Cushing, Paul Davies, W. P. Fuller, Jr., Atholl McBean, Paul McKee, Donald Russell, William Stewart, Alvin Eurich, and J. D. Zellerbach.

The Connecting Links

"At just the right time, David Jacobson and Paul Holden of Stanford University brought Atholl McBean in touch with Donald Tresidder and Alvin Eurich. The result is clear for all to see —SRI."

H. E. ROBISON — SRI

SRI was at last legally in being and ready to begin operations. Tresidder soon informed McBean and the nine other founding directors that the final organizing step had been taken.

It is abundantly clear that it was the initiative stemming from McBean, Eurich and Tresidder that led directly to SRI's formation. This was not, however, the only initiative as pointed out by Tresidder in January 1947, in his new capacity on SRI's board of directors. "The chairman reported that the University had for some time considered the need for a research institute on the Pacific Coast. A committee of three appointed by the president of the University visited research institutes throughout the country and recommended a similar institute be established at Stanford." He was, of course, referring to The Three Musketeers.

The first SRI board meeting was held at Stanford on January 8, 1947. Tresidder opened the session with a statement about the new institution.

> *"The organization of Stanford Research Institute as a separate*
> *corporation seems to me a significant step in the development of our*
> *industrial resources on the Pacific Coast. It is unique in that it will*
> *make available the resources of a major university for the study of any*
> *problems which confront industry, whether they are technical in nature*
> *or problems of management, personnel, or labor relations."*

Atholl McBean has long been recognized, along with the Board of Trustees of the University, as the "founder" of SRI. From the very beginning of his interest in the institute idea he provided financial as well as moral support. His first pledge for $15,000 was made in January 1946. A second in the same amount was made in December 1948. By 1957, he had given $160,000 to SRI, and six corporations of which he was or had been a director had contributed $255,000.

McBean's role in creating and stimulating the growth of SRI has not gone unrecognized by his fellow directors and by SRI itself. On October 20, 1958, a marble plaque commemorating his "founding" role was installed in the lobby of SRI's headquarters building in Menlo Park. It reads:

ATHOLL McBEAN

In recognition of his vision, perseverance, and leadership in cooperation with the Trustees of Stanford University in founding Stanford Research Institute.

The wording on this plaque was adopted the same day in a resolution passed by the board of directors in a meeting at SRI.

McBean and several members of his family (including Mrs. McBean and son, Peter) were present at the commemoration ceremony. He seemed greatly pleased to be recognized in this way. A few months later the directors passed a second resolution thanking McBean for his financial contributions and pledges to SRI.

The name of Atholl McBean will always be firmly associated with SRI's early history. He was indeed the "father" of the institution. Maurice Nelles has referred to him as the "foster father of SRI" and has mentioned his "wonderful" role in nurturing the Institute from "birth to maturity." As Nelles points out, McBean is rightly honored for his great contributions.

Clyde Williams also gave a later appraisal of McBean's role. Recognizing that many people contributed to SRI's creation, Williams said that "Atholl McBean made the greatest contribution of all through his foresight, his early activity in pushing its establishment through, and finally in aiding its growth."

Frank F. Walker of San Francisco, who was Stanford's financial officer in the 1930s and 40s and an advisor to The Three Musketeers, also wrote about The Northern Troika some thirty years after the events of 1976. "I was a friend of Atholl McBean ... and of Don Tresidder and Alvin Eurich. They all created a great institution." He went on to say that McBean in particular did "a wonderful job."

A troika always has a lead horse. Tresidder, Eurich and McBean, in effect, made a Northern Troika matching a Southern Trio in Los Angeles and The Musketeers at Stanford. However, the northern team might be named, there is no question about McBean being the lead man in a very effective troika.

I had the great pleasure of talking several times during 1945 and 1946 with Tresidder, Eurich and McBean but admittedly did not fully grasp what was afoot until September of 1946. I gained the impression — largely from Eurich — that a research institute in the physical sciences was in the making.

This is not what Eurich said but after all no one had ever attempted to create an institute fully embracing both the "hard" and "soft" sciences. Being still in the Air Force but occasionally visiting Stanford, I gave little thought to the exercise. My mind was centered on returning to the University's Business School for final work in its Ph.D. program.

It was from my wife, who was already back on the Stanford Campus, that I learned in September about a new Stanford institute in the final organizing stages. But this is another story for a later page. I did know that Tresidder, Eurich and McBean had done a good deed.

EARL P. STEVENSON
Arthur D. Little, Inc.
Adviser from Cambridge

The Holden Home in Palo Alto, California, where
McBean and Eurich
first met each other in 1945.

In later years, particularly during SRI's first decade, I came to know and work closely with Earl Stevenson, Ray Stevens, Clyde Williams, Eddie Weidlein (at Mellon), Henry Heald, Harold Vagtborg, and other friends in the eastern institutes (including also Charles Kimball, Vagtborg's successor at Midwest). They always were interested, helpful and generous with their time on SRI's behalf. They, too, deserve a great measure of credit for their contributions during SRI's formative years.

Not all of these men, however, were convinced that an economics and management research program could or should be created at SRI. But, from the outset, this was one of my roles. I knew only that Tresidder, McBean, Eurich — and before them the Musketeers — had said this is what was intended. This was all I needed to know, especially since the first executive director, William Talbot, thought it was "an interesting idea" and saw no reason why it should not be pursued "on a trial basis."

This brings the late Paul Holden of Stanford's Business School to the forefront again. His role along with David Jacobsen of the University in bringing McBean and Eurich in touch with each other has never been publicized in SRI forums. It was a key step at just the right time.

But Holden did more than help the Troika. He was one of my professors in Business School days and a member of my doctoral board following World War II. He gave freely of his time in helping me and others create the economics and management research program at SRI. We retained him as a consultant in this new activity. Holden deserves more credit on SRI's beginnings than has ever been accorded to him.

There were many actors on the shifting stage in SRI's history leading to its formation in late 1946. But, clearly, McBean was the leading light on the marquee. Charles Kimball of Midwest Research Institute once said that the SRI idea would never have flowered without McBean who forged the alliance with Eurich and Tresidder. Certaintly, they were the right men in the right place at the right time.　■

The Right Time

The Far West is the Golden West.

— PAUL MONTGOMERY (*Business Week*) - 1946

A KEYNOTE OF SORTS on the circumstances surrounding SRI's formation was sounded at a Newcomen Society dinner in San Francisco on November 30, 1967. The event marked the Institute's twentieth full year of operation. "... this organization was created at the right time, by the right people, in the right place, under the right auspices, and with the right concept." I had the honor of presenting this Newcomen Address.

Other parts of this book deal with the people, place, auspices, and concept in SRI's creation. All these features were indeed right in every respect. And so was the time. But more can and should be said about the environment of the days when "a new star on the western scene" was brought into being.

Everyone involved in this process during the immediate post-World War II days agreed that the American West, and particularly the Pacific Coast, was on the verge of an economic expansion. This was evident from the wartime upsurge in population, industry, and income.

There were, of course, some major problems arising from the phasing down of aircraft production and shipbuilding. Nevertheless, the western mood was buoyant, and there were all sorts of optimistic predictions. Furthermore, the feeling around the nation was that the West would continue its upward movement generated by the war. The clarion call "Go West Young Man" was being heard once again.

All this is significant in SRI's formation simply because one of the recurring themes in late 1945 and through 1946 was the need for an institute to serve the West's burgeoning needs. It was not wishful thinking. There were all kinds of signs that the American West was a new and promising frontier destined for rapid industrialization and broad economic growth.

Many words were used at the time in defining the western portion of the country. Some spoke simply of The West, others about the Far West, and still others of the Pacific Coast and the West Coast. But the Far West was most often used — meaning seven western states, California, Oregon, Washington, Arizona, Nevada, Utah, and Idaho.

Early in 1946, one periodical, The United States News, carried an article about a "boom in the Pacific States." It began with a flat statement, "The Far West is setting out to industrialize ..." Business Week surveyed the whole western situation in 1946 during which its publisher coined a new expression, "The Far West is the Golden West." A report on this survey was widely distributed in early 1947; the Golden West idea

appeared in the opening sentence of a feature article published in an April issue of Business Week.

At the end of the War, many of the nation's leaders were especially high on prospects for the West. President Truman said "the Pacific Coast is one of the brightest places in the country." Nelson Rockefeller was talking about the Far West as a land of great promise. Even Averell Harriman, a staunch member of the Eastern Establishment, described the American West as "the center of things to come." Herbert Hoover also spoke up now and then about the Far West. It seemed at times that only the head of Montgomery Ward was pessimistic about the western part of the United States. But, he was predicting a huge economic depression for the entire nation.

All this euphoria about the West came at a time when dire predictions on unemployment were being made for the nation as a whole. But a boom psychology was enveloping the West. As one news magazine reported, "an atmosphere of excitement over the future" was everywhere apparent.

Of all regions of the United States, the Far West had the largest wartime gains in population and income. In 1946 and early 1947 the western economy was vying for top national ranking in per capita income and accumulated savings. Population in the Far West had grown more than thirty percent since 1939 while the nation's numbers had moved up only some seven percent. During the same period, factory jobs had increased almost seventy percent versus less than fifty percent for the country as a whole.

Substantial gains were registered on other fronts as well. Farm production went up some 25% — slightly more than that for all the states combined. Government jobs rose by about 66% in the Far West compared to around 33% for the entire nation. Startling gains far beyond those for the 48 states and the territories (as a whole) had been achieved in construction, power generation and property values in the West.

In summary, the Far West had recorded an all-star performance since the last pre-war year. Total income was up some 180%; sales had risen by around 170%. The result was a higher proportion of the nation's economic activity being in the West than before World War II — population up from 9 to 11% of the national total, income from 11 to 13%, and retail sales from 12 to 14%. Another result of this wartime expansion was an early post-war increase in employment by the service industries.

At the wartime peak in 1944, more than a million workers had been added in the western chemical and metal industries. Hundreds of thousands more had joined government agencies. There is no question but that the Far West economy was bursting at the seams as World War II came to an end. But, in the meantime employment in the service industries had been squeezed down from some two-thirds to less than half of total employment. The comparable reduction for the nation was from one-half to two-fifths. As employment in the war industries declined, more and more people moved into post-war service jobs.

By the end of 1946, the American Far West had become a white collar region in comparison to the national employment pattern. One-third of the U.S. labor force was in clerical and professional pursuits. The comparable figure in the West was two-fifths. Conversely, the proportion of the West's labor force engaged in semi-skilled and unskilled jobs plus farming was considerably less than half the total while more than half was so employed in the nation as a whole.

As the calendar moved from 1946 into 1947, perhaps the greatest thing happening in the Far West involved a migrating population. People were moving to the region by the tens of thousands; most of them were heading for California. Still further, tourists were flocking to the western states. In 1946 alone, about two million people travelled to California in automobiles registered in other states. Tens of thousands more came by train and airplane. All this gave rise to an exploding tourist industry and to construction of more homes, schools, roads, and other public facilities. During the first post-war year, 1946, one-fifth of all U.S. construction was in the Far West; one out of every four dollars of the nation's home building was in the West.

The population of the Far West in 1946 was about fifteen million including nine million in California alone. There had been only some eleven million people in all the Far West in 1940. Many predictions were being made that the West's population would grow to almost twenty million by 1960 and that California would have a population of more than twelve million by that time.

The population gains in every western state except Idaho during the wartime years were much larger than for the nation as a whole — as they had been during the 1930s except for Utah.

PERCENTAGE GAINS IN POPULATION		
Area	1930-1940	1940-1946
United States	7	6
Far West	18	29
Washington	11	24
Arizona	14	31
Nevada	21	36
Utah	8	18
Idaho	18	4

It is no wonder, then, that during the immediate post-war period the economic emphasis was on the service sector before anything significant could be done on further industrialization or in agriculture. All together, the trades and other services, government, construction and related "people activities" in 1946 gave a special economic character to the Far West. They stood much higher on the western economic scale than for the nation and were far more significant than manufacturing.

Agriculture was important to the Far West during the pre- and post-World War II periods but not nearly so much as it was later to become. But the wartime income increase in the West — from 1939 to 1946 — was well over 350%, much higher than the 250% or so expansion for the nation. Even though farm output and population in the Far West had kept pace with each other for more than fifty years, there was a feeling in 1946 that western agriculture was nearing the end of its steady growth. Few perceived the great advances in productivity that were in the offing.

The manufacturing situation was, of course, far more significant in 1946 with respect to the research institute idea than were other economic sectors. Just prior to the war, manufacturing had provided only some 12% of the West's income. The national percentage was almost 19%. But during the War the West's income from manufacturing grew by some 225% in contrast with around 175% for the nation. The outlook for the West at the time was for much more growth.

This optimistic view prevailed in spite of drastic post-war employment reductions in several western industries. The wartime peak in shipbuilding of some 600,000 workers had declined to only 60,000 by 1946. The aircraft industry was then employing about 100,000 people, less than a third of its earlier maximum. Nevertheless, western industry had gained on the nation in employment since 1939; its share of the total went up from six to seven percent. In April of 1940, about 610,000 people were working in western factories; the 1946 total was over 1,025,000, a 68% gain.

The big movement in western manufacturing in 1946 was diversification. It was proceeding apace and without parallel in history. Several government aluminum plants in the Pacific Northwest were reopened after being closed at the end of the War. The big Geneva steel mill in Utah had also been put back in production. Pacific Car and Foundry (now PACCAR) had expanded its motor truck division in Seattle into a former Boeing building.

Eastern companies also were expanding their western production, or making plans to this end, in 1946. The Ford Motor Company announced that it wanted to buy $50 million worth of automobile parts on the West Coast. More and more companies east of the Mississippi River were opening branch plants in the West. An unprecedented boom in industrial building was under way. The expansion in a little more than a year totalled some three-quarters of a billion dollars. This was almost half of what the government had spent to expand industry in the Far West during the War.

A fifth of the nation's new industrial construction in 1946 was taking place in the West even though only one-fifteenth of America's industrial output was occurring in the region. It was well known at the time that eastern industrial executives were travelling throughout the Far West looking for new business opportunities to serve a growing western market.

In all this movement — especially by eastern companies — much more than a freight advantage was involved. A broad-based industrialization was in process throughout the West but especially on the Pacific Coast. Pre-war steel capacity at about one million ingot tons had been increased to 3-1/2 million tons. Both Kaiser and U.S. Steel were erecting new finishing facilities. Cheap power was an important factor in planning by several companies for new electro-chemical and electro-metallurgical plants. Aluminum plants were being constructed in the Pacific Northwest. Furthermore, many companies were interested in new western production because of the existence of a large skilled labor pool.

Even with this new drive for industrialization, there were few truly national, let alone international, companies in the Far West. There were no industrial and financial giants in the region. Nevertheless, some were in the making, for example, Standard Oil Company of California, California Packing, Crown Zellerbach, Kaiser Industries, Bechtel Corporation, and Bank of America.

Much of what the West used in 1946 still came from the East or Middle West. For example, about two-thirds of the furniture sold in the Far West was supplied by eastern producers. A similar situation existed in industry after industry.

Although California was the center of economic interest and western industrialization, all of the western states were moving ahead rapidly and held high expectations for the future. Every one of the states in the Far West outgained the nation as a whole in income and sales increases during the war years; every state except Idaho had grown more rapidly in population. All the states had benefited enormously from the rise in government spending. Farm gains were greatest in the inland states; industrial growth and prospects were greater in the coastal states. Per capita incomes in all the western states except California, Arizona and Nevada had outstripped the national gain from 1939 to 1946. California fell behind relatively only because of the great influx of people. Even so, the state's per capita income in 1946 was still 180% greater than the American average.

Although wartime economic expansion in the American West was pervasive, it was uneven in many respects. California claimed most of the upsurge in metals and chemicals as well as in shipbuilding and aircraft production. The state's manufacturing employment rose from 392,000 to 692,000. The timber industry in Idaho and Oregon increased its employment from 84,000 to 136,000 people. Steelmaking helped Utah's labor force to rise substantially.

The Far West did lag behind the nation somewhat in early economic conversion to peacetime pursuits but pulled about even in 1946. The biggest concern was whether or not industrialization could move ahead fast enough to keep pace with the continuing population increase especially by persons moving from the East. There were many unsolved problems including the need for more public utility services. Southern California was turning to Texas to augment its gas supplies. The Pacific Telephone and Telegraph Company announced an $800 million expansion program.

Some western companies were hoping for a step-up in international trade with China and other Far East nations. A San Francisco newspaper editor said that if standards of living for everyone in the Far East could be raised by only 25¢ a year, the trade impact would be great enough to "insure prosperity for the Far West for a century."

The western situation in 1946 is well illustrated by the industrialization movement in Southern California. Population growth was running two or three years ahead of industrial development. Housing was at high premium. Some 200,000 war workers were still gradually moving into peacetime occupations. Community drives were being organized to bring in manufacturing from other parts of the country. The prime targets involved automotive parts, cameras, textiles, cutlery, pianos, and many other high-value-added products. At least thirty eastern and midwestern companies had bought

Ready for lift off
— The West and SRI in 1946 —

plant sites in Los Angeles during the War. They were waiting for supply increases before starting production in the area. Local ports were hoping to export such things as aircraft, canned goods and motion pictures in far greater volume.

All these situations in the Far West generated two basic views among economic and business leaders in the area. One was a certain urgency in stepping up manufacturing. The other was a sweeping wave of confidence that potentials in the West were very great indeed. Nowhere in the country was there such high enthusiasm for the future. Practically everyone agreed that rapid industrial development was the key to success. Governor Warren appointed a special commission to speed up the process in California.

Another transformation was gradually occurring in the West and especially on the Pacific Coast. More and more commercial airline services were being provided. One could move overnight from Los Angeles and San Francisco to New York. The East and West were being brought closer together in many ways. This made it all the easier for eastern companies to become interested in the western economy and for western companies to think more about new markets in the East. New and faster transportation also stimulated the desire of easterners to move west; many of them wanted to return to an area they had found pleasant during wartime service. Also, more and more university graduates were reluctant to look for jobs in the East; they wanted to stay in the American West.

In all this environment, it is wholly understandable why many of the Far West's business leaders found the proposition of a western research institute to be an appealing idea. They saw it as one way to help speed up urgently needed industrialization. This is the main reason why almost all the proponents of an SRI at Stanford thought in terms of regional development and service to industry rather than about government-sponsored research programs.

A personal note may help bring the 1946 situation into focus. It is an experience shared by many young men and women at the time. I was in the process of completing more than six years of military service in the Air Force. Having been born in the West (Texas), followed by college in the West (Washington State), and graduate school also in the West (Stanford), I wanted very much to return to the area. So did my wife who had lived most of her life at Stanford.

The immediate decision was easy — return to Stanford and finish my Ph.D. work. But my father-in-law, Dr. Eliot G. Mears of the Stanford faculty, had given even more firm direction to my thoughts before he died in early 1946. He said — "The West will develop enormously and this is where you should plan to live." I never doubted what he had to say and readily accepted his advice. But in one respect, I was only an example from millions who were hoping that the West would indeed industrialize rapidly.

One other personal note illustrates how some people viewed the Pacific West in 1946. Having worked closely during the war years with General Robert E. Wood of Panama Canal and Sears Roebuck fame, I received some sage advice one day as we flew together on an Air Force flight.

There was widespread talk at the time about a post-World War II depression. Wood was dismayed by "such nonsense." He believed that the nation was on the verge of a sustained economic upsurge and said Sears Roebuck's plans would be based on this assumption. He kindly offered me a position in the company. I declined on the basis of wanting to return from Ohio to the West Coast. He promptly replied — "This is just what you should do; the greatest expansion of all will occur in the American West."

He was right. And so were McBean, Tresidder, Eurich, Nelles, Swain, and all their cohorts who helped bring SRI into existence. As one of our consultants in later years was to say — The timing of the Institute's formation was "pretty near perfect." It coincided with the beginning of a long-term and rapid economic growth period for the eleven western states.

It is crystal clear that the enthusiasms in 1946 for a research institute at Stanford reflected the mood of the times in the Far West and particularly in the Golden State.■

Prediction

"I think the institute will prosper; it is well located."

GOVERNOR EARL WARREN

The Founding Charter

The Institute is now officially in business.

— MORRIS M. DOYLE - 1946

SEVERAL TIMES DURING THE WINTER of 1945-46, Donald Tresidder and Alvin Eurich talked informally with Morris M. Doyle of San Francisco about the idea of creating an industrial research institute affiliated in some way with Stanford. A partner in the firm of McCutchen, Thomas, Matthew, Griffiths and Greene, Doyle had participated in a December 1945 meeting with Stanford's Three Musketeers on the institute concept.

Once the University Trustees had approved (in February 1946) the principle of forming such an institute, Eurich began discussions with Doyle and others on the legal implications. They considered various alternatives on organization, control, taxation, and related matters following which Eurich asked Doyle as University counsel to present his observations at a mid-March luncheon meeting.

Doyle and his associates drafted several papers on the institute concept, two of which were sent to Eurich a few days before the scheduled meeting. Their first concern was with possible approaches in organizing the institute so as to fully protect the University's position. Doyle's covering letter to Eurich on March 11, 1946, clearly shows that control and taxation questions were uppermost in his mind.

> *"The obvious problem is to establish control of the University over the Institute, especially if its activities are to be conducted on the campus, and yet to maintain a separate identify so that if the Institute should be held to be a taxable activity, the exempt position of the University would not be affected."*

Thirty-two years, one month and two days after writing this letter, Doyle repeated the message to SRI. He had indeed gone to the heart of the matter on how the Institute should be established. It is fully understandable that Doyle was worried about this situation. The Stanford name and the University's tax position were involved. He wanted to make sure that in gaining benefits from the research institute the University did not at the same time adversely affect its broader position and interests.

Although Doyle's further advice to the University remains in privileged form, it is perfectly clear what in essence he said. Both Tresidder and Eurich later indicated that they followed his counsel to the letter. On several occasions over the years, Doyle agreed that this was the case. Thus, the action taken testifies to earlier advice by Doyle and his colleagues.

Aside from advice to a client, Doyle wanted to make sure that Tresidder, Eurich, McBean, Swain, and others involved in the SRI initiative had ample background information on the issues involved and possible alternatives. This is why he prepared a few papers. He hoped they would be widely read by the institute proponents.

One paper outlined four possible structures for the institute. The first was direct operation as a part of the University. Another was a separate corporation having only a contractual relationship with Stanford. Still another was an affiliated nonprofit corporation wholly dominated by the University. The fourth was an unincorporated association with membership and direction in the hands of University people.

Doyle and his associates said that two criteria were of prime importance in deciding on the form of organization. One was sufficient control over the policies of the institute by the University to prevent basic conflicts between the two institutions. The second was possible impact of the institute's operation on the University's tax-exempt status.

The control and tax criteria are highly significant in viewing the formation of SRI within the Stanford structure. This was obvious in 1946 and remained so after SRI's formation. It was essential to the general welfare of the University that it maintain "a high degree of control" over the research institute.

Assuming that the new institute might be established as a Stanford-affiliated entity, some of the Trustees and University people were wondering about a "balance of power" with the institute proponents. Tresidder, Eurich and Doyle knew that Stanford had to be in a position "to offset the zeal of the supporters and management of the institute" against the purposes of the University if such a situation should ever arise.

One of Doyle's background papers illustrated the significance of this issue by referring to potential competition between the two organizations.

> *"If the institute is able to eventually build its own plant and have its own staff, it may be in a position of direct competition with the University for competent men ... and even absent such competition, unless the salaries paid by the University and the institute are kept at approximately the same scale, the existence of the institute ... would probably have at least a disquieting influence on portions of the faculty ..."*

SRI did begin building its own staff and facilities soon after the organization was established. Although questions were raised later about competition between the two institutions for research contracts, money, people, and to some extent, facilities, no particular problems arose in this respect during the founding years and certainly not in 1947. During this first full year, SRI had less than a dozen contracts, only a few people, practically no facilities, and was not yet seeking capital contributions on an organized basis.

Throughout 1947, there was frequent contact between Dr. William F. Talbot, SRI's first executive director, with Eurich and Tresidder about salary levels for the staff. Tresidder wanted to approve all salaries and always matched them up with University counterparts. Talbot felt that such salary constraints would handicap SRI somewhat, particularly in light of basic differences in operations of the two organizations. However, in almost all cases actions satisfactory to both Talbot and the University were developed. These and other solutions involving relationships between the two institutions were sought on an ad hoc basis; no attempt was made at the outset to develop underlying policies on potential problem areas that had been more or less predicted by Doyle and his associates.

Talbot felt that realistic policies could not be articulated until some operating experience had been gained. Tresidder and Eurich seemed to agree with this viewpoint, and in retrospect the approach was entirely reasonable. However, in the absence of some statement on the subject, speculation began to arise in both faculty and SRI circles about the future course of events. This resulted in some confusion on what was really intended when SRI was created.

Doyle's comments in 1946 on possible tax implications for Stanford arising from the institute idea were forceful and to the point. He often repeated these views in later years.

> *"The importance to the University of the ... tax-exempt status under*
> *Federal income tax statutes needs no emphasis... (An) extensive business*
> *enterprise through the use of the University's facilities and personnel for*
> *private research at a profit would threaten that status."*

Then Doyle moved to a most important point, particularly with respect to the future of the proposed institute. He put into words what many knew was the situation.

> *"If a research organization is created as a wholly separate entity, there*
> *may be grounds for securing a similar tax exemption. But sound*
> *planning requires the assumption that it won't enjoy such a status."*

The influence of this observation on the subsequent formation of SRI as a separate but affiliated corporation seems obvious. Although Doyle and his associates believed that the new nonprofit organization would qualify for tax exemption, they felt "sound planning" should take into account the possibility that such an exemption might not continue indefinitely. A separate entity seemed to be the choice with the least risk.

SRI did in fact receive tax-exempt status from the IRS as Doyle thought would be the case. But, the situation changed somewhat in 1961. A story of that change is pertinent to Doyle's background paper.

Treasury Department regulations had merely called for tax exemption on income of nonprofit corporations arising from activities related to their basic purposes in the public interest. However, during the latter part of the 1950s, some private profit-making laboratories and consulting organizations began to complain about "unfair competition" by institutes such as SRI. Several remedies were proposed by the Treasury; one of them was to tax income from applied research, leaving basic research income free of taxation. SRI and all its advisers felt this was an unworkable approach. The two types of research cannot always be clearly segregated.

A tax case involving New York University's ownership of a food company came to the forefront in 1951. The Mueller Macaroni Company had been given by its founder to the University. The IRS ruled that the company's income should be taxed as "unrelated" even though the money was clearly being spent for "related" purposes. Thus, in effect the basic guide on taxability became "how money was earned" and not "how it was spent." This decision soon became known in tax circles as "the Macaroni Case." More important, however, the word "unrelated" was not defined by the IRS. Thus, a threat to SRI's tax exemption remained on the horizon.

We were anxious in the late 1950s to clear up the ambiguity and proposed informally to the IRS that unrelated income be defined as money arising from any contract that placed ownership of patents, copyrights, and other research results in the hands of any private party. We were opposed on this idea by hundreds of nonprofit organizations around the country. Few of them had a parent university to worry about.

Being unable to settle matters with the Treasury, SRI took its views directly to the U.S. Senate, then considering a tax bill. This was done with tacit IRS support. The idea was legislative rather than administrative action. The plan was well received — so much so that the IRS went ahead on its own with regulations defining "unrelated income" essentially in SRI's language.

Thus, the first tax crisis in our history was resolved much to the relief of Stanford, Morris Doyle and his associates, and SRI itself. The main point of the story is simply that even in 1946 Doyle had foreseen such a problem. Making SRI a fully taxable operation at that time might well have had adverse repercussions on Stanford itself. The guiding SRI principle was to do all things necessary in light of its University affiliation to preserve a tax-exempt position.

But now back to the concepts underlying a proposed "charter" for the new institute. Doyle's paper in 1946 dealt further with taxes and control. One paragraph had a major influence on the University and its Trustees in the subsequent creation of SRI. In effect, it determined the basic corporate plan.

> "The third suggestion (i.e., a separate nonprofit corporation wholly dominated by the University) would permit the desired control over ... the institute and yet afford ... sufficient insulation to the University for tax purposes. Further, a nonprofit corporation which could only distribute earnings to a tax-exempt organization may well be tax-exempt itself. If it were to tax-exempt, the University would not only fully protect itself tax-wise, but would also realize the greatest amount of money from the operations of the Institute."

This matter of "control" appears also in a second background paper presented to Eurich in early 1946. While recognizing that the new organization should be subject to sufficient control by the University, the paper emphasized in principle that the degree of control must not be so close that the institute would lose its separate identity and be regarded as a "mere shell and front" for the University. However, the point was made that the board might be composed of persons "sympathetic" to the University's interests.

These comments on organization and operation of the proposed institute are important in that they soon focused the thinking of all those involved in creating the new institution. The main points soon became University policy and were adopted in due course by the Board of Trustees. Several discussions between representatives of the University and Doyle's firm occurred during March and April of 1946. Articles of Incorporation were drafted and revised, and by early May the document had reached an advanced stage. In transmitting a draft to Eurich on May 14, Doyle mentioned having deleted "teaching activities" while retaining in various places the words "education, learning, and knowledge." Also, by this time the University president's role as ex officio chairman of the institute's board of directors had been established as a guiding policy.

Throughout all these deliberations by Stanford officials and their advisers on possible formation of a research institute, two basic portions of Stanford's Founding Grant were kept in mind. One is that the University "should assist, by experimentation and research, in the advancement of useful knowledge, and in the dissemination and practical application of the same." Doyle felt that this provision most certainly encompassed the concept of "utilizing science for useful purposes" which on some occasions had been used to describe the basic SRI mission.

Doyle and his associates also took into account a Stanford Grant clause that "the public at large, and not alone the comparatively few students who can attend the University, are the chief and ultimate beneficiaries of Stanford University." In light of these provisions, it is not surprising that they believed an institute, properly organized and dedicated to scientific and industrial research, could be one more implementation by the Trustees of the intent of the University's founders.

A set of proposed Articles and Bylaws for the new University-affiliated institute was ready by early autumn of 1946. By this time, however, the first executive director had arrived on the scene. His early employment was made possible by a financial pledge arranged by Atholl McBean. Everything was at last in readiness for the formal founding of the new research organization.

The general practice within SRI over the years has been to recognize October 24, 1946, as

MORRIS M. DOYLE
Stanford University Counsel

Guiding Hand on the Charter

the institution's birthday. This is the day incorporation papers were executed by three attorneys acting on behalf of the Stanford Trustees. The attorneys were Morris M. Doyle, John L. Rockwell, and Robert M. Adams, Jr. However, Founder's Day might well be November 6, November 15, December 13, 1946, or perhaps January 8, 1947.

The SRI Articles were filed with the State of California on November 6, 1946. The three incorporating directors met for the first time as directors of the Institute on November 15. The Board of Trustees of the University acting as general members of SRI adopted the Articles and Bylaws (the SRI charter documents) on December 13. A full board of directors for Stanford Research Institute did not meet until January 8, 1947.

Stanford Trustees present at the December 13 meeting when SRI was "founded" were Charles Blyth, Leland Cutler, George Ditz, Paul Edwards, W. P. Fuller, Jr., Ira Lillick, C.O.G. Miller, Herman Phleger, M. C. Sloss, Alvin Eurich, and Donald Tresidder. They were SRI's first general members.

The Articles for the new institute soon became known within SRI circles as "The Charter." Among other things, the document designated Santa Clara County (the University's location) as the Institute's principal place of business in the eyes of California law. Although SRI's main offices were moved in the spring of 1947 to a nearby location in San Mateo County, the Articles were not amended in this respect until 1954.

The formal ties between Stanford and SRI were clearly spelled out in the original Articles and Bylaws. Nevertheless, many members of the University faculty and of the Institute's early staff did not fully comprehend the connection. They knew only that SRI had been created by Stanford and that the University president at the time was chairman of the board.

Some faculty members thought SRI was supposed to operate more or less as a department of the University. The public image of the relationship was dim and disjointed. This situation existed even though considerable publicity was given in late 1946 and during 1947 to the connection between SRI and Stanford.

Some of this confusion may have arisen from early use of a simple expression on the relationship — "SRI is affiliated with, but operates independently of, Stanford University." The public interpretation soon ranged from one extreme to another — from no connection whatsoever between the two organizations to SRI being part and parcel of Stanford. Unfortunately, the tie could not be described adequately in a short phrase.

One often heard in the early days that SRI was, in effect, a "sister" organization to the University, having been brought into being as a separate institution by the Stanford Trustees. On the other hand, some said that SRI was a subsidiary corporation "owned" and "controlled" by the University in the sense that the Trustees and the University constituted a single entity. Varying public interpretations of the SRI-University tie continued to exist in one form or another during subsequent years.

The specific affiliation between the two organizations as set out in the charter of 1946 involved five basic points.

- Members of the Board of Trustees of Stanford University became general members of the SRI corporation upon assuming office as Trustees. There were no other general members.
- The general members (i.e., the Trustees) were to elect annually a board of directors for SRI.

- The president of Stanford University was chairman, ex officio, of the board of directors.

- The basic purpose of SRI was to promote the educational purposes of Stanford University and to assist it in promoting and extending learning and knowledge.

- In the event of SRI's dissolution, its net assets were to go to the Board of Trustees for the use and benefit of the University.

As time went on, the first three of these ties were changed. In the late 1960s, the board chairman's post was made elective rather than ex officio. Then, in 1969, SRI and Stanford agreed to separate, at which time the SRI directors became also its general members and the group became self-perpetuating. Otherwise, the SRI charter is the same today as it was at the outset. It has stood the test of time, and this is a tribute to Morris Doyle.

As more and more Stanford faculty members became aware during 1947 of the Institute's existence, organization and purposes, their thinking and attitudes fell into two broad categories. Those who were familiar with and interested in western economic development and industrial research tended to view SRI as an important addition to the Stanford complex. Those who were not especially involved or interested in such matters tended to feel that SRI should not have been affiliated with the University.

Several people in the latter group maintained that the Stanford name should not have been used in connection with SRI and that the added burden of board chairmanship should not have been assigned to the University president. One faculty member who felt strongly about the use of the Stanford name likened the situation to local companies (e.g., a laundry) operating with a Stanford identity. Although a senior professor, he was unaware of any legal connection between SRI and the University. Nevertheless, he gave strong voice to his views.

Some of these early problems and confusions might have been avoided had there been a clear statement to both the faculty and new SRI people about the University-Institute relationship. On the other hand, such a statement might have resulted in even more questions and confusion — particularly if it had come from Tresidder. There was little SRI could say under the circumstances.

The basic purposes for SRI were — and still are — clearly stated in the Articles executed in October of 1946. These charter purposes have served SRI very well indeed. However, at least two of them very early became topics of considerable discussion and even controversy at times. One involved obligations to Stanford; the other had to do with the primary reason for SRI's existence. Both raised questions of original intent, mechanisms, and fundamental policy.

It seems clear from the record leading to SRI's formation that the first basic purpose in the charter was intended to be all-pervasive.

These words indicate quite clearly (see following page) that basically SRI was expected to do three things, i.e., promote educational purposes of the University, extend scientific knowledge, and devote all of its resources to these two causes.

The statement also says that the first of these objectives was to be pursued by "encouraging, fostering, and conducting" scientific investigations and research in several broad fields. It does not say that SRI automatically pursued its basic purpose in full simply by carrying out research within its own structure. On the other hand, the statement does not say explicitly that SRI had to encourage and foster scientific research within the University itself. However, the intent of the language was that in addition to its own research SRI was expected to take some action to assist the University in achieving its educational purposes. How this was to be done was left unsaid.

The second point in the first basic purpose seems clear indeed. SRI was charged with extending scientific knowledge, obviously through scientific investigations. In dealing with the third point in the initial purpose, the 1946 statement called upon SRI to devote its resources to advancing research *and* to assisting Stanford. This apparently meant to some that SRI was to advance research through its own staff or perhaps through the staff of other institutions but that in any case it was to assist Stanford in promoting and expanding learning and knowledge.

Although the new institute was in no position at the outset to do more than pursue immediate research objectives, questions did arise both within and outside the Stanford family about SRI's first purpose. Almost everyone involved seemed to have a definite view.

From time to time, the idea has been advanced that the language of the first purpose was put in "lawyer words" so as to assure tax exemption and was not intended as a guide in operating objectives. This, of course, is tantamount to saying that Stanford had an objective in mind that was not consistent with the public-service mission of the Founding Grant and that "lawyer words" were needed to obscure the situation. Both Tresidder and Eurich were clearly thinking along the lines of the first basic purposes as later articulated by University lawyers. No grimmickry in wording was involved.

Those who favored a highly independent policy with respect to the University soon argued that nothing in its charter required SRI to *give* or *donate* funds to Stanford. They felt that by the mere act of engaging in scientific research SRI was automatically devoting its resources to assisting Stanford in its broad educational and scientific purposes set down in the Founding Grant.

On the other hand, proponents of the "intent" point of view (including the author) argued forcefully that SRI was obligated to do at least two things in order to fulfill the first basic purpose. According to this view, SRI was to carry out scientific research that would assist the University generally in the pursuit of the broad mission *and* it was expected to use some of its resources (by mechanisms undefined) to help the University as a separate entity in both promoting and extending learning and knowledge.

One school of thought advanced the view that, even accepting these two requirements, there was no obligation for SRI to "give" or "donate" money or other resources to Stanford and that the "assistance" requirement could be met by placing research contracts or quid pro quo grants in the University, by purchasing technical services from University departments, or by some combination of these methods.

The opposite view held that the Trustees' basic intent in creating SRI was that in time it should be able to aid the University through grants, gifts, and various kinds of payments (cash, services, and property) with freedom on the part of the University to use some of the cash as gifts with no quid pro quo involved. I was, and remained, a strong supporter of this view.

Even as early as 1947, it was argued by some that one passage in the Articles supported the view that SRI as a matter of policy should not make other than sporadic gifts or grants to Stanford.

> "That the corporation is (one) which does not contemplate pecuniary gain
> or profit to the members... No part of the net earnings ... shall be
> distributed to ... any private member or individual."

Those who used this passage in supporting a "no gift" policy were, in effect, saying that Stanford was a private member of the Institute (which it was not) or an individual (which it was not except perhaps in the corporate sense of a "person"). Furthermore, the passage was included in the Articles for an entirely different reason — to meet a basic requirement for tax exemption.

One section in the first Bylaws shows an intent by the founders that gifts in some amount at unknown times would (or at least might) be made by SRI to Stanford. The very first of the duties of the directors said, among other things, that they had full power "to review and determine and vary from time to time ... the amounts which shall be devoted to, given, or turned over to, the Board of Trustees ... in furtherance of its general educational purposes."

On several occasions in 1947, during rather basic discussions on the gift question, the word "dividends" was used to describe the financial intent of the University Trustees in forming SRI. This idea did not, however, gain much acceptance in either the University or SRI.

There is no question that Eurich and Tresidder intended from the beginning that in due course (perhaps after three years) the new institute would be a source of financial assistance to the University. On more than one occasion in 1947, both of them said that financial support to the University was an important reason why they pursued the institute idea. This does not mean, of course, that financial return was the only objective they had in mind. They visualized an institute as one way in which the University could extend its influence in economic and industrial development in the western part of the United States.

This brings up another fundamental point on SRI's purposes involving the tie with Stanford. Even during the early days, varying interpretations were given, sometimes quite authoritatively, on original intent of the Trustees and others (e.g., McBean) who encouraged SRI's formation. One view was that the Trustees had in mind a relatively small SRI that would operate more or less within the University structure but with a separate board of directors clearly subsidiary to the University Trustees.

Another view held that the intent was to create as independent an operation as possible with only ultimate veto control by the Trustees. Some thought that financial return to the University was the prime objective; others stressed research for western industry; still others emphasized scientific and technical assistance to small industry as being the original motivation. Sometimes there seemed to be as many interpretations as there were persons involved in creating SRI, or who said they had been involved.

Several passages from a statement by McBean to SRI's board of directors in 1953 are pertinent in this respect. "There never was any intention that the Institute should be other than an integrated part of the University." He then referred to "an affiliation (with the University) that will operate to our mutual advantage." On the matter of financial assistance, he said, "We should like to see a plan whereby the Institute could contribute at least $100,000 a year to the University."

This attitude is consistent with many other comments on original intent made by McBean in later years. However, he did make clear on many occasions that in using the words "integrated part of the University" he intended that SRI should be a legal entity of the University but that its actual operations were to be independent subject to guidance by a board of directors elected by the University Trustees.

McBean often said that SRI should aid the University financially to the fullest extent practical. He was always firm that the first intent in the charter involved research on industrial problems. One of McBean's business associates during the 1940s later described the San Francisco executive's view in these words: "His expressed basic purpose for the interest he took in SRI was the providing of assistance to Western industry..."

Views similar to those held by McBean were expressed on many later occasions by persons who were University Trustees in 1946. W. P. Fuller, Jr., Paul Edwards, Charles Blyth, and Lloyd Dinkelspiel all agreed with McBean. The most authoritative voice in this respect is Morris Doyle who guided the writing of SRI's charter documents. His associate, Robert Minge Brown (later president of the Stanford Trustees as was Doyle) also was involved in preparing the SRI charter. They have always been (and still are) perfectly clear in their interpretation of original intent.

In their view, SRI was to be a legal entity in the University structure; its main purpose was to advance through scientific research and otherwise the purposes of Stanford University; its operations were to be conducted in such a way as to give maximum support and cooperation to the University; it was to assist Stanford financially when and as deemed prudent by its board of directors and the Trustees; it was to avoid competition with the University; it was to operate in such a way as to reflect credit on Stanford as a whole; and, it was to emphasize research in the public interest and welfare.

In SRI's first charter purpose the words "pure and applied research" are used in referring to the scope of the new organization. These words also were interpreted within SRI and Stanford in various ways during the early years. Both definition and principle were involved. Some maintained that SRI was created solely as an "applied research institute" with the thought that it would not engage in basic or "pure" research except perhaps on a very limited basis. Others pointed to the charter provisions and insisted that the Institute should play a much greater role in basic or fundamental research.

In most instances, these discussions turned on definitions. General agreement existed that SRI should devote its main energies to applying science for useful purposes. Also, the consensus was (and still is) that SRI in its own interests, and in line with its charter, should engage in some research designed to create new knowledge, particularly when this research is directed generally and ultimately towards useful purposes.

Most of the 1947 discussions on this matter hinged on the question: basic to what? There was wide policy agreement that SRI should engage in some research basic to its broad mission and that its role in this respect stood somewhere between university-type basic research and industry-type applied research. The question was somewhat academic at the time because the only research SRI could finance was that obtained through a few contracts.

The view from outside SRI even during the early years on the basic versus applied question varied from one extreme to another. Many people thought the organization was dedicated only to basic research whereas others used the words applied research or problem solving. All of this is not too surprising in light of the difficulty even within the scientific community of differentiating clearly between pure or basic research on the one hand and applied research on the other.

There has been over the years a rising appreciation within SRI that any first-rank research organization must engage in some basic work in order to attract and retain able scientists and as a basis for developing new applied research programs. However, in 1947 the matter was only a subject of discussion; no real action was possible at the time.

SRI's first charter purpose also designated the broad fields in which the organization was to operate — "the physical, biological and social sciences, engineering and the mechanic arts." It was natural, of course, that the new institute would be active in technical fields. The unique feature was the social sciences. This is what all the founding groups wanted even though it departed from a long-standing pattern in the eastern institutes.

Leaders of several of these organizations were quick to say that the social sciences could not be developed successfully in a research institute and that for one reason or another it was not an appropriate activity for SRI. In any event, new ground was being ploughed, thanks to the foresight of those who brought SRI into being.

W. P. Fuller, Jr.
Stanford Trustee when SRI was created.
One of the first General Members of SRI.

The second major purpose from the charter turned to facilities and their use.

THE SECOND PURPOSE

"To provide, equip, and maintain laboratories, experimental and other facilities for general and specific scientific and industrial research and to make such facilities available to ... Stanford University and other institutions and organizations, public or private, for the conduct of research and investigations; ..."

This provision was quickly interpreted as meaning that for the most part SRI should develop its own facilities apart from those of the University. On several occasions beginning in 1947, suggestions arose from various sources that perhaps Stanford should own the facilities and lease them to SRI at a going rate. While certainly permissible under the charter, it seems clear that this course was not really intended by the founders. No move of any consequence in this direction was initiated.

The second corporate purpose also was the basis for SRI's use of facilities in contract research for both public and private organizations including industry. Although nothing was said about financial arrangements, the intent of the founders was clear — facilities were to be used under suitable arrangements involving some net return to SRI. During the early days, however, SRI made its facilities available to Stanford on the basis of recovering only direct costs. This policy was not intended to include contracts placed at SRI by Stanford. These have always been on the same financial basis as other contracts at the Institute.

The third Institute purpose had to do with people and what they were expected to do in a public service institute.

THE THIRD PURPOSE

"To engage, maintain, and develop a staff of qualified educators, scientists, and research experts to carry on the investigations and research projects of the corporation; to provide for the development and improvement of research techniques; and otherwise to aid in the advancement of scientific investigation and of pure and applied research; ..."

Although some consideration was given by the founders to appointing Stanford faculty members as the principal staff of SRI, this charter provision clearly indicates that the Institute was free to develop its own staff and carry out its own projects. Some who were familiar with various pre-charter deliberations stressed on occasion during 1947 and early 1948 their understanding that one of the reasons for SRI's existence was to provide "an increment to faculty salaries," meaning that University faculty members were to participate widely in SRI's research program.

Although the charter most certainly did not prohibit such an arrangement, and in many respects encouraged participation by faculty members, Stanford and SRI adopted a general understanding in mid-1947 that these arrangements would be subject to inter-institutional agreements rather than being solely on a person-to-person basis. At the end of 1947, SRI had consulting or part-time employment arrangements with seven Stanford faculty members.

Many faculty members later served as consultants on SRI research projects; others worked with SRI during their University leave periods; a few people have held joint appointments in the two institutions; other SRI and Stanford people have worked together on joint projects and in many ways have collaborated with each other. A few SRI staff members have taught courses at the University.

In the main, however, the Institute's staff was developed independently of University faculty appointments. One reason was simply that the nature of SRI's research is such that full and undivided attention by principal investigators is necessary in most cases. Furthermore, the basic motivations and obligations of professional people in research institutes differ somewhat from those on university faculties. These two points were generally recognized within both Stanford and SRI by the end of 1947.

The fourth SRI purpose deals with a responsibility to disseminate information.

THE FOURTH PURPOSE

"To establish a center for the accumulation of information useful to scientific and industrial research; to foster the exchange of scientific and technical information with other research and educational institutions and to publish and disseminate such of its findings as may be deemed of general public interest; ..."

In many respects, this function was viewed at the outset as one of the basic reasons for SRI's existence. Nevertheless, while the Articles were still in draft stage, and as the first executive director was assuming office, a question arose on the publication objective. William Talbot thought the purpose as stated "might cause some businessmen a little fear." However, University counsel felt that the proposed tax-exempt status called for maximum emphasis on publication and the provision was retained.

The fifth and last substantive purpose for SRI laid down in the Articles covered ultimate goals for its research efforts (see following page).

This purpose was used at the very beginning to support the view that SRI's prime reason for existence was to engage in "applied research for western industry." This was certainly the intent of most of the people who were involved in SRI's formation. While this view was emphasized considerably at the outset, the purpose was only one of five placed before the organization. Furthermore, it was not intended to confine SRI to research for industry nor to restrict its activities to industrialization in the West.

Moreover, the final words were interpreted during the formative years as meaning that SRI should have a national as well as an international "visibility" and that research projects involving countries other than the United States were within its purview.

The Fifth Purpose

"To promote and foster the application of science in the development of commerce, trade and industry, the discovery and development of methods for the beneficial utilization of natural resources, the industrialization of the western United States of America, and the improvement of the general standard of living and the peace and prosperity of mankind."

The fifth purpose was intended to impart a sense of broad direction to the organization, this being to promote the "development of commerce, trade, and industry." A responsibility to serve the needs of national and international security was later recognized. Nothing was said along these lines in the charter.

Although SRI's Articles specified that members of the Stanford Board of Trustees were to be the members of SRI, and that there should be directors, the implementing steps were left to the Bylaws. These called for annual election of directors by the Trustees (acting as general members) and for the president of the University to be chairman of SRI's board of directors.

SRI's charter was drafted by able people who were prescient in several respects. More than anyone else, they foresaw some of the problems that would later arise and took them into account. They also visualized that the new institute might grow to an even larger organization than the founders had in mind.

Even as SRI expanded over the decades amidst changing legal and economic environments, no changes in its basic purposes have ever been necessary. When Stanford and SRI legally separated in the late 1960s, the situation was accommodated by a simple change in wording with the directors rather than the Trustees being the general members.

In marked contrast to SRI, the governing instruments of another research organization, Battelle Memorial Institute, had what amounted to a basic flaw. Its charter called upon the organization to devote its resources to the Ohio county in which it was located. As time went on, little attention was paid to this mission. In the meantime, Battelle's interests had spread around the world. It was no longer a "Franklin County" operation even though its charter said it was. Finally, Ohio's attorney general brought legal action against Battelle. The result was a far-ranging change in structure and operation.

The fact that SRI's Articles created a certain amount of controversy during the formative years does not in the least speak against the document. The main argument centered on what SRI was to do in assisting Stanford and vice versa. Neither Tresidder nor Eurich put any pressure on SRI in this respect during the late 1940s. McBean was not pushing matters. The problem arose in faculty circles and within SRI itself.

Some faculty members, particularly in the social sciences, more or less resented SRI's creation. They thought the University was investing funds unwisely and that in any case SRI should have been tied in closely with the faculty and also should soon begin helping the University financially. The head of the Food Research Institute felt strongly — and often gave vent to his view — that the name Stanford and even the word "institute" should never have been used. The basic problem, at least in part, was that he and so many other faculty members were not consulted when SRI was being formed.

Within SRI, the Stanford relationship did not begin in good fashion. William Talbot did not relish what he thought were excessive controls by Tresidder. Within a short while, Talbot was gone, Tresidder passed away, and the Stanford Trustees began worrying about SRI's financial situation. McBean's attention was fixed on finding a new executive director. Except for Eurich's guidance from Stanford, SRI was more or less on its own and was marking time at the end of 1947.

Meanwhile, the SRI staff was growing slowly — most of the new people being from outside the Stanford Community with no real dedication to the University. Only two or three of its leaders were actively promoting and explaining the basic concept on which the Stanford connection was designed.

With staff attention devoted almost exclusively to getting SRI in operation, it is understandable — particularly with changes at the helm in both institutions — that far too little was done to cement relations with Stanford. In addition, little was done on the University's side to help matters along — even though bills were being paid on behalf of SRI.

This climate was a breeding ground for rumors, complaints, and questioning. Jesse Hobson, SRI's second executive director, attempted to deal with the situation. But, alas, his drive for expansion and greater freedom of action in some ways compounded the problem with Stanford's leaders as well as with the faculty.

Action

"The charter is excellent; we are ready to move."

ATHOLL McBEAN

The charter events of SRI's first eighteen months or so made a deep impression on me. I was distressed about the situation at the time and have always felt the start was most unfortunate. I believed then — and always have — that SRI had a special obligation to Stanford and that far more should have been done by both institutions at the very beginning by way of exploring and promoting the relationship. From the beginning, I felt a deep commitment to Stanford.

The SRI charter was a stroke of genius. No one has ever suggested a change that, given the circumstances of 1946 — or even later —, would have made a better foundation for a nonprofit research institute.

Atholl McBean always felt that a "good job" was done on SRI's charter. He thought it combined very nicely his emphasis on industrial research and Stanford's criteria for an affiliated research center. He was immensely pleased when Doyle called on November 7, 1946, and said what he wanted to hear — "The Institute is now officially in business." Only the day before the Articles had been filed with the State of California. But, in fact, SRI had unofficially opened its doors in September.

Tresidder was soon to refer to the Institute's formation as a "significant step." It was even more. No other major private university not having a special endowment or assured financial support for an industrial research institute had ever taken such a move and made it succeed. Stanford was entering a fast track; no one suggested what the full implications would be.

DOCTOR'S ORDERS

In late 1945, Dr. Russell V. Lee, founder and long-time director of the Palo Alto Clinic, gave one of his patients some strong advice. Dr. Donald B. Tresidder told his doctor about Atholl McBean's interest in a research institute at Stanford. Lee promptly replied — "Don, you better move quickly; if you don't, Atholl will start one somewhere else; he believes in quick action." Fortunately, Tresidder did what his doctor told him to do.

During the early 1950s when SRI was beset by a financial problem that troubled the Stanford Trustees, I was involved along with Hobson and others in an informal meeting with the group. At one point, I used the phrase "bold step" in referring to SRI's formation. No one seemed to feel at the time that the words overstated the situation.

In some respects, the story of our charter centers on Stanford's motivations in creating SRI. Financial gain was certainly a key consideration, particularly in light of the University's money problems at the time. Alvin Eurich has addressed this point based on first-hand involvement. His words appear in a closing section of this book. ∎

The First Year

*"The Stanford Research Institute has been established
at a propitious moment — Western industry
has just scratched the surface of its potential."*

— WILLIAM F. TALBOT - 1946

ONCE THE STANFORD TRUSTEES approved in principle the idea of creating a research institute, Atholl McBean and Alvin Eurich began looking for its first chief executive. To be more precise, they were really seeking an executive director. The chairman of the board was the senior officer and thus responsible for broad policy direction. No mention was made of a chief executive officer; an executive director was to administer the Institute's affairs. It was not until the 1960s that the head of SRI was given chief executive status.

All this was not simply a play on words or a difference without significance. It was, in fact, intended at the outset, at least by Tresidder, that Stanford's president would be far more than a chairman at board meetings. He and the vice chairman (initially Eurich) were to make the principal decisions affecting the Institute's operations.

Some faculty members were to say later that, while Eurich was well tuned to be SRI's senior officer, the whole exercise was not Tresidder's "cup of tea." This was a reflection of some faculty attitudes at the time on his style as Stanford's president.

In any event, both McBean and Eurich maintained — and rightly so — that nothing significant should be done about the proposed institute until a director was in place. They consulted several people including Clyde Williams, director of Battelle Memorial Institute, and Earl Stevenson, president of Arthur D. Little.

By late spring of 1946, their search had ended. They selected Dr. William F. Talbot who was technical director of the Sun Chemical Company and president of its Fine Chemicals Division. No one else other than Philip Leighton at Stanford was seriously considered.

Talbot was "appointed" on September 1. Four days later, Tresidder reported the selection to the Stanford Trustees. No one questioned the arrangement — a director of an institute not yet incorporated. McBean had guaranteed his salary for three years; this was sufficient for Stanford to move ahead.

Talbot was not formally appointed until January 8 of the following year when SRI's board held its first meeting. He was also the corporate secretary. As events developed, he was to serve in these posts for a very short period.

Dr. William F. "Bill" Talbot

Staff Member Number One — The First Director

Stevenson had recommended Talbot to McBean and Eurich based on an earlier association when Talbot was with Arthur D. Little in charge of work for the General Printing Ink Company. Stevenson was director of the company; it later became part of Sun Chemical. When Sun created a new technical director position, Stevenson recommended Talbot who accepted the challenge. Knowing later that Talbot wanted to leave the firm, Stevenson thought the Stanford opportunity would interest him. In any event, he felt he had been helpful in "getting the Institute off the ground."

In mid-1946, while negotiations were under way on the appointment, Talbot wrote Eurich at length about his ideas for the new research institute. He stressed service to industry, an operation about midway between a university and an industrial laboratory, a tie between industrial research and the profit motive and the importance of promoting research projects. He went on to emphasize the need for a closely-knit and fast-moving staff, minimum rules and red tape, complete research and financial records, and the value of economic and marketing studies.

Talbot did not neglect finances in outlining his thoughts to Eurich. He said the Institute should operate so as to "provide for a profit over and above all operating costs," thereby building up a substantial earned surplus "to carry the organization through troublesome periods." This was not only the right approach; it was what McBean wanted to hear and was reassuring to Eurich.

Also at mid-year, Talbot visited the Stanford Campus and then met with Eurich and McBean at the latter's summer home in Woodside near the University. The three men soon came to a meeting of minds. In early August, Eurich advised his friends at A. D. Little that "we have settled upon Dr. William F. Talbot to be the director of our Research Institute." In fact, the decision had been made earlier subject only to final discussions in California.

Later that month Eurich wrote to Talbot about his forthcoming appointment saying, "We feel this is one of the most significant steps Stanford University has taken for some time."

There were, of course, other contacts on the proposed appointment. Information was sought from several people at the State University of Iowa, the National Industrial Conference Board in New York, Dennison Manufacturing Company, Lowell Chemical

Company, and two eastern law firms. Talbot was well known in these organizations. On the other hand, he was unable to find out anything about a Stanford Research Institute except from Stevenson at A. D. Little. His eastern industrial friends had not heard about the Stanford initiative.

Aside from Swain, Leighton, and a few others in Stanford's Chemistry Department, Talbot was unknown to the Stanford faculty. He was, however, well known in the chemical industry. A native of Nebraska, he had received M.S. and Ph.D. degrees from the State University of Iowa. After several years of teaching, he joined E. I. du Pont as a research chemist and later was a consulting chemist at A. D. Little. On leave in 1944 from Sun Chemical, he was assistant director of research and development in the Office of Strategic Services.

Talbot had invented melamine resins (a plastic) used for moldings, castings, and other industrial purposes and also held several patents. In both Swain's and Leighton's eyes, he was a good appointment for the new institute.

Thus it was that Talbot took up his post at Stanford in September of 1946. He had an "office" (18 square feet in the Chemistry Building) but no desk or telephone. He announced right away that the first task was "marshalling resources of the University —men and equipment — to participate in the Institute's program." Tresidder was quick to say to the media and in Stanford's 1946 report that SRI would "draw from the reservoir of outstanding scientific ability found within the University." Talbot made it clear to the press that "we will not sit back and wait for commissions to come to us." SRI was in business even though not yet in existence.

With Eurich's and McBean's support, Talbot did not wait for all the incorporation steps to be taken nor for the first SRI board meeting to be held before starting an operation. William E. "Bill" Rand, general manager of the chemical division of Sun Chemical, joined Talbot on November 18 as assistant director. I was employed in early October but was not able to join the staff officially until June 23, 1947. Discussions were under way even in September and October on SRI's first two projects — on the guayule plant and on aircraft production.

Word began spreading around the Stanford Campus in October that the new institute would be an offshoot of the University. This was the message from Talbot, and it fitted neatly into Tresidder's conception. Talbot spoke of "borrowing unblushingly" from University facilities and talent until separate facilities and staff could be created. But, few departments beyond Chemistry were in fact consulted.

Both Tresidder and Talbot mentioned on several occasions that professors interested in working with the Institute would be paid directly for their efforts. This idea of supplementing faculty salaries as an original objective of the Institute would be mentioned time and again by faculty members when SRI moved quickly to build up its own staff. This was Tresidder's thought at the outset, but it never materialized to any significant extent. The Three Musketeers had the same idea in 1945.

Talbot's idea was that a minimum of 100 persons would be needed "to carry on the Institute's many-sided programs" but even then it would continue to draw on faculty skills. Aside from chemistry, biology and business, this sort of University involvement simply did not enter the picture.

During his various talks with the press and around the campus in mid-autumn of 1946, Talbot did emphasize several points that were to be very much in SRI's future. He stressed that the soon-to-be nonprofit institute would operate with a "net gain" as a self-supporting organization. Referring to potentials in the American West, he said, "Increased population has expanded local markets tremendously and rising standards of living in the Far East promise huge new outlets for goods." Little did he know that within fifteen years SRI would open an office in Tokyo and begin serving Japanese industry.

Talbot was obviously enthusiastic about his new location and work. One Stanford publication quoted him as being high on "the willingness of Westerners to tackle new jobs and explore new fields." He said on several occasions that the situation was "an ideal setup for a research institute."

During November and December, five scientists were retained on a special basis for SRI's first project. It involved possible improvement of the guayule plant as a source of rubber. Most of the work was carried out in government laboratories at Salinas, California.

Since SRI was not yet officially in operation, Stanford assumed responsibility for about a million dollars worth of government property. The project was a joint one between SRI and the University with a Stanford assistant professor, Dr. Reed C. Collins, in charge of the laboratory work in genetics. Dr. Harris Benedict directed the biology program at Salinas.

For about four years ending on June 30, 1946, the U.S. Department of Agriculture had supported a project on developing a domestic source of natural rubber. The guayule plant, native to Northern Mexico and Southern Texas, was by far the most promising source. But in mid-1946 Congress cut off all project funds on the basis that the post-war need for a domestic rubber source was not great enough to justify the cost.

The military services did not agree with this position and the Office of Naval Research (ONR) entered the picture temporarily. A grant-type contract was assigned to SRI. The USDA staff at Salinas transferred to SRI. In due course, Congress changed its stance and appropriated funds for the USDA to resume its work. This took effect on August 1, 1947. Thus, the SRI project came to an end; most of the team except for Bill Rand (the manager) and Benedict went back to the Department of Agriculture.

DR. HARRIS M. BENEDICT
A Mainstay of the Guayule Project

The guayule project was number 102 in SRI's accounts. This is an amusing sidelight in SRI's early history. Rand set up the series and began with number 101 on a Food Acceptance Laboratory that did not develop into an income project. His view was — "To start with project No. 1 would admit a youthfulness that might just as well be concealed." Anyhow, #102 was really #1, and it brought SRI its first $100,000 project. No one ever asked about the first 100 projects, nor did anyone ask why project numbers should be mentioned outside SRI. But Rand reflected an attitude at the time. With only three regular employees at the end of 1946 in a two-room headquarters in the Physics Corner of the Main Quad at Stanford, there was an understandable sensitivity about newness and size.

A personal note now intrudes on the chain of corporate events. In the autumn of 1946 I was working temporarily with the Air Force Institute of Technology in Dayton, Ohio, after having completed wartime service in the Air Force. My one and only plan was to return to Stanford where I had attended the Graduate School of Business.

My wife preceded me in the move. She wrote in October about a news item on formation of a Stanford Research Institute. Some of my Air Force colleagues saw the article and were interested in the organization as a possible source of research assistance. I was asked to look into the situation during an upcoming visit to Stanford.

My first contact was by telephone. I asked the operator at the University to connect me with the Institute. She had never heard of the organization and said, "There is no such department." Following a brief pause at both ends of the line, she then testified to the newness of SRI, saying, "I think a research institute is just being started — one moment, please."

A man answered the phone; he did not give his name. Not knowing the director's name, and not wishing in any case to take his time on the assumption that others on the staff could help me, I identified myself and asked to speak to anyone he might suggest. I made it clear that there was no need to bother the director.

The reply was prompt and to the point: "My name is Bill Talbot; I am the director; there is no other staff." Talbot invited me to his office. We discussed the business at hand; he expressed interest in assisting the Air Force; we agreed to meet again in a few days. Then, responding to his question about my presence in the area, I told him of my plans on a doctoral program. Talbot also learned that I had no thought of leaving the area once the final Ph.D. requirements had been satisfied.

A few days later Talbot confirmed his interest in one Air Force project. Then he said he had talked with the dean of the Business School and asked to my surprise if I might consider joining SRI — if the project materialized. He said time could be arranged for my University work; very little time was needed in any event.

Having no other employment plans, I accepted on the spot without asking any questions about the Institute, its future, salary, or fringe benefits. The points simply did not occur to me since my understanding was that only a nine-month temporary job was involved.

Suffice it to say, I have never had cause to regret this quick acceptance of a "tempo-

A lift off in 1946

rary" position. Although being the second or third person to join SRI, I later received Identification Card #6. In the meantime, four other persons had joined. But they, as well as Talbot, were to depart in time, leaving #6 at the beginning of the list.

Prior to my arrival at SRI, I asked Rand if he would seek a few qualified persons who might assist on the Air Force project I was to direct (with Air Force approval). It dealt with the aircraft industry's "expansibility" in the event of another national emergency. Rand made several trips to Southern California and was able to obtain three or four people. For this I was most grateful. However, in Rand's words he "had not the faintest idea of how one went about substantiating an expense account for the U.S. Government." Months and even years later we were still trying to get paid for his costs. We were unsuccessful. On many occasions, I chided Rand for helping start a good project with "a bad financial entry."

THE FIRST HEADQUARTERS

Stanford Village
Building 100 — Room for Expansion — Menlo Park

STANFORD VILLAGE — 1947

The Dibble Hospital area with temporary World War II barracks-type building. Arrow points to first building occupied by SRI.

At their first board meeting in early January 1947, the directors talked about various research directions for the new Institute. Without limiting its fields, they decided that first emphasis should be on agriculture, food processing and petroleum. They agreed that SRI should not take on such a large number of projects as to scatter attention of the very small staff.

McBean mentioned a recent visit by David Minton of Battelle to SRI's office at Stanford. He quoted Minton as saying that a small, diversified, permanent staff would be essential if SRI was to receive any significant research contracts. The directors then decided that a food technology expert should be employed but with no commitments beyond a few months. They thought other staff should be added only as projects were developed and financed. Although this policy was necessary at the time, it did not augur well for the Institute's future. Even by the end of 1947, only one third of the research staff was on a continuing basis.

Much of the first board meeting had to do with finances, a situation that was to be repeated often during the first few years. There was an immediate need for working capital. Overhead costs were already running at some $153,000 per year. The 1946 deficit was about $7,100. The total value of research projects on hand was about $125,000 — with another $400,000 under discussion. These projects and inquiries had come in without particular solicitation. Talbot thought contract volume "could be doubled without too great effort" but this meant doubling the very small staff.

Talbot also told the directors that existing facilities could carry a load of about $500,000 in annual research revenue. A few buildings in Stanford Village (a World War II hospital area in Menlo Park near Stanford) already were being readied for Institute use. However, he said that "an appreciable amount of tools, scientific equipment, rehabilitation of space, and supplies must be secured, installed and put to work to serve the particular needs of projects." Meanwhile, monthly bills were being paid by Stanford and charged to an SRI account. This raised questions within the University. The situation was eased temporarily when the board approved a $50,000 loan from the American Trust Company in San Francisco.

The directors then turned their attention to longer-term capital needs. Talbot said that the outlook for self-supporting operations was encouraging. But he thought that capital contributions in the order of $500,000 would be needed to put the organization on "a firm operating base." His estimate was based on the idea that SRI "must be capable of remaining in being and active for at least three years with a skeleton staff even with substantially no projects."

Talbot thought that $100,000 should be set aside for salaries along with $30,000 for a sales campaign, $30,000 for facilities, $100,000 for working capital, and $40,000 for contingencies. He went on to say that the salary reserve might be reduced as more time was devoted to contract research work. No action was taken by the board but the handwriting was on the wall — growth ahead of money.

STANFORD RESEARCH INSTITUTE

The first logo

At the first directors' meeting, Eurich was elected vice chairman of the board. Thus began a practice that was followed throughout SRI's early years, i.e., a University vice president being the Institute's second officer.

Work on SRI's second research project on methylated napthalenes for the Richfield Oil Corporation was started in February 1947. This was the beginning of a long series of projects for Richfield. It was SRI's first endeavor for industry. The project was a "walk-in" in the fullest sense of the term. A Richfield geologist came in unannounced. He had heard about SRI and said Richfield wanted to be "the first company to support research in the new organization." Rand made all the arrangements and then induced Dr. Lawrence M. Richards to leave du Pont and join SRI as project director. Some years later he moved on to a research post in Richfield.

On May 21, the small staff moved from the Stanford Campus to a temporary building of the Dibble General Hospital in Stanford Village. Stanford had leased the site from the U.S. Government and was using most of the buildings for student housing.

Dr. Carsten Steffens was appointed director of chemistry and chemical engineering on June 1 and shortly thereafter became acting director of the Institute's entire research effort. Steffens later took up a faculty position in New Mexico, then returned to SRI and still later was first director of its office in Japan.

During a staff meeting shortly after my arrival in late June, Talbot held up an organization chart. It included a position for "industrial social sciences." Following the meeting, I asked Rand a direct question — "Who has been selected for the post?" My assumption was that whoever had been appointed would soon appear on the scene. Rand's reply told me more than I expected to hear. "You are the director of that program, aren't you?" With no further comment on anyone's part, I thus moved from temporary to permanent status!!

During the months from February through May of 1947, the directors met four times. They talked mostly about new research projects and, as they were to do often in the following two years, discussed a capital fund campaign. It was decided in March that any such plans should be left in the hands of Tresidder and McBean. In April, the board asked McBean to be a "clearing house" on assignments to directors of various companies to be solicited for funds.

The board dealt with two operating policies during the early 1947 meetings. One involved separate pricing policies for short- and long-term projects. In effect, no decision was taken and in time SRI practice resulted in a uniform pricing policy for projects — both large and small — sponsored by private clients. Pricing for government projects was not in question at the time, simply because no one was thinking about government contracts. The guayule project with ONR was a conventional university-type grant.

A few months later the government pricing question did arise; it was dealt with in precise detail. As the first Air Force contract was being discussed with military contract officers, one of them asked Rand and me about our government overhead recovery rate. We had no rate, because none had been needed. Rand had no experience in such matters, and mine was limited. He asked me to reply, I said that "something like 30% of labor costs — as at Stanford — would fit into our policy." This was acceptable to the Air Force. Then, we spent the next several years negotiating higher and higher rates in keeping with SRI's cost buildup.

The second early policy decision had to do with whether or not SRI could provide technical services in legal preceedings. The directors favored the idea. In later years this subject was to become quite controversial within the Institute and among the directors and Stanford Trustees. However, the basic 1947 policy was reaffirmed by the board several times on the basis that Institute experts would appear voluntarily in legal hearings only in connection with research they had undertaken at SRI.

In connection with his fund-raising assignment, McBean decided early in the summer that some professional help was needed. He met in late June of 1947 with Talbot and J. Henry Lang, a San Francisco financial consultant. Tresidder agreed with McBean and Talbot that Lang should be retained for one year.

Lang lost no time in presenting a plan to Talbot. It involved a "complete campaign counselling service" for a $5,000 fee plus expenses. He proposed to develop policy and procedures, prepare a prospect list of individuals and companies, write letters for individual directors, and submit progress reports to the board.

Talbot accepted Lang's proposal and arranged a kick-off meeting for August 4 with McBean. The immediate result was a prospect list including 47 companies (assigned to six directors) for a total of $855,000 and another twenty companies (with no amounts) to be handled by one director.

1947 Fund-Raising Plan		
Companies	Amounts	Directors
7	$135,000	Charles R. Blyth
9	75,000	John Cushing
10	180,000	Paul L. Davies
7	135,000	W. P. Fuller, Jr.
5	165,000	D. J. Russell
9	165,000	J. D. Zellerbach
20	. . . .	Wm. L. Stewart, Jr.
67	$855,000	

These assignments covered only part of the goal set by McBean, Lang and Talbot. Their idea was that the target should be $1,125,000. Talbot and Rand thought about one-third of this money should be used for working capital, another third for laboratory equipment, and one-third for construction.

Lang wrote to Williams at Battelle and to a few other research institutes asking for

information about their fund-raising programs. This and other independent actions (along with a decision to delay the whole fund-raising effort) soon led to termination of the arrangement with Lang. This occurred on September 30 only two and a half months after his appointment. No one had been happy with the arrangement.

One interesting aspect of this first fund-raising step is that no formal action was taken by the board in establishing the goal. However, an SRI booklet published during the summer of 1947, while the McBean-Lang-Talbot initiative was under way, announced that "the sum of $1,125,000 is now being raised." This was a harbinger of things to come. McBean made a decision that should have come from the board chairman. In any event, a decision was made and promptly announced.

The first SRI brochure appeared under the name The New Frontier. SRI was presented as the logical outgrowth of a firm belief among industrialists of the area that "the time has come when such an industrial research institute is absolutely essential to the continued healthy growth of the region."

The booklet was specific in including industrial social sciences within SRI's orbit. It called for scientific evaluation "all the way down the line — in accounting and administration as well as production and engineering — in sales and advertising as well as in raw materials and construction." The description of SRI was indeed expansive — "completely broad in its conception, embracing all kinds of research."

One section of The New Frontier dealt with the Stanford relationship. The idea of "full freedom to draw upon University resources" was stressed. However, the booklet went on to say that in time SRI would operate with its own plant and personnel within a concept of "complete independence." The full-freedom idea certainly did not set well with the Stanford faculty, particularly since they were not consulted on such a policy.

Working days at SRI during 1947 were pleasant in many respects. Each member of the staff knew all others personally. Although all were busy, the pressures of work were not too great. There were many administrative and service tasks to be performed, and often they were handled by merely dividing the work, including, for example, picking up and depositing mail at the post office. The staff moved furniture when an office would be relocated. They painted the interiors during a "fix-up" weekend.

A personal sidelight illustrates the closeness of the small SRI group at the time. Although my wife and I were not new to the community, this was not the case for most of the staff. As might be expected under these circumstances, we often visited each other during the evenings. Talbot and Rand liked to play a little poker on occasion. Although unskilled in the game, I nevertheless invited several new Institute friends to our home one evening for a session with the cards. I expected to lose a certain amount to my associates. To my great surprise, the evening ended with three losers and with me the winner. Both Talbot and Rand jokingly implied that my days at SRI were numbered because of carelessness in winning. Fortunately, they rose above principle and allowed me to remain!

The Institute's receptionist during the early Stanford Village days was a man by the name of R. E. (Roy) Sebern. Having earlier been a forest ranger, Sebern continued to wear his green uniform after joining SRI. Also, he was the bookkeeper. Even then the Institute had a double entry accounting system. Sebern would file invoices in the right-hand drawer of his desk and place incoming checks in a left-hand drawer. Periodically, both invoices and checks were sent to the Stanford business office where they entered a more formal system.

The coffee break has long since become a fixed routine in most organizations. The practice began at SRI during its very earliest days — except that it was called the "tea break." Midway during each afternoon the staff would gather for a few minutes in the reception area of a barracks-type building and enjoy conversation over tea and biscuits. The ritual had started in January, 1947, before the Institute moved away from the Stanford Campus. Perhaps, in retrospect, it is not surprising that the "tea break" annoucement appeared in a staff memorandum under the title "Miscellaneous Information."

> "At approximately 3:00 or 3:30 o'clock, we knock off and have a cup
> of tea for about ten minutes. If you find it difficult to get to the office
> when tea is ready, we will be glad to provide you with the necessary
> equipment so that you can make it in your laboratory and will
> reimburse you for the tea and biscuits you find it necessary to purchase."

Either SRI was ahead of its time on fringe benefit programs or it was simply overly generous. It must have been the latter; in due course, as the staff increased, the tea-and-biscuit program disappeared.

All of the Institute's policies and procedures during the organization's first few months did not, however, involve matters of pleasant privilege. We were admonished in no uncertain terms to maintain a high degree of security about our research activities.

A Closed-Mouth Policy

"Never mention to outsiders the name of any industrial sponsor ...

"Never mention research being sponsored by Government agencies ...

"Never discuss with outsiders the results of any research nor the types of research work being performed ... other than ... in the field of agriculture or food technology or aeronautics, etc ...

"Wherever possible at technical meetings, refrain from engaging in discussion about fields of research in which you are actively engaged.

"If you find yourself placed in a position that is awkward, state that such information is considered confidential and that you will have to check with the Director of the Institute before discussing the matter ..."

In looking back to the 1947 days and to this set of instructions, it seems obvious that there could have been little for anyone to reveal to prospective clients. Furthermore, in complying with the memorandum, the least embarrassing course would have been to stay away from professional meetings.

The truth of the matter is that everyone (including Rand who wrote the instructions) simply ignored the policy and used his or her own judgment on what could and should be said about SRI's work. The interesting point is that no one complained about it at the time. We were simply too preoccupied in getting various programs and projects under way.

Rand's memorandum of mid-summer left no stone unturned in making sure everyone understood the confidential nature of SRI's research work. There was a special message for wives and husbands of staff members.

SILENCE AT HOME

"Although the institute has not desire to create any unnecessary 'cloak and dagger' atmosphere, I would like also to point out the desirability of mentioning to your wife or husband or other members of your family the fact that work performed by the Institute is confidential in nature, so that in the event you may unwittingly mention things within your own home that you would not mention elsewhere, such information will stop and go no farther."

For some this was the beginning of complaints from the home front. For example, as my own work became more involved and complicated, I would sometimes jokingly respond to questions at home about the Institute by saying, "It's confidential." I soon found that others were doing the same.

Talbot thought the organization should have some distinctive hallmark or symbol to replace the atomic nuclei sheath used on the first SRI brochure. In an attempt to save money, Rand asked his brother (who was a commercial artist in Massachusetts) to make some suggestions.

His sketches included several stereotyped devices such as retorts, smoking factory stacks, and jagged sales curves on graph paper, none of which Rand felt were adequate. So, almost in desperation and in his words "without much real thought," Rand traced a map of the western states on a piece of transparent paper and with a compass drew some concentric circles from Menlo Park. He was trying to show that SRI was really quite well located to serve the western part of the nation. His handiwork was promptly adopted. In due course, the map was increased to cover the entire United States and later a global symbol was created.

A unique but exacting research opportunity arose at mid-year of 1947 and continued until late autumn. Standard Oil Company of California wanted to set up a basic research project in chemistry provided SRI could obtain a few highly qualified people from one or more of the nation's universities. It soon became apparent that perhaps only a half-dozen people in the country met the qualifications. The search gradually became known as "Aristotle at age 30." Several leading chemists were invited to SRI, but in the end the project was abandoned simply because the right people could not be brought aboard.

The search was not, however, without some interesting features. Dr. Robert Woodward, a Harvard chemistry professor, visited SRI to discuss the situation. Woodward was indeed an able chemist; he later won a Nobel Prize. Although he spent two days at SRI at the beginning of November 1947, he never seriously considered joining a small and as yet unknown institute in the West. This was fortunate in one respect. A skilled and inveterate poker player, he wanted to play for what some of his would-be associates thought were unfriendly stakes.

Another man who attracted SRI's interest on the "Aristotle Project" was Dr. Frank Mayo, a chemist with the U.S. Rubber Company. Several directors thought the Institute should not try to entice him away from the company. Years later, Mayo did join SRI but with other pursuits in mind. He was — and still is — one of the world's foremost polymer chemists.

When Tresidder heard that SRI was interested in getting Dr. Saul Winstein from UCLA, he quickly said that the University of California's permission to approach him was the "right way to do things in academia." Thereupon, he telephoned Dr. Robert Gordon Sproul, the University president. The reply was "Go right ahead, Don, but we value Winstein highly and have more money than you have." He shortly received two salary increases and a promotion. There was no joining SRI for a Stanford Oil project, but there was gratitude on Winstein's part for the approach.

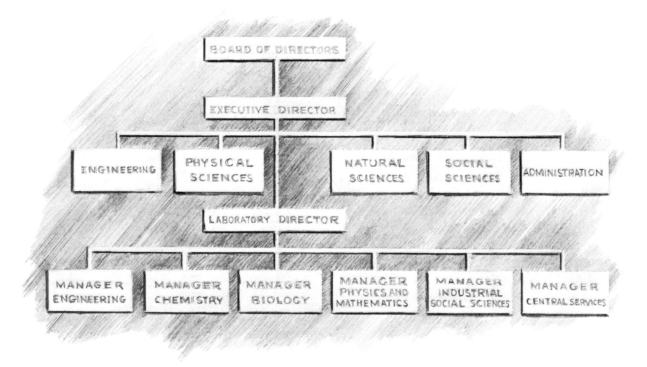

Dr. Carsten Steffens
First Director of Research — 1947

As the summer of 1947 came to an end — along with Talbot's first year at SRI — all seemed to be moving in reasonably good fashion. A project on the Los Angeles smog problem had been set up along with one for Pepsi-Cola on a possible new beverage. Also, a study on liquid surfaces, with help from Stanford's Chemistry Department, was under way with ONR. Several other projects were being discussed with prospective clients. The regular staff stood at around 25 people.

First Economics Project

SRI's Economics Division got under way in 1947 with an Air Force project on expansion potentials in the nation's aircraft industry. In addition to the author, the team included J. R. Crawford, D. N. McIsaac, A. J. Schulten, W. M. Stewart, J. E. Thompson, L. A. Wilkinson, and J. Yankie (all from the industry) with Dr. J. Knight Allen and Paul E. Holden from Stanford's Business School as consultants.

The results in 1948 were not encouraging to the Air Force nor to the first Secretary of Defense. Too much time would be needed in the event of a national emergency to bring production back to a high level. For SRI, however, the project was the beginning of a steadily-growing economics research program.

There was little to suggest that so soon after its beginning SRI was about to enter a holding pattern. Questions began to arise in Talbot's mind about the environment in which he found himself. And, Tresidder, along with Eurich and McBean, began to question Talbot's mode of operation. Although not evident to the staff at the time, the late summer decision to postpone a fund-raising campaign was a signal of things to come. A change was brewing. ■

Good Old Days

SRI space rental (including utilities) in 1947 — 13¢ per square foot per month.

The Gathering Clouds

Let's get organized and move out of the station.

— DONALD J. RUSSELL - 1947

TALBOT'S SECOND YEARS AT SRI began on a quiet note. In late August and early September 1947, he was thinking about ways in which the Institute could make a considerable leap forward with one or more new endeavors. Tresidder and Eurich returned to the campus soon after the Labor Day holidays. Talbot was looking forward to talking with them. Meanwhile, projects were under way for Richfield, the Air Force, and on Los Angeles smog.

The beginnings of SRI's research programs in the physical sciences and in economics were in place. An air of expectancy and youthful ethusiasm was amply evident. However, events soon moved in an unexpected way. Clouds began to gather over the new institute. A change at the top was in the making.

Tresidder began to worry about the growing expense advances to SRI. Talbot was disappointed with the tightening purse strings. McBean gradually realized that he would soon have to make good on earlier promises for financial support. The Trustees started asking questions about their investment and the future. The directors began worrying about being in the middle between SRI and the Trustees.

But amidst this emerging situation, business went on as usual. By early September, Talbot had run into questions from prospective clients about access by directors to proprietary information in the event project conflicts of interest should develop between a sponsor on the one hand and directors on the other. The board promptly responded with a resolution vesting "complete discretion and authority" for safeguarding research results in the executive director. This basic policy remains today.

At the September board meeting, the main point of discussion was the Institute's capital-fund needs. The directors' thoughts soon turned to industry. A membership plan was considered under which one-half of a company's contributions would be devoted to capital needs and one-half to research on behalf of the company. The proposal was tabled pending investigation by J. D. Zellerbach, an SRI director, on financing methods used by the Institute of Paper Chemistry in Wisconsin. Its executive director, Dr. Westbrook Steele, attended the November board meeting along with Zellerbach, where capital financing was again discussed. The board decided to explore the membership idea further; Tresidder and Talbot agreed to develop a plan.

Steele had already been helpful to Talbot by explaining in some detail how his organization operated. Through Zellerbach, he had provided information on resolving conflicts of interest among sponsors, handling of patents, self-sponsored research programs and charges to research clients. On the latter point, he said a 10% fee based on total estimated costs (direct and indirect) was used on research projects. This information influenced both Talbot and the directors to a considerable extent in their later fixing of income-recovery rates for SRI's industrially-sponsored projects.

Two significant matters were presented by Talbot at the September board meeting. One was a draft of a preliminary proposal to the Civil Aeronautics Authority on operation of the Landing Aids Experiment Station at Arcata, California. The proposal was approved but the project did not materialize. Also, he presented a proposal prepared for ONR on preliminary design of a supersonic wind tunnel. He said that the project, if obtained, would mean a tentative commitment to proceed with further contracts on the tunnel itself. The financial forecast was for some $4.0 million over a four-year period, with funds to be provided by the federal government. This proposal also was approved. Almost immediately, however, questions by individual directors began arising on the wisdom of seeking such large and involved projects at SRI's stage of development. Not enough groundwork was done with the directors before the proposals were submitted.

Had the wind tunnel facility been developed, it might have been an important factor in research cooperation between SRI and Stanford. The project was not discussed with University faculty members who would have been most concerned. Dr. Frederick Terman was dean of the University's engineering school at the time. Seventeen years later, he commented on the proposal: "I had never heard of this (project) ... yet, as of 1947 the availability of such a facility for even only a few hours a week at nights or weekends would have been of tremendous value to the aeronautical engineering program at Stanford..."

Although the Institute was making reasonably good progress in developing a research operation, ominous signs began to appear in personal relationships between Talbot and Tresidder. Talbot accepted the appointment at SRI with the understanding that the Institute was to operate quite independently of the University. He soon came to feel that this was not to be the case.

SRI being a new organization with no business office, the University handled all receipts, disbursements and purchases. Furthermore, the University was providing the working capital. Talbot found that most of SRI's business transactions were subject to detailed approval by Tresidder. This disturbed him greatly, and he became increasingly critical of the arrangement. He felt, perhaps rightly, that the chairman was involving himself needlessly in operating matters. In retrospect, it is perhaps understandable that Tresidder felt a personal responsibility, as senior officer of the corporation, to supervise its operations in some detail, particularly at the outset. Also, he more or less had such control in mind at the beginning.

Perhaps it could be argued that Tresidder was supervising SRI as board chairman and that this did not imply University surveillance. Tresidder apparently wanted to keep the Institute's operations completely separate from Stanford. But he was a man in two positions and Talbot looked upon him as acting in both capacities simultaneously.

One example reflects Talbot's irritation with some of the supervision exercised by Tresidder over the Institute's business affairs. One day Talbot held up a copy of a requisition for miscellaneous office supplies (pencils, paper, etc.) and said that the order was "on Tresidder's desk awaiting his approval." He sat for some time looking at the document and wondered aloud about the policy and system that seemed to require such close supervision. Tresidder on the other hand was worried about rising outlays and mentioned the "wind tunnel" matter (once in my presence) as a symbol of concern about SRI and Talbot.

Relationships between the two men became somewhat strained as the weeks went by. On several occasions, Talbot spoke quite directly to Tresidder, and at least three times offered his resignation as one means of overcoming what he thought were undue administrative restraints. The situation was not helped by a financial operation that seemed to be leading to a cumulative deficit of more than $50,000 by the end of 1947.

Talbot took the view, perhaps quite rightly in retrospect, that the Institute should never have been started if even much larger initial deficits had not been expected, or if arrangements had not been made for sufficient capital contributions. McBean had arranged for $48,000 of capital gifts, but even so it appeared that SRI would have a negative net worth at the end of 1947.

It it clear that no firm estimate was made at the beginning on the amount of money needed to create the new research institute. Several figures were advanced at various times, but most of them were merely quick-reaction guesses. Harold Vagtborg of Midwest Research Institute said some seventeen years later that he was invited to visit SRI in mid-1947. Talbot was ill at the time so Vagtborg called on him at his home. He later described one part of the conversation in these words:

> "It was during this discussion that we considered the minimum amount of money that it would take to initiate a program of this kind. I told him that even though we (had earlier) started Armour Research Foundation with practically no money and, indeed, did become indebted to Armour Institute of Technology to the extent of $50,000, I did not believe that anyone could ever start a research program with such inadequate funding...

> "I recall telling Dr. Talbot that in starting Midwest (which was about two years before our visit) I had recommended to the Governors at Midwest that, in my judgment, the minimum amount of money required to start a research institute was $500,000 and that had been raised and represented as 'cash in the bank' before I arrived on January 1, 1945."

Vagtborg went on to point out in his recollection that apparently Talbot seemed to feel the half million dollar figure was about right or at least that "some such amount was necessary." It is, therefore, quite understandable that Talbot was not overly concerned about the $50,000 deficit for 1947.

The tense situation that developed between Talbot and Tresidder over operating policy and finances was certainly heightened by the two proposals Talbot made at the September board meeting. The rumor soon started that Talbot had recommended "the construction of an expensive wind tunnel" by an organization with no capital. One thing seemed to lead to another and all the while Talbot became more restive. His personal situation was complicated by his wife's serious illness that developed soon after her arrival at Stanford. Mutual confidence between the chairman and the director seemed to worsen as the weeks went by.

One day in late autumn Talbot returned to his office from a meeting with Tresidder and said he had once again resigned in protest over a "minor administrative difficulty." But on this occasion his resignation was accepted. He seemed greatly surprised by this turn of events. He had been caught up in a game of Russian roulette.

One of the problems Talbot encountered almost from the time of his arrival was the absence of a clear understanding with Tresidder as to where the executive director's responsibilities began and ended. At one point, he turned for advice to Clyde Williams of Battelle, who many years later recalled his response in these words:

> "I told him that my understanding was that while Stanford University
> was the daddy, so to speak, of the Institute and President Tresidder had
> the top responsibility for the Insitute, he should not be the director and
> in fact Talbot should be... You have it in your power to direct the
> Institute in such a manner that you can retain responsibility for its
> management and at the same time keep the University happy."

Williams went on to advise Talbot that the greatest of tact should be used in his relationships with Tresidder. Williams reports Talbot saying soon thereafter that perhaps he had not been as tactful as he should have been and that he was leaving.

Some irony was present in this situation. Talbot was a courteous and considerate person. Rand found him to be so throughout their prior ten-year relationship. Moreover, Talbot was tactful in all his personal relationships except, apparently, on some occasions with Tresidder.

More than once Talbot grumbled aloud that Tresidder considered SRI as being on the same level as the University's Chemistry Department. On the other hand, Tresidder thought Talbot was trying to stand on a pedestal. Certainly, there were fundamental differences between them on how an "independent research institute" within the Stanford structure was to be run.

The portents of difficulties that were to come are revealed to some extent in a letter from Talbot to Eurich on August 30, 1946, immediately after Talbot's arrival at Stanford. He was asked for comments on the proposed SRI charter documents. In his reply Talbot mentioned the number and selection of board members. The draft called for two-thirds of the members to be from Stanford. Talbot thought "the board should be comprised of an equal number of Stanford Trustees (or officers) and businessmen with the director forming the odd number."

Eurich showed this letter to Tresidder who was later to leave a note referring to what he interpreted as Talbot's wish to be "the balance of control on (the) board." This impression was left with Tresidder even though Talbot's letter clearly dealt with principle rather than with his "own personal feelings."

Tresidder was concerned about Talbot and SRI on several counts including "no consultation," "wind tunnel" and "no budget." He left a note implying that he learned more about SRI during luncheons with McBean and others than he did from Talbot. Furthermore, he said he had talked with Talbot about these and other matters. Talbot's view, quite understandable in perspective, was that the chairman was trying to "run the show" rather than giving broad policy support and direction. In any event, the climate between the two men obviously was not cordial, at least from September of 1947 onward.

A special meeting of the directors was held on December 16; Talbot's resignation was accepted effective as of the end of the year. Tresidder announced that Rand would serve as acting executive director. Eurich said that the key scientific personnel on the staff "appeared to be thoroughly competent" and that their research was being carried out in a creditable manner.

Several names were mentioned for possible appointment as Talbot's successor. The directors decided to meet again in January to receive recommendations that would be made by Williams of Battelle. McBean then asked Williams to advise the directors on the selection of a new director.

Meanwhile, SRI ended 1947 with a staff of 43 full-time people and research revenue for the year of about $232,000. The year's operating deficit was almost $43,000; the year-end net worth was "in the red" by some $3,200 after taking the $48,000 gift into account. The University was holding SRI receivables totalling around $114,000 and had advanced the Institute about $133,000. This was a reasonable record, but Tresidder was not happy about it.

A few of the people who joined SRI in 1947 remained over the years and occupied key positions. In addition to Dr. Carsten Steffens (later director of SRI-Japan), the list includes, for example, Emery Bator (later the treasurer) and Dr. Harris Benedict (a senior plant physiologist).

Rand did an excellent job in handling the transition period following Talbot's resignation. Nevertheless, the year 1947 ended with an uncertain future for the Institute. Most of the staff, however, were so engrossed in their work that the crisis passed rather quickly with no undue effect on morale or operations. Little did anyone suspect that several other crisis points would be reached — and passed successfully — during the next few years.

The Talbot period ended before Christmas of 1947. He seemed both sad and relieved. Those of us who were brought to the Institute by the first executive director remain, of course, most grateful for the opportunity he gave us. I have always felt most kindly about Bill Talbot.

The state of the Institute's affairs as 1947 came to a close is aptly described in a year-end report to the directors.

> *"The day-to-day operation has been dictated mostly by expediency, and the resulting organic structure has many gaps and inconsistencies. These defects could be tolerated in the beginning, but will prove a serious handicap if they remain much longer."*

Since the Institute had no executive director at year end, the 1947 report was unsigned, having been drafted by Steffens and finally prepared by Rand in collaboration with Eurich at Stanford. Several of us on the staff at the time assisted on portions of the report.

I well remember some of the acts of "expediency" during 1947. Having been asked on a few occasions by high officers in the Pentagon about Institute policy on various matters and not knowing the answers, I asked Talbot how such queries should be handled. There were few, if any, policies in writing. Talbot's answer was clear. We should state what seemed to be the right policy and this would indeed be our policy for the time being. The system worked quite well as collectively we began to develop a body of operating policy for the new institute.

The basic impossibility of growing by expediency as well as a rising recognition of the need for a well-established center of applied research for industry in the western states impressed the Institute's directors with the need for a change in fundamental policy and development planning. In effect, the board decided at the end of 1947 to hasten the real establishment of Stanford Research Institute. Subsequent events show that the directors may not have appreciated fully the financial and other consequences of this broad policy decision. SRI was soon to be energized by a new and vigorous executive director.

It was in this setting of some disorganization and anxiety about the future of the fledgling institute that Donald J. Russell, a director, spoke in characteristic words —always directly to the point — at an informal meeting in San Francisco. "Let's get organized and move out of the station." As a railroad executive, these words came easily to him. They certainly reflected the mood among the directors and within the small SRI staff at the time.

The year-end report gives some indication of other problems facing SRI at the beginning of 1948. The principal one was to "explicate the objectives of the Institute." A second related problem was to select "the direction of ultimate growth..." These were followed by an urgent need for more space and the necessity to adopt a "sound and consistent personnel policy." Finally, a deficit for 1948 was estimated at $72,000. However, the report ended with a generally favorable report on the outlook for research projects on the West Coast.

Developments at the end of 1947 were doubly difficult for Bill Talbot. His wife was still seriously ill and in the hospital. Nevertheless, he maintained a calm disposition and a philosophical attitude about the situation. The Christmas season was not a particularly pleasant one for him or for others within SRI. We were sorry about the turn of events and were concerned about Janet Talbot's health. He urged all of us to continue a dedication to the Institute. And, at Talbot's suggestion, our small group gathered for a Christmas party and exchanged gifts and greetings of the season.

The Yuletide event was held in an officers' club house, still in place from the Dibble Hospital days of World War II. My wife reminds me that I doubled as Santa Claus and that our numbers were barely enough for a round of the Virginia Reel.

Although Talbot remained in the area for some time, he was soon engaged in industrial consulting work and we saw him on only a few occasions. His wife recovered her health in due course, following which Talbot accepted a position with the Rubberset Company and moved away from the area. Later, he joined Bristol Myers. He continued, however, to maintain an interest in the Institute and in the progress of its affairs. He died in 1967.

Although SRI was on dead center at the end of 1947, financing was not the main problem. Neither was the availability of research projects of which there were twelve during the year. After sixteen months the cumulative deficit was only about $51,000 and all but $3,200 of this was covered by contributions. The organization could hardly have been expected to do better.

The revenue forecasting system was certainly not perfected at the time. The estimate for the year was $283,000; the actual figure was $232,000. Some 80% came from the guayule, Richfield, smog, Pepsi-Cola, Air Force and liquid surfaces (ONR) projects. But, alas, the working cash balance at year end was only $450. With $114,000 in receivables, SRI was fully invested in growth — but Stanford was still paying the bills.

A far more significant point in retrospect involves the very essence of what some of the Stanford-oriented founders had in mind at the outset. Too little was done to develop joint programs with the University. Steffens and others of us did all we could along these lines. But there was no basic strategy.

On the Stanford side, few faculty members knew what was under way at SRI. The new dean of engineering, Frederick Terman, was hardly aware of the Institute's existence. Tresidder had not talked with him about it. On SRI's side, the only groups that could really interface with the University faculty were those in chemistry and industrial economics.

Terman had returned to Stanford after directing the Radio Physics Laboratory at Harvard during World War II. He found his alma mater to be "an under-privileged institution" in the engineering field. Believing that the military services would continue to support research at some of the nation's universities, he set about developing a program at Stanford including close relationships with high-technology companies. He was convinced that with good projects Stanford could build a first-rank graduate school with all the necessary faculty, equipment and buildings.

Terman and his associates did indeed succeed in achieving their goals. A vast array of sponsored projects was obtained; a top-flight faculty in various fields of electronics and communications was assembled; new laboratories were created and a strong graduate program came into being. One result was that by the mid-1960s the Stanford School of Engineering was among the top five in the nation. All this happened even though Terman had some difficulty in 1946 in getting Tresidder's support for the initial plans he had in mind.

Terman always felt in later years that "a great opportunity was missed" when joint efforts were not developed between the Engineering School and SRI. He knew little about its plans, and SRI had no one in 1947 in any of the engineering fields. By the time we began to build a program in electronics, the effort at Stanford was already on the way, and the die was cast, so to speak. However, during the 1950s and 1960s, some collaboration was developed, particularly in the communications field.

On many occasions during later years, Terman re-emphasized his view that too little was done in 1946 and 1947 to explore in some detail how good research programs could have been developed jointly by SRI and the University — not alone in engineering but also in chemistry, physics and other scientific and technical pursuits.

How successful all this would have been even if the goal had been pursued energetically, no one can say. The point, however, is that in Terman's view no organized thought was given to the matter. Tresidder did not encourage the approach; by the 1950s the whole idea of major cooperative endeavors had become more difficult and the mutual advantages present at the beginning had diminished.

There is another side to the story of Stanford-SRI cooperation during the Talbot days. Even with an unclear concept, there were some working relationships on specific situations. Steffens often called on University departments for staffing help and got a good response. Some discussions were held on possible joint projects in the biological sciences. Steffens did all he could to advance the general idea of cooperative endeavors. The Business School was most cooperative in our new economics program.

Steffens saw at first hand — as did I — some of the differences between Tresidder and Talbot. He felt that Talbot was not treated fairly on the wind tunnel matter. The project was being explored with the U.S. Government, several aircraft firms and the Pacific Gas and Electric Company. Knowing that the idea had come to the attention of at least one director, Talbot thought it is wise to mention the possibility to Tresidder.

The plan was certainly not ready for presentation to anyone. However, Steffens recalls that Tresidder did not grasp the nebulous state of the idea and immediately set his mind against it. He later told Steffens, "I have never before been responsible for such potentially-large financial commitments about which I had so little information."

Steffens' understanding on how Tresidder and Talbot viewed their roles in SRI differs to some extent from what Talbot often said, at least in late 1947. Talbot told Steffens before the two men arrived in California that SRI was to operate like a University department with SRI's director being equivalent to a Stanford dean reporting directly to the president.

This was certainly Tresidder's view and he confirmed it to Steffens in a conversation shortly after Talbot's resignation. Steffens recalls that he used the same words Talbot had used earlier "as though the two men had memorized the same speech." But, this was not Talbot's view in late 1947 on how things were supposed to operate. He came to feel that Tresidder's usual answer to a new idea was always "no." This may have been too severe a judgment given Stanford's financial problems at the time, but some deans may have agreed with Talbot.

In any event, the year 1947 ended with three points being quite clear to everyone associated with SRI. It had to move faster; an easier working relationship between Stanford's president and SRI's management was greatly needed; someone had to point the way to a better path. Much of the burden at the Stanford end was soon to fall on Eurich. As will be explained, he did an excellent job through 1948 before leaving the University. ∎

The Quiet Transition

The Institute has been founded,
but is not yet established.

— ALVIN C. EURICH / WILLIAM E. RAND
December 1947

SRI'S OPERATIONS WERE IN THE HANDS OF WILLIAM RAND from late 1947 until the second executive director, Dr. J. E. Hobson, was appointed on March 1, 1948.

During the Talbot days, Rand divided his time between administration and project negotiations. As mentioned earlier, he did a good job during the transition between two executive directors. However, there was little he could do on basic policies and development. These had to await the arrival of Talbot's successor. Rand was not interested in being the director because he knew the post would involve fund raising, a task he did not welcome.

Although the Institute's organization at the end of 1947 was necessarily quite informal, a plan had been developed earlier in the year by Rand and Talbot. It called for five assistant directors — at a staff level — covering engineering, physical sciences, natural sciences, social sciences and administration. Only the last of these posts had been filled in a formal sense prior to Talbot's departure. This was the appointment held by Rand until he became acting executive director.

The plan called for a laboratory director to be in charge of all research operations. The groups visualized at the time were engineering, chemistry, biology, physics-mathematics, and industrial social sciences. Rand assumed that I was to be in charge of all social sciences work and no one raised any question. He quietly moved my name from temporary to permanent.

At year end, Carsten Steffens was acting research director, which was equivalent to laboratory director. Both Talbot and Rand decided late in the year that the research director title was more suitable, particularly in light of the economics research program that had been started. Although several people in the research function were serving as managers of their respective activities, no formal appointments had been made by the time of Talbot's resignation.

Rand did attempt at the beginning of 1948 to put the Institute's operations in what he called a "form of organization." The new form, modeled after one used by the Armour Research Foundation, was in line with principles in a book published by Standard Oil Company of California on "The Co-ordination of Motives, Men and Money in Industrial Research."

The plan provided, of course, for an executive director. The next position was an assistant director and business manager followed by four associate directors and a research director. The associate directors were in a staff capacity (as had been visualized earlier for the assistant directors) covering aerophysics and meteorology, food technology, social sciences, and chemistry-chemical engineering. The plan also included a service department and several project leaders reporting to the research director.

Irrespective of the longer-range plan, the Institute's organization at the end of 1947 consisted primarily of an acting executive director, an acting research director and some ten project leaders. Although the latter did not consider themselves in an acting capacity, most were more or less on temporary status.

The first written notice that my nine-month temporary appointment had been changed to something more lasting occurred when the end-of-1947 staff list was released early in 1948. Asterisks appeared alongside the names of persons who were on a temporary, part-time or consulting arrangement. Fifty-nine names were on the roster. I was pleased to see that no asterisk appeared by my name.

Two other persons on this list were to accumulate long service at SRI. Emery F. Bator had taken over the accounting function in the autumn and years later became the Institute's treasurer. Carol Mosher had joined the chemistry group in mid-summer. In time, she was appointed to a senior post in organic chemistry.

Early in 1948, Rand wrote about the Institute's organizational difficulties in these words:

> "Realization of this plan of organization has been limited by the rate at
> which problems and personnel could be absorbed efficiently. The
> positions that are part of the line of authority have necessarily been
> filled, at least temporarily, so far as they relate to projects already under
> way. Some efforts were also made to fill the supporting, or staff positions
> ... because one of their functions, the development and maintenance of
> contact with potential sponsors, is especially needed by a nascent
> organization. These efforts proved unsuccessful and the positions are not
> now filled."

Rand's report goes on to point out that no SRI employee could be permanent in the sense that a professor in a university has tenure. He emphasized that the Institute could exist only so long as adequate support could be obtained for its people. Those who had been employed on a so-called permanent basis were told only that an effort would be made to provide continuing employment by shifting them from project to project and by getting new projects. The best way to make sure this happened was for each person to see that new projects were developed. Thus, the incentive was crystal clear.

Temporary employees were retained on the understanding that their terms would end with completion of their projects. At the end of 1947, only 26 persons were on a permanent basis. Seventeen were temporary (full-time), seven were from Stanford on a consulting or part-time arrangement, and nine were on a similar basis from other institutions.

This situation certainly was not conducive to healthy growth and development of the Institute. Rand emphasized this fact in the year-end report to the directors. His language was direct and to the point. "The foundation of any research organization is its permanent research employees. The Institute has but twelve of these and only one with a Ph.D."

As 1948 began, no clear-cut and comprehensive statement had been developed on SRI's basic reasons for existence other than those in the Articles. Strange as it may seem in retrospect, most of the senior people did not see the charter papers until early in 1948 when Rand was working on the report to the board. Being fully occupied with research projects, most of the key people had given little thought to the philosophical basis for our existence nor to the charter objectives aside from the industrial research mission.

Rand, Steffens and I had studied the charter early in 1947. However, we gave little thought to SRI's obligations as a public service, tax-exempt, scientific research organization. Our view of the Institute's role appeared in a small brochure (The New Frontier) issued in the middle of the year. We had helped Talbot put it together.

This booklet — our first — opened on the theme, "Industrial Research Comes of Age," and described briefly the growth of research and development in industry from 1920 through World War II. The point was made that "at a definite stage in the industrial development of any area, the increasing burden and complexity of applied research calls for centralized research groups ..." Then, following a reference to Mellon, Arthur D. Little, and Battelle, the brochure turned to the need for a research institute in the West.

A WESTERN INSTITUTE

"Today the rapid industrial growth of the West Coast region has greatly heightened the demand for research in many fields. While most large industrial concerns maintain research departments, the work of these departments can be accelerated ... by calling on well-organized research institutions to carry out projects which ... may not be suited for assignment to the (company) staff...

"The need for an independent research organization on the West Coast at this time is further emphasized by the fact that all industry is faced ... by a severe shortage of technical personnel and facilities ..."

The pamphlet went on to explain that the "pooling of scientific personnel" in an institute staffed and equipped to "carry out any kind of research project" could help on some of industry's problems. The idea was emphasized that ways must be devised to bridge the gap between academic institutions and industry and that SRI provided one way in which this could be done. The section ended with a statement that SRI "is the logical outgrowth of the firm belief among industrialists of the Pacific West that the time has come when such an industrial institute is absolutely necessary to the continued healthy growth of the region."

The most important section of the brochure dealt with the role and scope of the new organization. The opening words set no bounds on the operation: "The Stanford Research Institute is interested in, and will be equipped to handle, any problem that will yield to the research approach, and which any individual, enterprise, or agency is willing to sponsor." The language was certainly all-inclusive, but no one questioned it at the time.

The booklet then recognized two additional points. The first was an assumption that the majority of research problems brought to SRI would be in the physical and life sciences and engineering. The second involved what was called the industrial social sciences.

A New Dimension

"Business is rapidly recognizing that in order to enjoy the full benefits of much promising scientific and engineering progress, vital information is needed in labor relations, marketing, and other problems of a social and economic nature. The Institute is prepared to conduct research in these fields to strengthen and supplement the research that will naturally be carried on in the more traditional sciences."

Although this passage gave ample basis in policy for the social sciences program, the statement that SRI was "prepared" to carry out research in several fields was more of an intent than a capability. Nevertheless, I went along with the wording.

Our economics group included only a few people selected for their experience in the aircraft industry. We were by no means prepared to undertake projects in the fields mentioned. Furthermore, we never attempted to develop a capability in labor relations. In any event, the mid-1947 pamphlet defined the scope of the Institute as being "completely broad in its conception, embracing all kinds of research." This was far too encompassing; the statement should have been toned down.

More than three decades following work on The New Frontier, Rand reflected on how SRI was "prepared" in 1947 to take on economic studies for business. "I remember choosing (the word) quite carefully... We were 'prepared' to take on almost anything and, once the project was secured, we went out and found the people."

This is exactly how things happened in the beginning days and especially during late 1947 and early 1948. There was no other way to move ahead in a fledgling institute with no development money, a very small staff, no firm plans for the future and most of the time in a holding pattern between executive directors.

As Rand quite correctly recalls, there was a tendency at the time to retain people who were "inventor types" or who had "special knowledge or skills that met our immediate needs." This is what took place on the first Richfield project; the same steps were taken on the Air Force study.

In the latter case, the immediate need was for people with experience in aircraft production. The group assembled for this purpose had little background in broader economic and management studies for commercial enterprises. Thus, in due course, they moved on and were succeeded by others with a different mix of skills. New projects were then brought into SRI.

This sort of building process may seem shortsighted in looking back to the first days. But, given the circumstances, there was no alternative. We are fortunate that the approach worked as well as it did up to the spring of 1948 when it became possible to get some people before projects rather than having to bring in projects and then get people. Everyone breathed a sigh of relief when that day arrived. In reality, the change occurred only because the new director said it should; there was no sudden shift in financial resources.

Although nothing had been done by the beginning of 1948 to narrow the Institute's announced scope, a few basic policies had been created. SRI would not "endorse products, lend its name for advertising, or promote enterprises." A pricing system had been set up based on charging sponsors (later to be called clients) for the cost of direct salaries and expenses plus an overhead allowance plus a "small amount" for growth and security of the organization. Also, it was clear that patent rights arising from a project were the property of the sponsor. In addition, the Institute had pledged to decline projects in conflict with those already in process.

Recognizing that our operating objectives and purposes had not been clearly defined, Eurich asked that the 1947 report to the board include the basic purposes from the Articles. Then, he added:

> "The exigencies attending the organization of the Institute have precluded much discussion of these objectives, but it is now clear that many of the difficulties of the past year, such as those that led to the resignation of Dr. Talbot as executive director, have arisen from a lack of clear understanding of the objectives and from a failure to pursue them consistently ..."

There was indeed a lack of understanding on the Institute's objectives in the sense that no one attempted to spell out the implications of the charter. But even if this had been done, the parting of the ways between Tresidder and Talbot would have remained. They simply had differing views on how SRI was to be managed.

Rand had ideas on how the Institute's purposes and objectives should be formulated and explained in some detail. But, quite properly, he felt this should await the arrival of the new director. The year-end report merely says that an examination of objectives and their implications, and creation of a consistent policy based on them, must be completed before financial needs of the Institute could be determined.

At the end of 1947, and through the first quarter of 1948, SRI was occupying 9,730 sq. ft. of working space in three barracks-type buildings in Stanford Village. In addition to the executive offices, the main building included the economics research group, the Food Acceptance Laboratory, and a test chamber used in smog research.

One building had been a hospital laboratory and was being used for chemistry work more or less in the shape it had been received. Another building with chemical laboratory equipment was only partly occupied on a makeshift basis. The general view at the

WILLIAM E. "BILL" RAND
Leader of The Quiet Transition

time was that the three buildings would be sufficient until sometime toward the end of 1948 when one more unit was to be leased from Stanford.

These facilities, with equipment and improvements having a book value of less than $21,000, were obviously not impressive. They certainly made an impact on Jesse Hobson when he first visited SRI in early 1948. He was greatly depressed after seeing the makeshift quarters and meager equipment on hand. During later years, he mentioned several times that this weak condition seemed almost overwhelming as he pondered the possibility of joining the Institute.

Early in 1947, the directors had suggested that SRI concentrate its first attention on research in agriculture, food processing and petroleum. It was understood that first emphasis would be on research for western companies. These guidelines were followed to a considerable extent throughout the year. As indicated earlier, twelve projects provided revenue of almost $232,000; two projects and almost fifty percent of the revenue involved agriculture. Five projects and seven percent were in food processing. One project and eight percent came from the petroleum industry.

Nevertheless, Rand quite correctly pointed out in the first annual report that these results were accidental. He said that "in the absence of a sales staff, the Institute has necessarily developed principally to solve those problems that came incidentally to the attention of the staff and that seemed possible of solution." He was well aware that seven of SRI's twelve projects and almost 80% of its revenue for 1947 came from clients located in the eastern part of the United States. Government projects accounted for some 70% of revenue for the year.

Rand might well have mentioned that almost all of our revenue in 1947 came from eight projects. Two provided less than $1,000 each and two were below $100.

Three projects produced more than three fourths of 1947 revenue. One of these —the guayule operation — ended at midyear. It alone accounted for almost half of the research volume. The other two projects, one on air pollution for the petroleum industry and one for the Air Force on the aircraft industry, carried over at full scale into 1948. The only other carry-over project of consequence was for ONR on the properties of liquid surfaces. It had been transferred from Stanford when Dr. J. W. McBain retired as professor of chemistry and joined SRI on a part-time basis.

The Institute was in a precarious position on contract backlog. This was one reason why only six persons joined the staff during the first quarter of 1948. All arrived by February 1, having been employed prior to Talbot's departure.

Rand did not have an easy task on his hands during the two months between Talbot's departure and appointment of a new director. The average monthly deficit for the last four months of 1947 was almost $6,200. Rand was expecting the deficit to continue at about the same rate for the next twelve months.

Also, Rand was greatly worried about the acute shortage of scientific equipment and estimated the urgent need to be in the order of $240,000. He and the rest of us knew there was little possibility of meeting even a small portion of these needs during the transition. And, it seemed quite possible that the Stanford Village buildings might not be available beyond June of 1951. The possibility of financing construction of even 10,000 sq. ft. of space elsewhere seemed too remote for serious consideration. There were too many immediate problems at hand to worry about one that was three and a half years away.

Rand recognized the need for a greater feeling of security on the part of the staff. He knew this could not be accomplished by superficial changes alone. However, one suggestion he made was "to institute a retirement plan of some kind." In his view the precise form of the plan was far less important to morale than the existence of some arrangement even though it could not be financed immediately. In making a proposal to the directors, he knew that the Institute was hardly in a position to take the step.

Those who were devoting time to research projects were more concerned with developing their programs in one direction or another than they were about the state of the Institute's affairs or about various fringe benefit plans. Rand gave all the encouragement he could. But he was quite candid about uncertainties confronting the organization.

Along with others, Rand was hearing all sorts of rumors about the future of the Institute; they ranged from closing down, to integration within Stanford's Chemistry Department, to an expansion with contributed funds. My own project for the Air Force was to end in May of 1948 — less than five months away. I quickly followed Rand's cue and within a few weeks obtained follow-on projects from the Air Force and the Navy.

Air travel cost at the time was no problem. We flew many times back and forth to Washington, D.C., on the Navy, non-stop, "Hot-Shot" flight from Moffett Field near Menlo Park. This travel was free under our contract with the Air Force.

But, as the saying goes, there is no "free lunch." The DC4 flight took all night. I left one evening following a telephone appeal to be on hand for a Pentagon meeting the next day. This was followed by an overnight flight home. No sooner was I in the office than another call announced another meeting the next day. So, four consecutive nights in the air was the result — all in the line of duty to meet commitments at both ends. None of us thought much about such inconveniences simply because we were engaged in an exciting venture.

Steffens knew no more about what the future might hold for SRI than did Rand and others. However, he was a steadying influence with a fundamental faith that all would turn out in good fashion. It seemed incredible to the small staff that the marriage of an institute and a director had come to a divorce so soon. Steffens gave some assurances to a puzzled staff by saying on several occasions — "I do not know what will happen, but everything will be alright in the end." Nevertheless, information from outside the Institute was not reassuring.

Eurich and Rand said in their year-end report that no more government projects would, in general, be accepted unless the contracts provided sufficient overhead income to cover expenses, and then only when surplus space could be used and when industrial research might be expected to arise from the work.

I promised Rand that my follow-on contracts with the Air Force and Navy could have higher overhead rates when we had sufficient information to document our request. This proved to be the case when later the rates were raised from 30% to 40% and then to 80%. Also, additional economics projects were attractive because no capital equipment of consequence was involved. Furthermore, the group required little space. I told Rand that as soon as we could build a nucleus staff on the basis of government contracts we would seek industrial projects. This is exactly what happened in 1948.

Rand devoted a lot of time in late 1947 and early 1948 to assessing the Institute's opportunities with western industry. Having been in the area only a little more than a year, he was not yet fully familiar with the western economy. However, he made it his business to study the situation. We often talked about prospects and how the Institute could increase its research for companies on the West Coast. However, I was too preoccupied on projects to give the matter much attention.

In appraising potentials on the West Coast, Rand soon arrived at several conclusions, in most cases following discussions with executives in the industries concerned. He felt that the petroleum industry offered the greatest possibilities. It seemed to him that the industry was "alive to its research needs" and that SRI had a good start on air pollution projects for the Petroleum Industry Committee on Smoke and Fumes (part of the Western Oil and Gas Association).

He thought the chemical industry potential was rather small, primarily because the headquarters and laboratories for most western chemical companies were located in the eastern part of the country. Food processing was high on his list because of the large part it played in the economy of the West. Rand felt that if the Institute could not obtain research projects of this type it could not exert the influence the founders had expected it to have in the region.

As things turned out during the early years and to a great extent later on, food processing was not a high-potential field for SRI. One reason was a tendency for companies to look to state and federal agencies such as the Department of Agriculture. For example, freeze-dry techniques were developed at the USDA laboratories in Albany, California.

Rand saw only limited opportunities in the forest products field, primarily because most western companies were turning to industry-sponsored organizations for their outside research needs. He viewed the ceramics and glass companies as being too small to support a significant amount of research. Fishing and agriculture were low on his list, not that they had no important technical problems but because they relied primarily upon federal and state agencies for research assistance.

He also viewed potentials in the public utility and transportation industries as being low, partly because they did not "feel the need for research" and in part because they tended to turn to the older, established eastern institutes. Rand believed also that the motion picture industry had major technical problems but little concept of its real research needs.

Two general conclusions formed a part of Rand's view on the western research picture. He was somewhat discouraged by the fact that on a national basis some of the most important western industries had relatively low research-spending rates. He put forest products, food, paper and nonferrous metals in this category. Also, he had noted a tendency for industries "just awakening to their need for research" to form associations and laboratories for the general benefit of their members.

It is difficult to appraise Rand's conclusions. In the first place, he was thinking of the immediate future. Also, SRI had only limited facilities and research programs to offer industry. Furthermore, his survey came at a time when many industries were just beginning to think in terms of greater research efforts. In any event, subsequent events proved him right on high potentials in the petroleum industry and on limited possibilities in the motion picture field. However, he was wrong about the transportation industry and gave little attention to banks and financial institutions which in due course became important clients.

Thirty years later in looking at what he wrote at the beginning of 1948, Rand took himself to task on his assessment of the future. "In retrospect, there is no doubt that my imagination ... was much too narrow, compounded perhaps with a somewhat negative point of view."

This self-appraisal is far too harsh. He deserves high marks for what he did and tried to do. Although limited in time and attention, his look ahead was the first of its kind within SRI. He was virtually alone in the exercise. Within the internal environment of the times and given SRI's meager resources, it is wholly understandable that he was somewhat discouraged. But, he did insert the beginnings of a planning process, however limited, into the system.

Although Rand was not in a position to do much financial planning for the Institute during the early part of 1948, he did develop one prediction on overhead expense rates that is quite interesting in light of later developments. Project labor at the time was running at less than $5,000 per month. The overhead rate on labor costs was about 114%; capital investment subject to depreciation was less than $21,000. Realizing that the overhead rate would or should decline along with rising project labor, Rand developed a set of curves to show the relationship, assuming, first, no additional equipment investment and then a further investment of $240,000. The curves showed that with $30,000 of project labor per month and the added investment, the Institute might have an overhead rate of 100%. His predicted rate with $60,000 of project labor was 80%; he and others thought this should be the target.

The Institute did add $240,000 in depreciable assets by April of 1949. Project labor reached the $30,000 level at the end of 1948 and the $60,000 point in February 1950. But with an entirely different set of operating conditions, overhead rates were over 160% and 108%, respectively. SRI was then rapidly building for the future and not alone for the present.

Early in February of 1948, a rumor began to spread among the staff that a new executive director would soon be appointed. We heard that he might be a man from Armour Research Foundation. Later in the month the message circulated that his name was Jesse Hobson. None of us knew much about him even though he had visited SRI on December 26, 1947. Although Armour was one of the country's largest eastern research institutes, we knew little about its activities.

CHANGING OF THE GUARD AT ARMOUR
March — 1948

Jesse Hobson looks on as Dr. Henry T. Heald, president of Illinois Institute of Technology, *at right*, congratulates Hobson's successor, Dr. H. A. Leedy of Armour Research Foundation, on the occasion of Hobson's farewell to join SRI.

We had more or less assumed that the new man would be in his high forties or early fifties, and that he would be a chemist. Consequently, it came as a surprise when Rand said that Hobson was only 36 years of age and an electrical engineering graduate of Purdue with a Ph.D. in the same field from the California Institute of Technology. We also heard that he had been an instructor in mathematics at Earlham College, a faculty member in electrical engineering at Armour Institute of Technology, a central station engineer for Westinghouse, head of the electrical engineering department at Illinois Institute of Technology and finally director of Armour.

Hobson's special field of technical competence was "extra-high voltages, surge voltage, high voltage insulations and power transmission." We did not know, however, that he was a high voltage man in many other respects. Perhaps we should have suspected from his earlier Westinghouse connection that he was a builder and an energizer. In any event, we soon found that here was a man who would not be content until SRI took its place as a significant entity among the nation's independent research institutes. All of us were immediately attracted to him personally when he visited SRI while considering the new position.

An event occurred in late January, 1948, that almost resulted in Hobson's changing his mind about SRI. Tresidder died on January 28 in a hotel room in New York City. He had been instrumental, along with Eurich, in gaining Hobson's enthusiasm about the new position. Eurich promptly telephoned Rand who was in Chicago, and asked him to assure Hobson that Tresidder's death signalled no change so far as the Institute was concerned. Years later Rand recalled that Hobson was greatly disturbed by the news and was tempted to "call the whole thing off." Rand feels he was successful in reassuring Hobson and in convincing him that he should not let this unfortunate development change his thinking about SRI.

Jesse Hobson was appointed as the second executive director only two months after Talbot's departure. He arrived on the scene late in March and took immediate and active direction of the Institute. Rand continued to serve as assistant director. A quiet transition had come to an end, and Rand seemed relieved that it was over.

One can only speculate on what would have happened had Tresidder and Hobson been associated with each other on SRI affairs. Hobson was a strong-minded individual accustomed to running the Armour operation. Rand wondered years later whether or not Hobson "could have coped" with Tresidder who intended to run things at SRI. In any event, he was the senior officer and was entitled to take a strong hand.

There surely would have been a clash between these two men with great but unknown impacts on SRI. A second crossing of swords, however tactfully handled, might simply have been too much for the Stanford Trustees who were already worried about the SRI situation. Also, McBean and Tresidder might well have grown at odds with each other, particularly as McBean involved himself more deeply in the Institute's operations.

All this is speculation, of course, but it is on reasonably safe grounds. Others have posed the same question. Even before 1948 was out as Hobson made one bold move after another, I jotted down a note — "This would have been an explosive situation with Tresidder." Perhaps Hobson would have moved differently but who knows?

As will be unfolded later, the trend of affairs with the new chairman was in an opposite and highly favorable direction. Eurich and Hobson worked exceedingly well together with SRI as the beneficiary.

The Institute's revenue for January 1948 was $27,731; the February figure was $25,865. The deficit, however, rose from $4,990 to $8,918. Even so, net worth changed from a negative figure at year end to $10,505 at the end of the Rand transition. A $15,000 gift from Stanford Oil Company of California had put the Institute in a "solvent" condition.

It is convenient in taking a perspective of SRI's early history to say that its founding days ended in early 1948. The keynote is sounded in the Eurich-Rand report to the directors — "The Institute has been founded, but is not yet established." Although beset by various problems during its first year and a half, SRI was in being and was operating in March of 1948. A new stage was about to begin.

The end of the quiet transition is a good point at which to glance backward over our Founding Years. From one point of view a slow countdown to creation began in the mid-1920s. But the real countdown got under way in mid-1945 at a summer encampment of the Bohemian Club of San Francisco. This was when The Three Musketeers first outlined their thinking to Stanford's president, Donald B. Tresidder.

The countdown soon picked up momentum, especially after McBean entered the picture in the autumn of 1945. Within a year, SRI had been incorporated and the first director was at the helm.

This might not be a rapid course of events in a business enterprise but it is not exactly a slow one either. Deciding on such things as form of organization, gaining support from the business community, preparing a charter and finding an executive director are not simple matters. The remarkable thing is that all this was done within a university structure in so short a time.

One can well imagine a long drawn-out process in a major university as it looked into the possibility of creating a research institute. A plan in some detail would be needed even before a faculty committee could begin work.

Then, surely, a trustee's committee would be needed, especially on financial plans and in testing the interests of business. Some consultation with students would be in order — and the views of various alumni groups would be sought. Lawyers and tax specialists would be called in; everything would come to a standstill while government examined the proposed nonprofit and tax-exempt features. Only then would a search committee begin looking for a leader.

Much of this time-consuming chain of events would simply be a reflection of administrative needs within a university. Many of these features were present in universities in the mid-1940s and long before. Why, then, was it possible for Stanford to move so fast in the immediate post-World War II period?

In a way the situation was fortuitous and unique, and the answer to the question is fairly simple. Separate motivations of a few key poeple within and outside Stanford came together at what The Three Musketeers rightly called "The Golden Time."

The American West was on the verge of an economic upsurge; Stanford was regrouping after World War II; Swain and Leighton wanted to move the University's Chemistry Department closer to industry; Swim wanted to play a key role in Stanford affairs; Tresidder was looking for a unique "president's project"; Eurich thought an institute would greatly benefit Stanford; McBean was enthusiastic, could command resources, and was ready for a new public venture. Finally, Nelles and Black wanted to combine their Pacific Research Foundation with Stanford.

The Stanford Trustees at the time were largely from the business world. They, too, were interested in a new institute. Recommendations to move ahead were coming in from the East. Herbert Hoover, a Trustee, favored the project. So did Gwin Follis, head of California's largest company. Also, Donald J. Russell of Southern Pacific, was solidly behind the idea.

In all this wave of enthusiasm and urging to go ahead, hardly anyone raised a "go slow" signal or a word of special caution. Those familiar with research institutes were saying such things as — only one contract is needed, the organization can be self-financed, it will be profitable, it cannot fail, time is of the essence, Stanford must be a leader, business is ready to move, money is available, and so on.

In all this emphasis and a rush to formation, little attention was given to such things as physical location, size and growth rates, fixed investment, working capital, operating relationships with Stanford, and other planning usually involved in a new venture. The general idea was to get a corporation and a director and go from there. No one thought in detail about the sort of problems the new institute might run into during the first one or two years or later. Even the reports that were prepared were briefs devoted almost entirely to principles.

All this was probably the right thing to do at the time. Otherwise, the whole movement might have been delayed one or two years or even set aside. Whether or not "the golden time" would have passed is open to question. But there is no doubt that SRI was created at the right time and under the right auspices.

Charles Blyth, a San Francisco financier, was a Stanford Trustee when SRI was created and became one of the founding directors of the new institute. With a smile but meaning what he said, Blyth observed some ten years later that had a "later-day SRI" been commissioned to look into the feasibility of a Stanford institute in 1946, its report would have carefully presented all the facts and consequences and perhaps "led to the wrong conclusion."

Blyth went on to say that with all the potential problems outlined in such a report the institute proposal might have been set aside. His comments came in the 1950s after SRI had just passed through a financial crisis. In any case, Blyth never wavered in strong support for the organization. He had a point; too much advance study might have deterred the whole effort.

Being familiar in considerable detail with preparations leading to formation of all the earlier institutes of SRI's type, I have often marvelled at the dedication of those who guided the countdown to SRI's creation. They did a service for the future far greater than any of them realized at the time.

During the 1950s and 1960s, many groups from various parts of the United States visited SRI in connection with proposals to create local research institutes. They had witnessed the swift rise of SRI and were much interested in the decision process leading to its formation. Their questions could not be easily answered. They always seemed a bit surprised that so much was done in so short a time by so few people — all having so much faith that in the end all would turn out in good fashion.

In any event, the countdown was completed by mid-autumn of 1946. The decision to go ahead had been made; the lawyers had finished their tasks; the first director was on the scene; the initial project was at hand. No money was in the till but Stanford stood ready to pay the bills, based on McBean's promise to raise funds. SRI had a small office at Stanford; the new institute was indeed at "ground zero."

Aside from the Stanford Trustees who were consulted from time to time and who finally authorized SRI's formation, very few people were involved in the decision to launch SRI. The action was almost entirely in the hands of Tresidder, Eurich and McBean during the final stage. Swain and Leighton knew what was happening but by and large the Stanford faculty knew very little about the idea until long after the decision was announced. Outside the McBean circle in San Francisco, the California business community was unaware of the University's quick moves in the autumn of 1946.

Tresidder, Eurich and McBean were in a hurry as far back as late 1945 to bring matters to a head. It was characteristic of McBean to be impatient once he got behind a project. He often followed up Eurich by telephone and in person. Eurich, too, wanted to move quickly so as, among other things, to keep up McBean's interest.

Eurich told Dudley Swim in March of 1946 that he wanted to get the organization set up soon. He gave the same assurances to Swain and Leighton in the summer. By early autumn he was telling McBean — "We are anxious to get the institute started as quickly as possible." This was music to McBean's ears but still the tempo did not fully satisfy him. He was fond of saying in later years: "Dr. Eurich and I really put the heat on to get SRI off the drawing board."

McBean did not confine his follow-up to Eurich. He urged his Stanford Trustee friends to do something. He was afraid they would ponder the idea too long and thus kept saying that he was ready to raise money for the institute.

McBean's father-in-law, W. Mayo Newhall, had been a close friend of Leland Stanford and was an early Stanford Trustee. McBean often mentioned Newhall's response at a Trustee's meeting when someone wondered aloud how the departed founder would have felt about a certain question up for decision.

Newhall, then in his eighties, is supposed to have said, "I do not know but I will see him soon and find out." McBean was anxious to move ahead on the Institute and was fond of saying, "I will tell Governor Stanford about it when I see him." For the rest of his life, McBean kept telling listeners one and all with great pride and satisfaction how he and Eurich got the Trustees to move quickly in founding SRI.

The driving forces in SRI's quick formation were McBean and Eurich. McBean in particular was the sparkplug. As Russell has emphasized, "SRI would not exist today had it not been for (his) perseverance ..."

It was, of course, unusual for a director to be in place before a corporation existed. In hindsight, it was all a part of the rush to action in 1946 — and it was a wise decision. Unfortunately, things did not work out in the short run as planned.

Great reliance was placed on Clyde Williams' recommendation on the first director. But, he had not known Talbot personally. On his part, Talbot did not look carefully into the setting and circumstances. His industrial background was right for the new institute, but he had no real "feel" for a university environment even though he had a teaching background. Neither was he personally motivated to a high degree (as was

Hobson) in planning and promoting an organization. He did not discover before arriving that Tresidder intended to "run the institute" leaving the director largely to the research function.

Eurich dealt fairly with Talbot in all respects and did not interfere in his management activities. But even with Eurich, Talbot was often impetuous, particularly in his comments about resigning.

Talbot was a fine person and wanted very much to create a strong institute at Stanford. He simply found himself in an environment in which neither he nor the directors found comfort.

Quick decisions and speed on staff additions were characteristic in SRI's beginning days. The approach was more or less necessary. Staff could not be added without research projects on hand. Once a project was in place, speedy action was needed to get people and finish the task at hand. There was a better way to do things, but it really was not open at the time.

As the first transition approached an end in late February of 1948, the staff did not know what was in store and was not prepared for what happened. But it was an exciting time of expectancy.

In many respects, my wife captured the mood of the times. Upon hearing about the new director and some of his ideas for SRI's immediate future, she said: "It all sounds very interesting," and then raised a question no one could answer — "But will it really work?" SRI was about to begin anew. The Founding Years were not quite completed but they were soon to pass into history. ∎

A Vigorous Thrust

I am recommending a development program simultaneously on five fronts.

— J. E. HOBSON - 1948

ON JANUARY 20, 1948, ATHOLL McBEAN GAVE A LUNCHEON at the Pacific Union Club in San Francisco for Clyde Williams, director of Battelle Memorial Institute. McBean had invited Williams to visit the West Coast and meet with SRI's directors. He thought Williams could be helpful in finding a successor to William Talbot.

An SRI board meeting followed immediately after the McBean luncheon. The two events led quickly to what might be called a vigorous thrust in the Institute's affairs.

Williams talked about the importance of research to American industry and how programs were being developed in the eastern part of the country. He used Battelle to illustrate what could be created on the West Coast and said that SRI could become a significant national as well as a regional institute.

Tresidder then told the group that an extensive search was already under way for a new executive. Williams had earlier recommended Dr. Jesse Hobson, director of Armour Research Foundation, as "the best man in the country" for the position. But he doubted that Hobson could be attracted away from Armour. However, Tresidder had already invited him to visit SRI and soon thereafter had offered the position to him. The directors were awaiting a reply when they met with Williams. This was not, however, known by any of the Institute's senior staff.

Furthermore, Williams did not know that events had moved so fast; as he later wrote, he thought no decision had been made at the time of his January visit.

> *"President Tresidder placed on a blackboard ... several names under consideration for the job. As a first action on this, Atholl McBean asked me whom I would recommend. I saw Jesse Hobson's name on the list and said, 'If you can get Hobson, he's your man.' President Tresidder flew that night to Chicago to interview Hobson ..."*

Meanwhile, Williams was thinking about other candidates to suggest to Tresidder, McBean and Eurich. He had one or two Battelle people and two or three industrial executives in mind.

Tresidder saw Hobson in late January and arranged for him to visit SRI again in February. This was the last move Tresidder was to make for SRI. As indicated earlier, he died in New York on January 28.

During a one-day visit, Hobson met the key SRI staff and talked with Eurich and McBean. He was an engaging person but little was known about him around SRI, in San

DR. J. E. HOBSON
Second Director — A Man of Action

DR. HAROLD VAGTBORG
Voice of Experience
Armour — Midwest — Southwest

Francisco or at Stanford. He left an impression of being reluctant to leave an established eastern institute to join a fledgling organization in the West.

Nevertheless, Hobson was attracted by possibilities on the West Coast and soon accepted an appointment as of March 1. In the meantime, Eurich was made acting president at Stanford. He became SRI's chairman on April 6, the same day Hobson's election was confirmed by the directors.

During the first several days following Tresidder's death, all was not tranquil about SRI among the Stanford Trustees. At a meeting in San Francisco, there was general agreement that the Institute was going nowhere fast. A proposal by one Trustee that the Institute be closed down found several in agreement. Eurich acknowledged that from lack of experience in such matters some mistakes had been made. He asked for support to keep things going with a new executive.

Many years later, Eurich said that during most of this debate, Charles Blyth, the San Francisco financier and an SRI director, said nothing. But, then he brought the discussion to an end by saying, "I'll borrow the money and keep it open." In Eurich's words, "That turned the tide." The Trustees approved the idea of getting Hobson aboard.

Hobson lost no time in sizing up the situation soon after his arrival in March. He quickly decided that SRI could never become an important research institute without an immediate and vigorous development program. Feverish activity took place around the Institute for a couple of weeks as he created a plan with occasional help from some of his new associates.

Most of the work, however, was done by Hobson alone. He had not known any of SRI's senior people before his first visit in February. Furthermore, he felt that a new look was necessary. By early April he was ready to make a move. "After reviewing the situation..., I am submitting recommendations ... regarding the promotion and development of the Institute, with recommended expenditures for the remainder of 1948."

Because SRI had been in operation for about eighteen months and had not moved rapidly in assuming its "rightful place" on the West Coast, Hobson felt strongly that an aggressive program should be put in motion "at the earliest possible date."

This appraisal reflected much of Hobson's energy and philosophy. He came up with a plan that was soon to reshape, completely and in diverse ways, our entire operation. Some of his very first words foreshadowed what was to come. "I am recommending a development program simultaneously on five fronts." We did not fully realize it at the time, but this short sentence was to have an enormous impact on SRI for years to come.

Hobson was convinced — and he was right — that the Institute's previous policy on cautious growth with new staff following — rather than leading — projects had to be changed and changed quickly. He felt it was necessary to have some money for self-sponsored research. The purpose was simply to increase SRI's prestige and to carry some projects until they became attractive to industrial clients.

These two moves were indeed much needed at the time. This is not to suggest that Talbot's emphasis was wrong under the circumstances. There was little he could have done with such limited resources. He knew very well that SRI could not grow properly on a complete bootstrap basis and had some plans to change the situation. However, the environment that developed with Tresidder and with other directors was such that long-term planning was not really feasible.

Hobson wanted to create "a nucleus of scientific men with outstanding ability" so as to develop several fields that he thought would be immediately useful to the West. For this purpose, he said a "technical development budget" of $76,500 including $40,000 for self-sponsored research was absolutely necessary. This was the first of his five "fronts."

His plan then turned to equipment and facilities. Hobson was dismayed by the pitifully inadequate facilities he found at SRI. He thought that more equipment was "desperately needed to provide tools for science" and wanted $100,000 for this purpose, another $50,000 for new space and $25,000 for shops. All this made up his second "front."

Even before arriving, Hobson thought that immediate steps should be taken to bring SRI to the attention of business and industry. The new director was development-minded to a high degree and everyone was soon to see this characteristic. He wanted $36,000 for "promotional expenses" including a person "to handle publications, talks, news releases, and other items of public information."

This third "front" in Hobson's plan soon led to G. Edward Pendray, a New York public relations adviser, being retained by SRI. Pendray was a well-known specialist in public relations programs for scientific and technical organizations. He was one of the nation's early pioneers in rocketry and had founded the American Rocket Society. Also, he had created the annual, worldwide, high school, talent search by Westinghouse. Pendray and Hobson had known each other from Westinghouse and Armour days. Like Hobson, he was energetic and full of ideas.

It was abundantly evident to Hobson and his new colleagues that SRI had no organized program to get new research projects. Thus, an "aggressive sales program" became his fourth "front" in the Institute's development. He felt strongly that this was no less needed in a research institute than in any business enterprise and he wanted $17,000 to get something under way.

Then Hobson took up a matter that had bothered Talbot no end. SRI had no business office, the function being handled at Stanford. He wanted to change this situation quickly by having a small staff "to organize accounting, purchases, billing (and) accounts receivable, and to have charge of the physical plant." For this fifth "front" he wanted $20,500. This proposal would have run strickly counter to Tresidder's concept on controls over SRI affairs. But Hobson had discussed the matter with Eurich and found him entirely agreeable on the move.

All this added up to $325,000, a sizable sum at the time, for the balance of 1948. Hobson was confident that the five-front program would see the Institute on the way to

Dr. Alvin C. Eurich

"SRI was — and still is — the beneficiary of Alvin Eurich's great work as its principal 'architect' in 1945-46 and its guiding hand in 1947-48."

WILLIAM E. RAND

"becoming an effective institution of service to industry and the region" by the end of the year. But he was already calling for $200,000 to $250,000 for 1949. His planning was based on the idea that SRI could not be self-supporting until the annual research volume reached about $1.0 million. He thought this would happen "under normal circumstances" by 1950. No one asked what these circumstances might be and indeed they were not to be normal for several years to come.

Hobson's proposals were literally breathtaking to his new-found associates. We had grown accustomed to a vastly different environment. Few expected that much would happen, but we did not know how persuasive our new director could be in board circles. Nevertheless, to say the least, he had all the internal support he needed. Everyone was fascinated with his confident beliefs and firm predictions.

This was the first of several Hobson predictions on a break-even in finances. SRI did in fact reach the point by mid-1950 but research revenue was almost double his early-1948 figure, and in the meantime a sizable deficit had been accumulated. Even so, being self-supporting at a $2.0 million revenue rate was misleading. By that time capital needs had mounted and there was no way SRI could go to the equity market.

Developing this new program so soon after arriving (less than a month) called for no small measure of courage on Hobson's part. The directors were a bit startled, but they knew something was needed. They agreed with the plan but promised to get only $100,000 in contributions. So, the five fronts became policy with only one third of the money. SRI was launched on a risky course, but a decision had been made.

The directors then turned to the capital problem. Eurich had been told by Harold Vagtborg of Midwest Research Institute that MRI had raised more than $1.0 million since its formation shortly after World War II. He said that $225,000 had been spent on promotional activities before MRI opened its doors. Hobson had urged Vagtborg to write to Eurich about his experience.

This was not the last time Vagtborg was to give a helping hand to SRI. He and Hobson were close friends, having known each other when both were at the Illinois Institute of Technology. Vagtborg was head of its Armour Foundation while Hobson was an IIT faculty member. When Vagtborg left for MRI, Hobson succeeded him at the Foundation.

By April of 1948, the idea of retaining a professional fund-raising organization was being reconsidered. The directors had not liked the earlier brief experience with a San Francisco consultant. Thus, they finally decided to do nothing for the time being.

The new development plan was launched immediately after April 6. It was not helped by early returns on the financial front. By the end of the month, the cumulative contributions of $63,000 had been used up, leaving SRI with a negative net worth of some $1,800. But Hobson was undaunted. He said that "the volume of operations is yet too low for the 'break-even' point" and maintained that the new outlays "should be considered as over and above normal operating costs." It was certainly too early to expect

anything other than deficits, but the explanation was to be repeated in various forms in
the months to come.

In May, the Civil Aeronautics Administration asked SRI to accept a management
contract for operating the Landing Aids Experiment Station at Arcata, California. The
situation offered possibilities for a communications research program. Furthermore, a
net income of $30,000 or so per year was attractive at the time. A plan was developed and
approved by the board. However, later changes in the CAA brought negotiations to an
end for the second time. Hobson was surprised to hear along the way that this very same
project had raised serious questions between Talbot and the directors and especially
with Tresidder.

A public relations plan was ready by June. It included a brochure to be used in a
fund-raising program. Also, a series of one-day conferences on research for industry
was announced. The purpose was to acquaint executives of industry, patent attorneys
and bankers with the need for industrial research in the West and also to tell them about
SRI. These meetings were held in the autumn and played a key role in general development of the Institute.

The mid-1948 pamphlet was, of course, based on Hobson's development plan. Following a description of SRI, it moved directly to the main point. "During the early stages
of its development ... the Institute needs more funds ... to obtain topflight personnel,
adequate research equipment and special apparatus to increase its effectiveness."

Then, the booklet mentioned the amounts of money from the April plans —
"$325,000 is needed to complete essential expansion initiated in 1948 ... and $275,000
will be required in 1949 ..." For both years, the amounts for particular activities differed
somewhat from the earlier plan. But in the final analysis this was not significant; the
booklet was not used to any great extent until 1950. The fund raising was again delayed.
Some of the directors were concerned about seeking money on a wide-ranging basis
while SRI was operating in the red.

Another more-useful brochure was soon prepared for project promotion purposes.
It emphasized research for industry in the West and pointed to faculty and scientific
equipment at Stanford. In some respects, the text was expansive and all-encompassing,
perhaps understandably so. And it certaintly was not modest. "No matter what your
problem, the Institute very likely provides the unusual facilities you need to solve it."

It is just as well that some of industry's more difficult research problems were not
brought to SRI at the time. Later, of course, the Institute became far less ambitious in
what it could undertake and wanted to do.

In various ways, the brochure emphasized contract research as our main objective.
"The Institute was established to make applied research available to industry, particularly industry of the eleven Western States." However, in referring to both basic and
applied research, the publication indicated that "the Institute bridges the gap between
the academic world and industry."

Then, the main interest of the young organization was put in one sentence. "SRI" is interested in any industrial or economic problem that will yield to the research approach, and which any individual, company, trade organization or governmental group is willing to sponsor." In due course, SRI found it could not do all things; it had to be selective in seeking projects. But, the brochure did rule out one activity by saying that the organization "does not endorse products, lend its name to advertising or promote enterprises."

SRI's research operations at the time were divided into five broad fields — physics, industrial economics, chemistry and chemical engineering, electronics and geophysics-seismology. The brochure briefly described each of these fields. Some of the contents were prepared rather hastily. Edward Pendray asked one day for an outline on industrial economics; he wanted it then and there. He got what he needed, and it appeared in print without editing — statistical analysis and forecasting, community industrial programs, industrial development studies, market development, transportation economics, population studies and related research in the United States and abroad.

This was the first time any SRI publication had ever mentioned or even implied that somehow the Institute would stray beyond national boundaries into foreign lands. The thought was not premeditated. It arose as Pendray waited for the text. I wrote it quickly and next came the words in print.

Perhaps the most important feature of the 1948 brochure had to do with the role of a research institute on the American scene. Various interpretations had been given on this role during the events leading to the Institute's creation. The new statement, approved by the directors, carved out a place for SRI, at least for the immediate future.

Recognizing that most large companies maintained their own research groups, the thought was that "these departments can be supplemented, stimulated and accelerated"

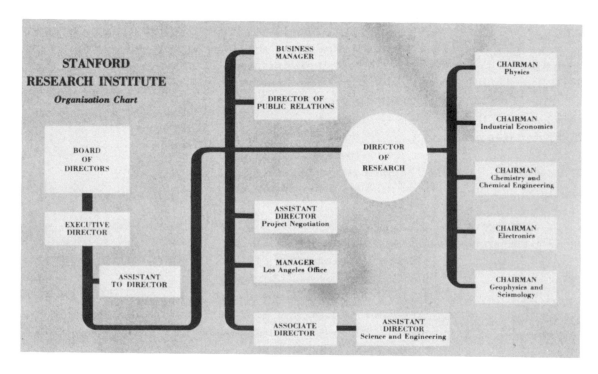

The mid-1948 organization

SECOND DIRECTOR OF RESEARCH
1948
Ralph Krause (*center*) with Paul Cook *to the left* and Dr. Lawrence Richards *to the right*

by external projects when special equipment or knowledge is involved. Also, it was visualized that "smaller or newly-organized businesses ... can likewise be well served by the independent research institute."

Special attention was given to the regional mission. "The modern independent research institute ... is equipped to play a constructive role in the development of special regions of the country, and in the progress or defense of the nation." This idea was amplified by saying that projects sponsored by government, private sources or industry can "promote the growth of a region through technological audits of its mineral, chemical, agricultural or other resources, by developing new uses for present products of the soil or mines, or finding new uses for hitherto useless deposits, soils or by-products."

The need for objectivity in research was mentioned. "The independent research institute takes problems away from the day-to-day service demands on the company laboratory, into the objective research atmosphere which is so often necessary for successful results." Also, the concept of multidisciplinary research was stressed as being especially helpful "where the problem is an unusual one, or where a unique combination of research effort is needed."

As time went on, this latter feature was often referred to within SRI as the "wide angle of research inquiry," the "multidisciplinary approach" and "organized team work in R&D." It was and still is a special dimension of a research institute and especially so in SRI.

The brochure then turned to the nation's rising need for highly-qualified research people and how they could be more productive. "The pooling of scientific personnel in a research institute, staffed and equipped to carry out virtually any investigation, leads to more efficient use of ... scientists and engineers and better employment of specialized equipment." This probably staked out more than could be done, but the thought was certainly in the right direction.

Picking up the theme from SRI's mid-1947 brochure, the new issue spoke of "new frontiers," pointing out that unprecedented growth of the West in recent years was powerful evidence that "ever-widening horizons of research" were moving in diverse and exciting ways. The nation's industrial research laboratories had, in fact, increased from about 100 to more than 2,500 during the preceding three decades. Although American industry was spending about $750 million a year on research, SRI certainly did not fully foresee in 1948 the tremendous expansion of the next two decades.

In a signed message in the new publication, Hobson said that "Research creates industry" and that continued expansion for economic purposes, national security and higher standards of living depended on an "intensive program of applied research." He went on to say that this was why SRI was created by a group of industrial and business leaders. More to the point, he emphasized — to the great satisfaction of the directors — that SRI's main goal was "translating fundamental science into products and processes of commercial value, particularly for the benefit of the West."

Thus, a basic philosophy for SRI was outlined, including a dedication to the region in which it was located. But, as the Institute grew in size and scope, the emphasis was soon to shift to the national and international scenes. In any event, the title of the mid-1948 brochure staked out a key point in SRI's search for purpose. The phrase, "Applied Research Center for the West," gave a strong regional goal. It was clear from the text that Stanford and its business friends had felt in 1946 that the Institute was vital to "continued economic growth of the West."

The publication was intended to promote, among other things, the concept of more research by industry wherever it might be done. Hobson's message mentioned a view by Dr. Roland P. Soule (vice president of American Machine & Foundry Company) that "one of the best tests of sound management ... is its attitude toward research." The foreword ended with a quotation that was often to be used within SRI during Hobson's tenure. "The biggest gamble is to do no research at all."

Amid all these calls on industry, the new brochure kept returning to a western orientation. The cover included Rand's design of a symbol with a map of the western states, a star in Northern California and concentric circles covering the West. Then there was an even more direct message. "The mountains and the forests and the rivers and the plains of the West are rich with a multitude of natural resources. It is the region that the Institute serves."

The last page of the brochure included a note of high purpose selected by Hobson (a Quaker) from the Bible. It was one of his favorite passages. He thought it reflected the ultimate goal of research — useful ends for mankind. It was from Psalms 144: 13-14.

"That our garners may be full, affording all manner of store; that our sheep may bring forth thousands and ten thousands in our streets; that our oxen may be strong to labour; that there may be no breaking in, nor going out; that there may be no complaining in our streets."

The new publication prepared under Hobson's guidance — but with strong support by his associates — set a tone for SRI. Some of the same thoughts had appeared a year earlier in The New Frontier. But, for various reasons, it had not created a unity of purpose. The new product did the job in this respect, perhaps due in large measure to the forceful and enthusiastic way in which Hobson expounded his concepts — both within and outside SRI. He certainly sold the Institute's staff on the basic ideas. Hobson was always most persuasive in whatever he set out to do.

This journal on SRI in 1948 now turns back to operations. Everyone was greatly concerned about the meager equipment on hand. There were no electron microscopes, spectrometers, spectrographs, x-ray diffraction devices or computing machines anywhere in sight. A special list of urgently-needed equipment — some $113,000 in value —was prepared. J. D. Zellerbach, one of the directors, approached RCA for a possible gift of an electron microscope; he succeeded in getting an indefinite loan. About $80,000 worth of equipment gifts soon came from other organizations including the Public Works Administration.

One research program started during the Talbot regime was terminated in mid-1948. SRI had been operating a Food Acceptance Laboratory. It included a series of Taste Panels made up of housewives, staff members and others who would taste foods and fill out questionnaires. The whole exercise was unattractive financially and was not a real research program. It smacked of routine testing or polling, perhaps not even repeatable in results from one day to another. In any event, it went away.

By mid-summer, SRI was in high gear on Hobson's development plan. About half of the $100,000 special fund had already been spent. Deficits also were mounting, having reached about $88,000 by the end of June. However, negative net worth was only $25,000 after contributions. But, Stanford's investment had grown to $208,000. It is a vast understatement to say that both University officials and the Trustees were concerned.

By this time the directors had again taken up the problem of capital needs. They heard once more about monies that had been raised by MRI in Kansas City. Hobson now felt strongly that $750,000 to $1.0 million was needed so that SRI could get on a self-sustaining basis. This was his first estimate of capital needs. As events developed, he was very much on target. But, more important, it looked as though the fund raising would start by early autumn.

GEORGE R. HERBERT
Executive Assistant to the Director

Hobson was never satisfied if he was not worrying about something. He and those around him were soon thinking about our position in Southern California. The area was a key research market, and there was talk about creating a research institute in Los Angeles. SRI's move was to set up a small office in the city with Dr. A. M. Zarem, a physicist, in charge. Zarem came from the Naval Ordnance Testing Station in Pasadena. He and Hobson had known each other since their graduate school days at Cal Tech.

Economics research at SRI in mid-summer of 1948 was on a one-track course but going along reasonably well. Everything had to do with the aircraft industry; all was for the Air Force and Navy. The first project on airframe production had been completed. Then, Secretary Forrestal at DOD asked for a study on a proposed five-year aircraft production plan. Two other projects on production problems were already in place. All this work was scheduled for completion by early 1949.

There was no long-range plan for economics research except somehow to develop something for industry. Everything was indefinite. Then, late in the summer, a call came from Pan American Airways. Having heard of SRI, the company's treasurer asked about assistance on some route studies involving Guatemala. A few days later, our first business-sponsored project in economics was agreed upon during a between-flights meeting at San Francisco's airport. The final result of the project was a non-stop PAA flight between Los Angeles and Guatemala that continues today.

The Air Force, Navy and PAA projects began to suggest ideas for the future, and it was not long before a steady growth in economics and management studies got under way. Throughout his time at SRI, Hobson gave enthusiastic support to this new field for research institutes. He did this in the face of advice from heads of several institutes — made especially to me — that the whole idea was "fraught with danger." But all soon changed their minds and started their own programs in limited ways.

By the middle of the year, the Institute staff had grown to about 100. There had been less than fifty in May. Hobson was pushing hard on growth. His first organization was in place. All but three of the top positions were held by people who had joined SRI since Hobson's arrival. Only Rand, Steffens and Gibson in the central administrative group had been employed by Talbot. Herbert had arrived in May. He was one of Hobson's first appointments. Krause was employed at the recommendation of Dr. Frederick Terman at Stanford. Poulter had accompanied Hobson from Armour; he was SRI's senior scientist and devoted all of his time to research.

The Institute was divided into five research groups. Poulter was handling geophysics and seismology; Zarem was starting a physics group. Dr. Raymond Ewell from Shell

Chemical had taken over chemistry and chemical engineering. Thomas H. Morrin was beginning a buildup in the electronics field. I was head of industrial economics and had been since the Talbot days.

Ewell's name brings to mind one of Hobson's amusing traits. He could be highly enthusiastic about some of his colleagues' activities and then move quickly to the other extreme. As a gourmet, Ewell had written a small book on dining in San Francisco. Hobson always worked this in when introducing Ewell. Then, one evening he dined at one of the featured restaurants and found the food not to his liking. Never again did he mention the book but on occasion would speak privately about how some people wasted their time on less-than-helpful pursuits.

By the end of September, Hobson had been on the job about seven months. The staff had grown to 125, including 70 on a permanent, full-time basis. Project revenue was running at some $600,000 per year, twice the rate when Hobson arrived. A vigorous spirit prevailed around the organization; ambitious plans were being developed. The Institute was indeed on the move.

There were, however, some difficult problems. The cash balance was only $1,200. On at least three occasions, payroll checks for the senior people were issued but not cashed until money became available. Deficits were running at $15,000 or more per month. Negative net worth had reached $82,500. The Stanford debt had risen to $266,000. Some $141,100 against the $100,000 development budget had been spent or committed with three months yet to go.

But even in the financial arena there were some favorable signs. Revenue had increased about 70% in three months. The contract backlog was quite satisfactory. Government research was down to 27% of the total. Although the directors "expressed satisfaction" with all that had been done, the Stanford Trustees were more than ever concerned about the trend of Institute finances.

Meanwhile, Hobson pushed ahead even more vigorously on the development program. More than 11,000 copies of the new brochure were mailed to business executives. In addition, a periodical called Research for Industry (R for I) had been created. It remained on the scene until 1964 and certainly was a key factor in acquainting business and government with a growing SRI. The mailing list eventually included more than 25,000 people.

Edward Pendray was the father of R for I. Many years later he said, "I developed (it) as a means of reaching sponsors and potential sponsors with greater frequency than was possible with booklets or folders, and with some element of 'news' to make the material more timely and interesting." With very little money for the project, he used a low-cost format and wrote the first two issues himself. Many agreed that his handiwork was "an effective promotional tool." It was widely read in business around the country.

As autumn got under way, many other things were happening at SRI. Research conferences in San Francisco and Los Angeles were soon to be held. Equipment for a new magnetic materials laboratory was being moved into place. Plans were afoot for new programs in the life sciences and mechanical engineering. A research agreement form for use with companies was being introduced. But, the big need was for more equipment — in Hobson's opinion about $500,000 as a minimum.

During the autumn, Poulter won first prize (his third) in a national AAAS competition for color photography on scientific subjects. An arrangement had been worked out with Matson Navigation Company for joint work in transportation studies. But, for various reasons, it was never used. Finally, the board was planning to increase its size so as to be in a better position for the long-delayed fund raising.

In the meantime, Hobson was urging McBean and other directors to get this program under way. He told McBean that three directors (Cushing, Stewart and Eurich) hoped Stanford would loan SRI some $500,000. Then he said, "It is urgent that contributed funds be secured at the earliest possible date." The facts would have justified an even stronger statement. Time was running out.

Nevertheless, Hobson added even more energy to the expansion drive. A senior staff meeting was help in Aptos (California) the weekend of September 24-26, 1948. It had a profound effect on our development. Hobson drove home his view that the Institute had to expand in size, scope and research quality. One by one all those present were asked to present plans for the future. Hobson's usual comment was — "Not enough — you must get your sights higher."

The SRI contingent returned from the Aptos weekend all fired up to move the organization ahead in Hobson's image. He said over and over that all of us were young in age and experience, thus all the more reason why everyone must be vigorous in building programs, getting good people, promoting SRI and making a future for our-

DR. THOMAS C. POULTER
Associate Director

A Hobson Colleague from Armour Research Foundation

WILLIAM RAND

CARSTEN STEFFENS

R. VAN VALKENBURGH

WELDON GIBSON

PAUL MAGILL

selves. As time went on, we looked back on Aptos with amusement but respect. A new shot of adrenalin was flowing and Hobson was clearly the instigator.

Some thirteen years after the events of 1948, Hobson recalled his first efforts to develop SRI. He was justifiably proud of what had been done.

> *"... I was asked ... to prepare a plan and budget for the development of the Institute. That plan was prepared to essentially build — from the top down and to operate ... at a loss until June 1950. It was certainly more luck than management that we met that target date exactly on schedule and to the best of my knowledge has been in the black since."*

His recollection on the basic idea is right. However, the first break-even target was at $1.0 million in revenue. This rate was reached on an annual basis by the autumn of 1949. But, then a new expansion was set in motion, aimed at break-even by June 1950. This was achieved only one month behind schedule. However, these are perhaps details. The important point is that Hobson had started things moving toward the goals for which SRI was founded. The Institute was never to be the same again.

Although SRI's affairs during 1948 were certainly dominated by finances, it was fast becoming a more-important institution. Sixty research projects were active during the year, forty-one having been started since Hobson's arrival in March. Work on the smog problem and on land subsidence in Southern California, along with six other projects, continued into 1949. Thus, Hobson was joined by others on the staff in saying — "The growing service of Stanford Research Institute to industry, government and other sponsors is reflected directly in the increased number and scope of its active research projects."

Three quarters of our research revenue ($600,000) in 1948 came from industrially-sponsored projects. Several major companies had joined the client list — Union Oil, Southern Pacific, Shell, Pan American, Pepsi-Cola and Rheem, for example. These and other projects covered a wide range — from synthetic detergents to western development potentials to food chemistry.

Several new laboratories were started during the year. They included, for example, a general electronics facility, an ion exchange laboratory, an air and water pollution complex, a gage laboratory, and an analytical service facility in chemistry and physics.

SRI's engineering program began in August with the arrival of Thomas Morrin from Raytheon. Seven people joined him in this effort before the year was out. Their first project on a television converter started in September. The second involved single sideband transmitters. These endeavors soon led to a major program in electronics.

Although the Institute made considerable progress during the year on many fronts, the financial problem was most difficult at year-end. This might have been expected. The year's deficit was $160,000; the new year began with a negative net worth of $127,000. The bank balance was only $1,300. A cash crisis was at hand.

Even so, Hobson was brimming with confidence and was eagerly looking forward to 1949. He said it would be "one of continued growth" and that it would be necessary "to expand the staff and physical equipment" and to move the Institute into new fields. His whole attitude was remarkable under the circumstances and it rubbed off on others even though the directors were concerned about finances. He kept saying that SRI had been "well launched," and that its efforts had been "well received." He could hardly wait for approval of a new development plan.

Perhaps having in mind some of SRI's earlier problems, Hobson in a year-end statement gave high credit to Alvin Eurich (the chairman) for his "vision, courage and wise guidance" during the year. This was a well-earned plaudit. Eurich had stood with Hobson during some trying but exciting times.

The year of the Vigorous Thrust ended with 204 people, a fivefold increase in twelve months. Revenue was one and a half times greater than a year earlier. Three additional buildings in Stanford Village had been occupied; space had multiplied five times. More expansion was being planned.

Some of the directors felt that the Institute's interests were becoming too broad and expansive. Nevertheless, Hobson added these words to the annual report — "(SRI) is unique in the breadth of its interests." He was convinced the path was right and felt he had McBean on his side.

The Christmas season was, nevertheless, an apprehensive time for the staff. A financial crisis was enveloping the organization. Rumors abounded that its doors would be closed within a month. Growth had consumed all available resources and deficits were moving upward. Meanwhile, Hobson was proposing various solutions and promoting a new development plan.

I have always felt that Hobson's initial moves in 1948 had an enormous impact on the future of SRI. When he arrived in March, the organization was standing still; at year-end it was energized even with the money problem at hand. The Institute was never to lose the energetic force that Hobson inserted almost immediately after he took charge.

Questions were to be raised later about Hobson's seemingly-insatiable drive for expansion. Much more was yet to come as 1948 came to an end. Inherent in his character was a strong enthusiasm, tremendous energy, great entrepreneurship, and a drive for success. His impact was all-persuasive and it was lasting.

Along with others, I was deeply involved in the Hobson thrust. He was a great salesman, and we were with him all the way in 1948. Some of the questioning at the time (and in retrospect) was certainly justified, but his associates were not questioning him. There was a price to pay for the speed of the movement. But there would have been a penalty in the long run for doing less, at least in 1948.

The year was not without some personal sidelights in a backward glance.

THOMAS MORRIN

J. W. McBAIN

LAWRENCE RICHARDS

LEV MEKLER

EUGENE STALEY

V. LORRAINE PRATT
Good Librarian-Small Library

My original temporary appointment should have come to an end about the time Hobson arrived. However, he knew nothing of the beginning arrangement (nor about Rand's change in my status at the end of 1947), and I did not elaborate. Soon after taking over, he asked me to handle a second job temporarily; he had the business function, along with my economics posts, in mind. He could have picked a less hazardous task; it was certainly more than a part-time job.

Then, one day he asked me to choose "for the long term" between the business and research positions, suggesting a decision in a week or so. I did not need to think it over; I would stay with economics research. Thus, my position again became "permanent." No one said we should seek new economics projects in the spring of 1948. But, more importantly, no one said we should not move ahead. Thus was born an ever-growing industrial economics and management sciences program.

Certainly, I shall never forget the Aptos weekend in September 1948. Before Hobson could tell me to get my sights higher on adding staff in economics, I confirmed by telephone with a few people (with whom earlier talks had been held) that they were indeed invited to join SRI. All of them accepted. Hobson was satisfied with this sort of action.

But it was on the way home with Hobson's comments on "young of age" in mind that I realized fully what he meant. I was 31 at the time; several others were around this

STRATEGY SESSION IN ECONOMICS
From left to right: Dr. Weldon B. Gibson, D. B. Myers, Jr., Robert O. Shreve and Dr. Bonnar Brown.

JANE GOELET
Affirmative Action-Office Manager

age. His call to help make a future for ourselves had a new appeal.

The full story of SRI's upsurge during Hobson's tenure from 1948 through 1955 must await another volume. But there is no question about the upward turn of events during his first year. Hobson's initial impact was enormous even though the Institute was still small and seeking its place in the research spectrum.

To anyone not at SRI in 1948, it is difficult, if not impossible, to portray fully the tenor of the times. The days were exciting and exhilarating even with the developing financial problem.

During the Christmas Season, in a play on Rand's words of a year earlier, I jotted down what seems in retrospect an appropriate keynote. "The Institute is being reorganized and refounded at the same time — an exciting experience."

During 1947 and 1948, I often talked with McBean in San Francisco, at SRI and by telephone. Just before Christmas in 1948, my wife and I called on the McBeans at their San Francisco home. We quickly fell to talking about SRI. I mentioned the quiet events of 1947 and the great change that had come our way during the last nine months.

McBean spoke directly to the heart of the matter and with great enthusiasm even though he knew — as I did — that a money crisis was at hand. "Everything before is but a quiet prelude; we will surge ahead in dramatic fashion. The Institute will be a big success — it was not founded to be otherwise. Don't forget what I have just said." I have never forgotten his words and told him so not long before his death twenty years later.

Thus, we come to the end of a chronology on our Founding Years. It is well that we never forget what our founding directors said and did; the next two chapters may help in this respect. ▪

A CLIENT MEETING

From left to right: Dr. Thomas C. Poulter, Thomas H. Morrin, Paul J. Lovewell, E. Finley Carter of Sylvania and later SRI's third executive director, Dr. Weldon B. Gibson, Ralph A. Krause, Dr. Robert L. Benedict and Dr. Carsten Steffens.

The Policymakers

Like a person, an organization is known by the company it keeps. The SRI Board is first rank; I am impressed.

— HENRY R. LUCE - 1956

URING A NEW YORK SESSION in early 1956 when SRI and Time, Inc. were discussing possible joint sponsorship of the first International Industrial Conference in San Francisco, Henry Luce took one look at our board list (with the founding directors identified) and more or less made up his mind to join a new endeavor. He put into words a basic fact about SRI's formative years.

A good board of directors obviously is important to any organization. This was especially so during our early years. Some crucial decisions dealing with the very existence of the Institute had to be made. Fortunately for SRI, its early governing board included some able, influential, energetic and highly motivated senior executives. Luce was especially impressed — as were others — by the quality represented on the founding group of policymakers.

These men were always willing to devote time to SRI affairs and on several occasions took strong steps in shaping and guiding its development. They recognized the key role of the Stanford Trustees and the frequent need for decisive action in cooperation with the Trustees.

Without in any way abdicating their policy positions — quite the reverse in fact — the founding directors always gave a great measure of freedom to management. Although from the outset there were some problems and differences among the directors on the future course for SRI, a basic harmony always prevailed. Pride in the organization and an honor in association were evident over and over again.

The power and influence of the founding board are evident from even a casual review of its membership. When SRI had little or no experience and no real accomplishments, it depended to a great extent on a public image created by its board. This was an image of integrity, forward thinking, and dedication to a concept.

On occasion, someone unfamiliar with the setting would question the whole idea of SRI. The board always rallied to the cause. One director responded in force to such a critic in the early days. "I suggest you take a look at the list of board members and perhaps reassess your perspective."

Of prime importance was the willingness of a few directors to work together almost as one in solving problems that threatened to bring the Institute to an end. These times of crisis — and there were several — are recounted elsewhere. Many more await a second book.

Contributions of the early board as a whole — and especially by a few of its members — are reasonably well known today even with the passage of time. The efforts of some are known to only a few people. They deserve more credit than has been publicly accorded.

The group begins with Morris M. Doyle, one of our incorporating directors, and includes 53 business executives, seven Stanford officers and a professor from Cal Tech. All in all, 60 outside directors served SRI at various times during its first nine years. However, this account deals only with the founding group plus one, the first addition to their midst during the vigorous thrust of 1948 and early 1949.

In many respects, Doyle was an SRI founder. He helped write its charter and advised Tresidder and Eurich on how the organization should be brought into being. A highly respected lawyer and counsel to Stanford University, he was a conscience to SRI, being aided along the way by his partner, Robert Minge Brown. Doyle's term as an incorporating director lasted only about a month but later as a Stanford Trustee, he always took a great interest in SRI. Following his election as president of the Trustees, he became an SRI director for the second time in mid-1962.

Doyle and Brown were especially helpful after the formative days when steps were under way with the IRS and the U.S. Senate aimed at removing at least some of the ambiguities in tax regulations affecting nonprofit, tax-exempt research institutes.

Being a modest man, Doyle has always down played his early activities on SRI, but the record is clear. He made a great contribution and occupies a special place of honor in our history.

The roles played by Donald Tresidder, Alvin Eurich and Atholl McBean in bringing SRI into existence are portrayed elsewhere. Because of his untimely death, Tresidder was a director for only about fifteen months. Eurich was vice chairman of the board from the beginning and was elected chairman upon Tresidder's death. He resigned from Stanford in late 1948 and thus from the board chairmanship. A little over a year later he resigned from the SRI board. Clarence Faust, Stanford's acting president was SRI's interim chairman from January to May of 1949.

STEPHEN D. BECHTEL, SR.

PAUL L. DAVIES

DONALD J. RUSSELL

Three Close Friends and Early Directors — A Magnificient Triumvirate

The Founder

Eurich's first great contribution was during the 1945-46 days of the Northern Troika. But, equally important, was his reassuring and steady hand during 1948 following Tresidder's death. He held the place together and thus deserves the accolade "savior" as well as "architect." There is more than ample reason why he is given "Highest Honor" in the opening pages of this book.

From the outset, McBean was recognized by his fellow directors as SRI's "founder." He was certainly its most active backer and protagonist. His major efforts in advancing the cause and welfare of the organization are at the forefront in several parts of this book. In some respects more important, but largely unknown outside a small circle, were McBean's activities on a day-to-day basis in an unofficial "father" capacity. It was in this arena that the full force of his character, personality, likes and dislikes, convictions and concepts were so fully evident. This story on "One of a Kind" appears in the next chapter.

Two of the first eleven directors, Paul L. Davies and Donald J. Russell, served throughout the formative years and later upon reaching retirement age were elected "founding directors." Davies was head of the Food Machinery Corporation (now FMC) and Russell was vice president (later chairman) of the Southern Pacific Company (SP). Both men were energetic, direct and forceful, and always very active in SRI affairs.

An intrepid traveller in connection with FMC, Davies was especially helpful on our expanding international activities during the 1950s and 1960s. Both FMC and SP frequently placed research projects at SRI, and in most cases their chief executives were directly involved. Both men were extremely busy but always had time for SRI.

Russell in particular brought a friendly but direct approach to his activities as a director. He insisted on tighter cost controls and better cash management. He wanted board meetings to be run on time and efficiently; he grew impatient when discussions

LOS ANGELES DIRECTOR

William S. Stewart, *right*, and his close friend, Jesse Hobson

150   *The Policymakers*

strayed away from the essentials; he expressed himself forcefully about events within his acquaintance.

A Stanford alumnus and Trustee, Russell became over the years one of the nation's most highly-regarded railroad executives. He stepped up Southern Pacific's R&D efforts and early turned to SRI for help. The most significant result of this association was the development and later widespread use of a DF (damage free) shock absorber system on thousands of America's railroad freight cars.

During the very early SRI years, Russell was not particularly involved in international affairs and knew only a few foreign executives. But, as time went on, he became greatly interested in the field and devoted a lot of time to SRI's worldwide operations. He soon developed very close relationships with scores of top executives around the world. He was — and still is — a generous and gracious host and greatly enjoys the international environment, particularly when SRI is involved. No director has ever been a greater backer of the Institute.

Both Russell and Davies were forces to be reckoned with in SRI's boardroom. They always spoke directly — often with a sprinkling of humor — to the question at hand. They were close friends and shared opinions on most matters. They were totally dedicated to SRI's welfare and future.

While McBean was known as the "founder" of SRI, Charles R. Blyth, a Stanford Trustee and one of the first eleven directors, was in many ways its "protector." He was head of an investment banking firm bearing his name and was highly respected in financial circles. On at least three occasions, Blyth did yeoman service for SRI when his dedication and influence were greatly needed.

During a late 1948 and early 1949 financial crisis, he was instrumental in working out a refinancing plan for SRI. At a time when even some Stanford Trustees felt that the organization should be liquidated for financial reasons, Blyth held firm in his faith in SRI. Almost singlehandedly, he prevailed upon the American Trust Company and five other San Francisco banks to loan $600,000 to the Institute. He was elected Treasurer in May of 1949 and thus helped see that the loans were retired in good order. There was no problem on the matter with SRI; the management was determined to exceed Blyth's expectations, and in fact did so.

CHARLES B. BLYTH
Treasurer *Par Excellance*

Furthermore, at his urging the Stanford Trustees converted a working capital advance into a $500,000 long-term loan. Blyth often said then and later that Stanford should turn the loan into a gift investment. However, John F. Forbes, our financial adviser from 1949 onward, always argued that the loan should remain as tangible evidence of the SRI-University affiliation. Blyth did not press the point with his fellow Trustees, and it is well that Forbes' view prevailed. Otherwise, the University undoubt-

PAUL B. McKEE

Founding Director from the
Pacific Northwest

edly would have been criticized by some of its fund raisers for giving money outright to SRI. Never, however, was there any Stanford gift suggestion from SRI.

In the early 1950s, when the Trustees again became concerned about SRI's financial affairs, Blyth added his full support to McBean and others in convincing them that all would be well in due course.

Then, in 1956 when SRI had to get a building program started (but had no cash reserves), Blyth gave a crucial assist. He brought management into contact with top executives of the Prudential Insurance Company. A financing plan was soon arranged. Blyth's involvement was the key to Prudential's participation.

Whatever financial success SRI may have had in later years — and it has been considerable — is in many respects a testimonial to Blyth's firm support when it was so greatly needed in the late 1940s and early 1950s.

Paul McKee, a Stanford graduate and a leading business executive in Portland, Oregon, came into contact in 1946 with the San Francisco movement that led to SRI's creation. He was interested in a possible research institute for the Pacific Northwest. By joining with McBean and Stanford and becoming an SRI director, he symbolized (along with William L. Stewart of Los Angeles) the Pacific Coast scope of the new Stanford organization.

A forceful and direct individual, McKee served SRI faithfully during the early days. He resigned from the board in mid-1953 with the feeling that he had completed his commitment to McBean and others who had invited him to membership.

McKee continued, however, to be greatly interested in the Institute's welfare and one year later rejoined the board when plans were afoot (with his strong support) to open a Pacific Northwest office in Portland. He resigned again two years later — feeling once more that a promise had been fulfilled.

As head of a private utility company and a staunch advocate of power generation by utility companies, McKee was not a supporter for various federal power projects in the Northwest, especially Bonneville. He was greatly disturbed in the mid-1950s when he felt an SRI study on aluminum production in the area gave too much backing for federal power generation. He voiced his views forcefully but continued to support SRI in many ways. McKee's criticism of our report centered on a very few words that were not intended in any way to diminish the cause of private enterprise. But he was highly critical of the author —always referring to him as "Mr. X."

This whole episode was somewhat traumatic at the time, but SRI stood by "Mr. X" while increasing its respect and appreciation for McKee's support. I was not the author of the report but did handle most of the relationships with McKee.

William L. "Bill" Stewart of Union Oil Company represented Southern California on our first board of directors. He later became vice chairman of the company, one of the Institute's early clients.

Stewart and Hobson were immediately attracted to each other and became warm friends. Hobson often sought his advice and help more or less in a "brother" relationship. Their close association grew in part out of SRI's early work for the Western Oil and Gas Association on the smog problem in and around Los Angeles. Among other things, with Stewart's encouragement, the project led to an SRI office in Los Angeles under Abe Zarem's leadership. Stewart and Zarem soon became close friends and strong advocates for an SRI operation in Southern California.

Also, in late 1948 and early 1949, Stewart helped arrange a $125,000 loan by WOGA to SRI when we were desperately short of working capital.

Following Hobson's resignation in late 1955, Stewart was less active on the board, particularly after he became an even more ardent yachtsman and began taking long journeys to the Caribbean and Europe. However, he always responded when called on for special help.

J. D. Zellerbach of Crown Zellerbach Corporation, one of the original board members, served until 1956 when he was appointed by President Eisenhower as Ambassador to Italy. He had earlier been head of the U.S. Marshall Plan in the country.

Zellerbach's single most important service as a director was in bringing SRI in touch with the Italian Government. This resulted in a 1950-51 project on recovery and

J. D. ZELLERBACH

A Founding Director
Ideas from Jack's Restaurant in San Francisco

reconstruction plans for Italy's mechanical industries. Many of the discussions with Zellerbach before, during and after the project were held at a luncheon table in his favorite dining place, Jack's Restaurant in San Francisco.

During board discussions leading up to the Italian project, our first major effort abroad, some directors raised questions — as they were to do later — about the wisdom of taking on projects outside the United States. J. D. Zellerbach and S. D. Bechtel, Sr., stoutly defended the project. In doing so, Zellerbach said that in time the European recovery program would lead to strong competition for many American companies but

---

THE ELEVEN FOUNDING DIRECTORS
(Elected December 13, 1946)

Charles R. Blyth .... Died, August 25, 1959
  President, Blyth & Company, Inc.

John E. Cushing .... Died, April 22, 1956
  President, American-Hawaiian Steamship Company

Paul L. Davies .... Retired, July 1972; Died, November 1975
  President, Food Machinery Corporation

**Alvin C. Eurich .... Resigned, March 1950
  Vice President, Stanford University

W. P. Fuller, Jr. .... Resigned, June 1961; Died, August 1970
  Chairman of the Board, W. P. Fuller & Company

Atholl McBean .... Retired, March 1963; Died, December 1968
  Chairman of the Board, Gladding, McBean & Company

Paul B. McKee .... Resigned, June 1956; Died, February 1968
  President, Pacific Power & Light Company

Donald J. Russell .... Retired, January 1973
  Vice President, Southern Pacific Company

William L. Stewart, Jr. .... Died, August 30, 1963
  Executive Vice President, Union Oil Company

*Donald B. Tresidder .... Died, January 1948
  President, Stanford University

James D. Zellerbach .... Resigned, January 1956; Died, August 1963
  President, Crown Zellerbach Corporation

Note: Atholl McBean became Director Emeritus in April 1963; Paul Davies and Donald Russell were elected Founding Directors in June and December 1972, respectively. Titles are as of 1946.

*Chairman.
**Vice Chairman.

that SRI should assume an international rather than a purely domestic stance. His comment about European competition seemed remote at the time, but later events proved him right.

The two remaining members of the founding board were W. P. Fuller, Jr., and John E. Cushing of San Francisco. Fuller was a Stanford Trustee and strong supporter of the University, but neither he nor Cushing had been particularly involved in the events of 1945-46 leading to SRI's formation. Nevertheless, both men were active directors and always most cooperative and helpful.

Four of the first eleven policymakers (Blyth, Cushing, Stewart and Tresidder) died while still directors. Eurich is president of The Academy for Educational Development in New York. Russell is retired and lives in San Francisco. All others have died since retiring or resigning as directors.

In January 1949, the twelfth policymaker entered the picture. During 1948, the board had discussed on several occasions the idea of expanding its size. One reason they decided to increase their numbers was to broaden representation both geographically and by types of business. They felt this would be helpful in a fund-raising program then being planned.

Donald J. Russell

"No person has served SRI longer — almost three and a half decades — and with greater dedication than Donald Russell. He was — and still is — an able and distinguished Founding Director."

S. D. Bechtel, Sr.

The first new director was Stephen D. "Steve" Bechtel, Sr., who was to become one of the most influential, most interested and hardest working board members. Bechtel's election was recommended by Russell. The proposal was promptly endorsed, but then Russell found Bechtel reluctant to accept. He was already active in Stanford and University of California affairs and was less-than-enthusiastic about Russell's idea. Moreover, he was terribly busy running the rapidly-growing Bechtel Corporation. But his friend of many years persisted and, as Russell said later, "I finally got him into the fold." It was one of the greatest assists Russell could have given to SRI.

JOHN E. CUSHING
A Founding Director with
Hawaii connections.

DONALD J. RUSSELL
A Founding Director
Making His Point Clear

Soon after becoming a director, Bechtel began urging the board and SRI to pursue opportunities in the international field. Although there was a continuing response over the years, it was never enough for Bechtel. He kept asking that the amount of international work be "doubled and doubled again" in short periods of time. Furthermore, he constantly urged that a greater proportion of our research be for business and industry rather than with government. In all this thrust, his perseverance was exceeded only by his insistence.

Being the chief executive of a large worldwide engineering and construction company, Bechtel clearly foresaw the trend toward greater internationalization of business. He thought it highly important that SRI keep pace with — and indeed lead — the movement. Time after time, he assisted in broadening our U.S. and foreign contacts and urged all of us to leave no stone unturned in developing international projects.

Bechtel's service was by no means limited to the foreign field. He was chairman of the board's Membership Committee and a member of its International and Stanford Liaison Committees. On one occasion after another he would propose a new board member on the basis that "he will bring a lot to the party." He was always right.

Steve Bechtel went about his board activities with great energy, ability, vision and enthusiasm. He was full of ideas and initiatives. He inspired confidence, planning for the future, intense loyalty and thinking on new scales by all who worked with him. He could not have been more interested in or dedicated to SRI. Bechtel kept emphasizing that anything could be done if management — with "strong tail wind from the board" —would pursue its opportunities, especially abroad, with "sights set high" and with ever more determination.

Bechtel's dedication to the Institute was so great that in later years he and others in the family helped make possible a magnificent International Building. That story, including honors bestowed on Bechtel, appears later in this book. His goal for SRI was that it should become "a significant international institution." His contributions along these and other lines have been magnificent. He was, in effect, a founding director together with the original eleven.

I have had the great satisfaction of working closely with every SRI director of the formative years. It has been a great experience with men such as McBean, Eurich, Russell, Bechtel, Davies, Blyth and Doyle. They hold very special places of honor in my mind for all they have done.

With Blyth I was intimately involved in arranging financing for our first permanent building. It was my lot to receive the full wrath of Paul McKee on the power generation issue but our close friendship remained intact. It was my good fortune to work closely with Zellerbach on our first major international project in Italy. With Russell, Bechtel and Davies, I spent long hours on countless occasions in connection with our worldwide interests, especially the International Industrial Conferences in San Francisco and many similar events abroad. My relationships with McBean ranged across the full spectrum of SRI activities.

The personal story could go on and on. But suffice it to say that SRI is everlastingly fortunate to have had such strong support from its founding directors, especially when the issues were crucial. I think it is no exaggeration to say that without their rallying to the cause SRI would simply not exist today. And, in addition to all this, from the staff's viewpoint, the whole experience has been fun — and certainly exhilarating. I shall never forget it and have always tried to see that each and every founding director knew full well that SRI remembers all they did.   ■

THE FIRST TEAM

Two of the first eleven SRI Directors, Donald J. Russell and Paul L. Davies, served on the board for almost 27 years and then were formally elected as non-voting founding directors. In this capacity, Russell is still active in SRI affairs.

Alvin C. Eurich was a director for about four years. He and Russell are the only two living members of the first team.

Atholl McBean continued as a director for 16 years and then served almost six years as director emeritus. Donald B. Tresidder's term of about a year ended with his death in early 1948.

William Stewart and W. P. Fuller, Jr. were board members for almost 17 and 15 years, respectively. Charles Blyth served about 12 years, John E. Cushing 10, and J. D. Zellerbach 9. In two terms, Paul B. McKee was a director for some 10 years.

The first addition to the founding group, S. D. Bechtel, Sr., was a director for 26 years, becoming director emeritus in 1975.

Morris Doyle, one of the incorporating directors, later served 16 years in two terms on the board and was elected director emeritus in March 1979.

Both Bechtel and Doyle are still active on behalf of SRI in their honorary board positions.

SUPPORT FROM HOME

There were times in SRI's early days when our directors were most helpful in client relations. One such case occurred in 1948.

The first Secretary of Defense, James Forrestal, was interested in an SRI report on expansion potentials in the aircraft industry. At a meeting in his office, he read a key sentence from the report. "The aircraft industry is not now capable and will not be capable on July 1, 1949, of expanding sufficiently to meet mobilization requirements within the time required."

This was forceful language from a new and quite unknown institute. The Secretary was preparing a report of his own for President Truman. He accepted our conclusion but wanted to know more about SRI.

We answered his questions and in the process gave him a list of the Founding Directors. At a meeting the following day, he said — "I called a couple of your directors and am fully satisfied. Now let's get to work on my report."

Forrestal had called McBean who said that western industry was solidly behind the Institute. McBean later said, "I gave the Secretary the big picture on SRI." The other call was to Blyth who emphasized that contrary to some rumors the Institute was "here to stay." Apparently Forrestal had heard some of the whispering about our days being numbered for financial reasons.

With help from two of the founders, an immediate question had been answered. More importantly, however, the project marked the beginning of a long and growing research relationship with the Department of Defense. Our first project had brought the Institute front and center in national security affairs.

During the latter part of 1950, President Truman mentioned the SRI Report and then remarked — "It was helpful in my efforts to get more money from the Congress for aircraft production." He might have added that the advent of the Korean War had something to do with the action.

W.B.G.

ONE OF A KIND

*My horse, Old Pueblo, earns more money in
one race than SRI makes in a year; you must
do better financially; I insist upon it.*

— ATHOLL McBEAN - 1956

OTHER PAGES IN THIS ACCOUNT cover in various ways the contributions of
the founding directors during SRI's formative years. Several brought even more than
substance to the affairs of SRI. They were engaging personalities and often drove home
their reasoning with humor and anecdotes — sometimes preplanned, other times not,
but always with effect. These pages deal with the color that surrounded one director. He
was indeed "one of a kind."

The story has to do with Atholl McBean, a legend in western business even before
SRI was founded. McBean literally dominated the object of his affections for almost two
decades, and SRI gained immensely from all his efforts. He had a strong personality,
well-known likes and dislikes, an iron will, and an impatience second to none in dealing
with organizations for which he felt a responsibility. McBean could be exceedingly
"high" on particular individuals for extended periods and always wanted to help them.
But most, if not all, felt his wrath in some way sooner of later.

There was no question about McBean's "toughness" perhaps sharpened from his
business days in San Francisco during the great dock strikes and strife in the 1930s. He
could "hire and fire" with equal force — sometimes doing so more than once for a
particular person. Jesse Stanton of Stanton and Stockwell, the architects for SRI's first
permanent building, went through this double experience with McBean. But, as with
most people who came into McBean's orbit, he never faltered in respect for the man.
Stanton once remarked that "one has not really been honored in working for McBean
until having been fired at least twice."

During McBean's active days with SRI,
he had plenty of time to devote to its affairs.
At least a third of his time — and often half
or more — were spent on the Institute. He
was intensely proud of the organization.
His contributions were enormous by any
measure. He deserves all the accolades and
honor bestowed on him — publicly and privately — for all he did before and after SRI
was founded.

To say that McBean was dedicated to the profit motive is a vast understatement. "I am a Scot, and I know the value of earning a surplus even in a nonprofit organization." His eyes always went immediately to the "bottom line" in any financial statement. And to say that he pushed and cajoled SRI towards profitability is even a greater understatement. He was never satisfied with any financial performance — always urging that a better job be done.

This pressure was so great at one point during our buildup period that he responded with a stern lecture to an explanation he did not like. "Young man, never ever let me hear you say that again." Jesse Hobson had unwisely said, "But, Atholl, we simply cannot run the Institute like a brick factory." Hobson might have used a telephone, petroleum or farming company analogy. But, it would not have mattered; McBean was a director of companies in all these fields — and many more. Unfortunately, Hobson struck at the very heart of McBean's pride and joy — Gladding McBean, a ceramics company including a brick factory.

Even though McBean kept strong pressure on Hobson to build the Institute — especially its financing — and in spite of the latter's exasperation at times with the founder's persistence, the two men gradually evolved a sort of father-son relationship. McBean thought of Hobson as "my boy at SRI." Hobson looked upon McBean as a mentor and father-advisor.

Shortly after SRI began to break even financially in mid-1950, McBean looked at the net earnings — small but positive — for one month and retorted — "It looks like a clerical error — let's have a bigger number next time."

It was during these days of small but rising surplus figures that McBean often said in various ways that his racehorse, Old Pueblo, earned far more than SRI. But, as the horse began to fade from the winning circle and as SRI's black figures increased, no one in SRI had the nerve to mention Old Pueblo. One reason was that the well-known come-from-behind Silky Sullivan was consistently winning horse races in California. By this time, McBean was asking — not humorously — for a magnifying glass to find SRI's earnings amidst rapidly rising revenues. The returns were quite good, but he insisted on higher rates.

Persistence in building SRI was an abiding feature in McBean's life after he had reached age 65. Everyone including his fellow directors recognized as much, and many in SRI felt his sting from time to time. Upon being shown the text for a proposed plaque honoring McBean, Wallace Sterling, SRI's chairman, changed the word "perseverance" to "persistence" but agreed with a smile that perhaps the original word might portray McBean's magnificent role in "softer terms" to persons who had not experienced institutional life with "the one and only" father of SRI.

Few details in SRI's early affairs escaped McBean's attention. Most people in the management group were young in age — some in their late twenties and many in their thirties. His self-appointed mission was to "train them for the future." He wanted a business-like operation with one person always in charge when the principal executives were away from the office. He telephoned one day — as he did almost everyday — and asked the operator for "the director." Upon being told he was in New York, McBean asked for "the assistant director." Not knowing who was calling, the operator replied — "He is away today. Can anyone else help you?" This was enough for McBean. He curtly

HONOR TO THE FOUNDER

Permanent Plaque at SRI Headquarters honoring Atholl McBean installed
in 1958. *From left to right*: Dr. Weldon B. Gibson, vice president,
Dr. J. E. Wallace Sterling, chairman of the board of directors,
McBean and E. Finley Carter, SRI's president.

observed, "That is the $64 question," and hung up. A stern lecture on the subject soon followed in person.

McBean's phone calls were demanding — yet highly beneficial — in a special way. Placing his own calls and with no need to identify himself to SRI executives he would go directly to the point. "How are things; what's important today?" A reply lasting more than a couple of minutes, or hesitancy in any way, simply left the question unanswered. McBean had already hung up his phone. He wanted people to be on their toes.

Although McBean was not an officer of the SRI board, he acted in effect as an executive chairman, always saying he only wanted to be helpful. Two or three times a week, trips to his San Francisco office (in the summertime to his Woodside home) were necessary to bring him up to date. He always wanted a session just prior to board meetings "to get things lined up."

Also, he was fond of just "dropping by while in the area" — having come, of course, only to visit SRI. Furthermore, he would often do the driving even though for some time he did not have a driver's license. He wanted to check up on developments and would not wait for a driver. His many involvements were awkward at times for management, but all were patient with "the founder" — and well we should have been. When important help was needed, McBean was always out in front with energy and dedication for his favorite organization.

McBean's fund raising work was organized influence with perfection. He would set a target, more or less guarantee the whole amount, and then one by one "put the arm" on his business friends. He was fond of recounting how the last of six San Francisco banks was brought into SRI's Associates Plan in the early 1950s. Taking the chief executives of the bank's largest depositor and borrower, he simply marched in unannounced to see the bank chairman.

Upon seeing his visitors, the bank executive said with a touch of humor, "Never have I had such distinguished people visit me in my office. Please sit down while I bring in some of my senior people to meet you." The leader of the visiting party promptly replied, "Oh, neither is really necessary; we simply came in to talk with you about the bank becoming an SRI Associate for $15,000." The meeting ended as quickly as it had begun — "Atholl, my mind was made up the minute you walked into the room."

McBean was a director and member of the Executive Committee of Standard Oil Company of California. His respect for its management was very great indeed. But with the company as with SRI, he did not hesitate to ask searching questions and delve into matters in some detail. He knew SoCal's ranks — deep in talent — could surround him with care on whatever questions he might raise. In some respects this only whetted his appetite. He would simply march in unannounced or keep telephoning until he was satisfied with answers.

But, McBean was not without a sense of humor. Once he asked a SoCal executive for details on oil production in Indonesia and received a long written reply filled with numbers. Calling for a "small memo" on the subject, he received a quarter-size reproduction of the original. With a laugh, he often said to SRI thereafter — "Give me a short regular-size memo on what you have in mind."

Being an all-out supporter for SRI, McBean always felt great pain when he heard criticism — direct or implied — of its operation if he felt the critic had not done all his

McBean's Summer Home — Woodside, California

Atholl McBean

"Among all his qualities, Atholl McBean was first and foremost a man of action. It is to his everlasting credit that he persevered in founding SRI."

DONALD J. RUSSELL

homework about the matter in question. He would promptly set about "straightening out that fellow" and often did so indirectly through the power and influence structure of the business world he knew so well. This sometimes was embarrassing to SRI but again most people in senior positions around the country understood the situation; on occasion, some would say something like the following to SRI — "I got taken over the coals by Atholl, and he sure straightened me out."

But when McBean felt that SRI had made a mistake, he did not hesitate to tell the management how they had "gotten things all fouled up." One instance illustrates his approach. He became convinced that one of our projects having to do with oil exploration techniques had been mishandled. Assembling the principals within SRI along with the head of an upset oil company, he said directly and forcefully to management, "If you want to dance the Turkey Trot, you simply have to pay the fiddler. Now listen to what this man has to say and do something about it."

McBean believed that whatever might be done should be done first class. When SRI's first permanent building was completed, the inner courtyards were left without landscaping. He took a dim view of the situation and wanted to know why nothing was being done. A response on cost and budgets was not convincing. He wanted "Tommy Church, the best in the business," brought into the picture — "and have the bill sent to me."

But even with his exasperating memory for details, McBean could conveniently forget when it suited his purposes. The bill for the landscaping went from the architect to McBean (as he had specified) and then came to SRI with a cryptic note — "for payment." When asked about the matter, McBean simply said, "I think the job is first class and I know you like it." We did indeed like it; the bill was promptly paid.

He also insisted at the time that a line of yew or cypress trees be planted in front of the new building even though there was no budget for such an expensive adornment. I suggested in a joking tone that perhaps he had an oversupply around his Woodside estate and that a few trees might be moved to SRI. He never brought up the subject again.

McBean had a habit of opening small meetings with long accounts about Standard Oil, Pacific Telephone and Telegraph, Gladding McBean, Newhall, or SRI, no matter what the subject at hand might be. He was not easily derailed on these organizations, and seldom bothered with opening statements about the reasons for his interests.

At a New York meeting in the late 1950s, he took up these companies in succession without apparent reason before the main subject could get introduced. He spoke about flying on a company plane, being able to telephone anywhere he wished at any time, how best to fatten cattle, new technology in ceramics, and finally about SRI. Not having done his homework on McBean, the chairman (an eastern lawyer) finally asked about his interests. In rapid fire McBean said, "I am on the Executive Committee at SoCal, on the board at PT&T, the family executive at Newhall, the major stockholder at Gladding McBean, and the founder of SRI."

Upon being asked if he kept abreast of all these organizations, McBean said, "I think you should know more about SRI" and spoke about it for some thirty minutes. By this time the meeting had to be adjourned with the agenda untouched. A few days later,

Assembling the principals 163

McBean said he thought "such eastern meetings were most helpful in explaining SRI," and that he would arrange more of them. No one ever asked the chairman of the New York luncheon how he felt about the approach.

Having been successful in getting some bankers involved in the Newhall (California) farming and ranching company in the depths of the Great Depression and in keeping them engaged under some trying circumstances, McBean often mentioned the idea of getting their "hands in the wringer so they couldn't let go." He often used this analogy in referring to bank financing at SRI and to keeping the Stanford Trustees behind the Institute. He was, of course, immensely pleased when SRI paid off its bank loans and offered to retire a Stanford loan ahead of schedule.

Even while SRI was a relatively small organization, McBean was constantly talking to its youthful leaders about modern management practices and techniques. To some this seemed a bit strange in view of his general reputation for "strong-arm" administration. But it was another indication of his abiding desire to see SRI succeed. He visited the Institute one day during his 75th year for the sole purpose of hand-delivering a set of management principles. "This is how I want you to operate. Put copies on your desks and on the walls. Never forget these points."

How well his guidelines were followed may be open to question, but the paper was duly circulated and displayed. McBean often checked to make sure. The accompanying text is what he gave us.

The 1956 list of management principles does not include one often given expression by McBean. He always insisted that each of his business associates come up with at least one constructive suggestion a month. Perhaps this originated with his father. McBean often said that in earlier travels — whether for business or pleasure — his father expected him to return with at least one idea that would more than pay for the trip. He wanted the same thing done at SRI.

McBean thought anyone below his age — no matter how close — was a young man and looked upon anyone above his age as "getting along in years." In 1956 when he was 75 and his long-time friend, John F. Forbes, was 80, a decision on SRI's permanent building was pending. As financial adviser, Forbes said, "No prudent man would proceed." But this ran counter to McBean's strong desire. So, he merely observed in an aside that "John Forbes is getting old; we should go ahead anyway." Based on hard facts at the time, Forbes was right. But based on a "hurry up" concept in building SRI — and on confidence in its future — McBean was right. His view prevailed once again.

Age was the basis of another McBean characteristic. In a meeting he would often follow a strong personal opinion on the matter under discussion with a question to some younger associate — "Isn't that right young man?" One had a real problem in these situations if the answer was anything short of "yes, it is." Perhaps the main point, however, is that McBean was usually right. Certainly, he did not hesitate to speak his piece.

McBean was always decisive when any business matter involving Gladding McBean came up with one of his other organizations. The face brick for our first building was developed by Gladding McBean. The architect turned down the trial installation for aesthetic reasons. McBean simply ordered the bricks removed and instructed the factory to "get things right immediately and call back tomorrow." The job was completed post

PORTRAIT FOR POSTERITY

A portrait of Atholl McBean hung in 1972 in the lobby of SRI's headquarters. *On the left*, Dr. Weldon B. Gibson, *and on the right*, Peter McBean, son of the founder.

haste; otherwise, McBean would have taken over personal direction on site. As the architect said later, McBean always felt there was "a right way and in the case of SRI, the only way."

A strong constitution and physique were amply evident in McBean. He added to the idea of longevity by occasional joking reference to "if I die." It was never when, only if. But in a more serious vein, McBean did in fact enjoy talking about his age. He wanted to see a lot more in his lifetime. He once brought a Newhall research project to SRI, got a cost estimate and asked how long it would take. Upon hearing the words, six months, he retorted, "You must speed it up. I may not be here in six months and I have to take care of this matter." We did indeed speed things up.

In 1954, McBean thought it would be a good idea to travel to Washington, D.C., and "let those fellows back there know about SRI." He had Richard Nixon, then Vice President, in mind. A session was soon arranged. But, McBean was not accustomed to waiting long periods in any outside office. Furthermore, he was upset at not being led to the vice president's office by the shortest possible walking route within the building. Upon entering Nixon's room he started right off about SRI and all the things it was doing "to help you fellows back here in Washington." It was a one-way conversation, and the vice president got the whole story. McBean thanked him for his time and departed with his SRI associates in tow. Nixon seemed a bit nonplussed.

Shortly after leaving the Senate Office Building, McBean said he would like to visit Arlington Cemetery, not having been there before. While parked in the quiet of the area, he was speculating about SRI's great future. His views were fascinating, but his Institute companion wondered aloud if we could indeed become as significant as had been outlined. McBean was a bit startled and went on in dramatic fashion to support his view.

"The United States is a big country; the West is the biggest part of the country. SRI is in the West. The future of the country is in the West. Think big thoughts about the West and about SRI."

McBean always enjoyed events and circumstances when people in high places, especially in the eastern part of the country, were brought into our activities. So it was when arrangements were made with Henry Luce and Time, Inc. to cosponsor the first International Industrial Conference in San Francisco in 1957. He insisted that Luce be invited to SRI long in advance and to San Francisco where a dinner could be sponsored in his honor. The arrangements were duly made; McBean and S. D. Bechtel, Sr., gave the dinner at the Pacific Union Club with 88 people around one table. It was a magnificent affair. A few days later, McBean remarked in characteristic fashion — "I congratulated Mr. Luce on getting SRI as a joint sponsor." This may have surprised Luce; Time, Inc. and its financial resources were enticed into the fold by SRI — not the other way around.

From today's perspective, one might well ask how it was possible for McBean to act for so long in so many ways as a sort of combined senior executive and guiding hand for SRI. There were several reasons why he was able to be in the forefront on almost a day-to-day basis. He had time on his hands; everyone respected his founding role and motivations; he had good ideas and strong views; no one wanted to tangle with him, and; all hoped that the relationship could be worked out by management. But the latter was not an easy task.

Finally, the very structure of the board during the 1950s made it fairly easy for McBean to operate especially after 1948. The ex-officio chairman, Dr. J. E. Wallace Sterling, had a backbreaking task as Stanford's president and often said he could spare little time for the SRI function. This was wholly understandable and everyone sympathized with him. As McBean often said, he only wanted to help the chairman, and he did so with vigor and concentration.

The Pacific Union Club in San Francisco was always dear to McBean's heart. He had been president of the Club at one time. He certainly was a staunch protector of its rules — both written and unwritten. He noticed one day in the mid-1950s that an SRI board meeting announcement referred to the Club by name. He called to caution against such a transgression — "Some members might get the impression you think the P-U Club is a restaurant." We promptly started using "1000 California Street," an address not displayed on any building but one that fits the Club's location. McBean was satisfied.

Two additional encounters with McBean — both of a personal nature on my part — have always illustrated in my mind two of his characteristics. One was his intense desire to see SRI succeed no matter what and his readiness to offer advice on any point to this end. The second was his strong sense of personal leadership and direction of affairs.

McBean came into my office one day in 1956 and closed the door behind him. I knew his advice would be direct and personal. Taking note of my travels around the world, a Ph.D. degree and my SRI title, as well as an almost exclusive use by others of "Hoot Gibson" as my name, he wondered aloud if I had any thoughts about a new name — one that might be better accepted far and wide. Knowing he liked "Doctor" and the practical impossibility of changing a long-used nickname (even if one desired), I meekly suggested the possibility of "Doctor Hoot"!!! McBean promised to think about such an idea and never mentioned the problem again.

The second event occurred in 1964. Having lost a teenage son, I was planning a long European backpacking trip with our second son, thus taking the place of his late brother. I asked McBean if he thought such a venture might be inappropriate. He emphatically

McBean's San Francisco Home

favored the idea, saying that at age seven he had "gone all over Alaska including some of the most remote areas." Seeing that I was a bit astonished, he added, "of course, I took my parents along."

The story of Atholl McBean could go on ad infinitum. He was a character in many respects; he was a dominant figure in all respects; he was a successful businessman; he loved to organize important projects; he was a stern taskmaster; he had great faith in the West; he was totally dedicated to SRI; he could build up or turn on an associate in short order; he was accustomed to having his way, and; he certainly was persistent.

More importantly, he got things done and especially was this so for SRI. All the honor implied by the word "founder" is fully justified. Without McBean, SRI might never have been created. Without his continuing perseverance, its progress may have been long drawn out or even halted.

An SRI director from the beginning, McBean was appointed to the Executive Committee when it was created in 1949. He was the first director emeritus starting in March 1963, but was asked by the board to continue meeting with its Executive Committee as well as with the full board.

More than three decades after McBean's driving efforts culminated in SRI's creation, one of his fellow founding directors, Donald J. Russell of San Francisco, gave full plaudits to his friend. "He was a great man... I respected his efforts, his judgment and his sincerity... I did not always approve of the way he did everything, but the final results are what counts." Then he went on to say, "SRI would not exist today except for the perseverance of Atholl McBean."

To say that McBean was much involved in SRI's affairs throughout the formative years is redundant in the extreme. Things were to change in the 1960s when a silent gulf gradually developed between McBean and many of the other directors. In failing health, he withdrew quietly to a background of recognized honor. He died in December 1968.

I worked closely with McBean for many years, enjoyed his friendship, benefitted from his support, experienced his wrath, and saw at firsthand his proprietary interest in SRI. I was present at the famous Nixon meeting, heard his Arlington proclamation on the future of SRI, and received countless telephone calls aimed at "getting up to date."

Although I saw him less and less during the 1960s, we always maintained contact with each other. As author of the words of honor on the McBean Plaque at SRI, I shall always look upon him with high respect and gratitude for all he did in founding the Institute.   ∎

A Stanford Motivation*

As THIS BOOK ON SRI's FOUNDING YEARS points out, I was intimately involved in the events leading to the formation of Stanford Research Institute in the autumn of 1946. Also, I was directly concerned with its activities through 1948.

In light of this experience, I am especially pleased to respond to the author's invitation to comment on the circumstances at Stanford University that had a bearing on SRI's creation. The University's financial situation was certainly a factor.

In my view, the story really begins in late 1941. The weekend of December 7 changed my life as it did for many people throughout the world. Along with six Stanford Trustees, administrators and faculty members, I had been invited by Dr. Donald B. Tresidder to be his guest for three days at the Ahwahnee Hotel in Yosemite Park, California. Tresidder was then president of the University's Board of Trustees. Deeply absorbed in Stanford's problems at the time, he wanted to talk over its future with a few representatives from the University community. I was one of the faculty members among his guests.

We arrived on Friday and immediately began our discussions. At mid-morning on Sunday, a call came in from Edwin Janss, a Stanford alumnus in Los Angeles. He wanted to know if we were listening to the radio. We were not but quickly turned it on and in a state of shock heard about Pearl Harbor.

Together, we listened to the news for an hour or so and then, silently, walked to our cars and drove home. With a national crisis at hand, Stanford's future seemed not too important. Several of us soon turned our attentions to other pursuits; within a few weeks, I was in Washington engaged in war service.

But what has this to do with the creation of Stanford Research Institute? It was simply my first realization of the urgent need for more research facilities in the West not only for the nation's security but for future economic development. At our meeting, Tresidder had mentioned some initiative along these lines at Stanford.

During World War II, Tresidder and I met occasionally in Washington to talk about Stanford. Little did we think that he would become president of the University and that I would have the good fortune of serving with him as vice president. Nor did we even remotely realize that both of us would soon be greatly involved in creating SRI.

In many respects, SRI's formation was one result of a set of circumstances that existed at Stanford when Tresidder took office in the 1943-44 academic year. The

---

*Written by Alvin C. Eurich. (As vice president of Stanford University, Dr. Eurich was one of SRI's founders. He was chairman of its board of directors in 1948. See chapters on The Northern Troika, A Quiet Transition, and The First Year.)

University had great natural and physical resources. But it was cash poor. Its income was very meager for what it was trying to do.

When Stanford opened its doors in the early 1890s, it was reputed to be one of the richest universities in the world. For the first quarter century or so, its students paid no tuition. Neither then nor for another thirty years or so did the University develop a tradition of raising large sums of money.

Stanford's land holdings were extensive — some 9,000 acres with less than 1,500 being used for the campus. Most of the remainder was leased for grazing purposes at about a dollar a year per acre. Even in the mid-1940s, land along the main highway bordering the University was worth $60,000 or more per acre. Nevertheless, the vacant land was producing virtually nothing for Stanford.

Faculty salaries were abominably low. In 1944, the minimum salary for a full professor was only $4,500 per year. The highest being paid was under $9,000. One result of this situation was simply that Stanford could not compete effectively with other leading universities in attracting and holding top-notch faculty members.

The pleasant environment around Stanford helped in some ways to retain faculty but in no way offset the salary problem. Some drastic action was needed to position the University among the country's leading institutions of higher learning.

Some constructive steps had already been taken. For example, Stanford had broken with its tradition of limiting the enrollment of women to 500. Also, in the mid-1930s the Stanford Associates had been created to help raise money. But far more was necessary. The new administration was faced with a severe financial problem.

To fully understand what took place in 1945 and 1946 as the SRI idea came into focus, some comments about how the new administrative team operated may be helpful. Tresidder and I worked together closely. When both of us were on campus, we met regularly at eleven every morning and often talked on through luncheon.

Each of us knew the thinking of the other. Each knew about conversations the other had with people inside and outside the University. Naturally, we disagreed at times but always continued our talks until we reached full accord on the issues at hand. Our relationship was a close one indeed.

The late Palmer Fuller, Jr., a San Francisco business executive, was president of the Stanford Trustees. With our enthusiastic encouragement, he generally spent a day a week on campus talking not only with the two of us but also with the deans, other faculty members and students. Within this setting, we began to talk about the SRI idea on which a faculty committee was at work.

Uppermost in our minds in tackling some of the critical problems of the University was getting additional income to help meet the salary problem, attract outstanding scholars from other institutions, expand research both theoretical and applied, refurbish a neglected physical plant and, in general, to improve Stanford's position.

The main question was obvious. Without experience in raising large sums of money, how could we reduce costs and get additional income to help meet urgent needs? Some of the possibilities involved a reorganization for more efficient operations, better utilization of University land, better use of physical facilities, and an all-out effort to raise research funds. In this context, the idea of an SRI seemed most attractive to both Tresidder and me. But, our major concern was, of course, to see Stanford become a University of even higher quality.

One of the first steps involved organization. A financial vice president was directly responsible to the Board of Trustees. In essence, there were two administrations. The University president and his office handled academic matters while financial and business affairs were in the hands of the vice president working with the Trustees.

All this was changed when the University's chief financial officer resigned. My role was changed from academic vice vresident to vice vresident and, in effect, I became the executive vice president.

Further steps were soon taken. We merged four Schools — humanities, biological sciences, physical sciences and social sciences — into one with Dr. Clarence Faust as the dean. We also placed all student services under the direction of Dr. Lawrence Kimpton who came to Stanford as dean of students from a vice presidency at the University of Chicago. Also, the School of Health was eliminated and a new health service created in cooperation with the Palo Alto Clinic. New deans were soon appointed for all Schools of the University except for medicine and business.

As a start in planning better land use, Tresidder sought help from the Janss family in Southern California. They had sold part of their ranch to the State of California for the UCLA campus and went on to develop the surrounding Westwood Village. Shopping areas were built and leased to operators.

This approach seemed to be a good prototype of what Stanford might do with its extensive land holdings. A director of planning was appointed; he held the first position of this type in any college or university. A road system was planned so as to accommodate a shopping center, an industrial park and additional home sites. We had in the back of our minds that a research institute might be added in due course.

In searching for better ways to use the educational plant, we made a survey on the use of University buildings. On the basis of a seven-hour day, five days a week, we found that classrooms were being used at only 31% of capacity and seats at only 15%. Laboratories were used primarily in the afternoons and classrooms in the morning. Obviously, our facilities were not being used efficiently.

Plans were made immediately to increase the enrollment, a step with which the Trustees quickly agreed. In one year the student body was more than doubled — from 4,200 to 8,500 persons. From tuition fees alone, this move provided additional income enabling Stanford to increase its basic faculty salaries by some 33%, begin renovating old buildings, start attracting new faculty members, and to initiate some new research programs.

In the meantime, the University's regular research programs were making considerable progress. Some excellent government-sponsored projects were being developed within the Engineering School. In physics, Dr. William Hanson was perfecting the linear accelerator which led later to a major facility at the University. At the same time, Dr. Paul Kirkpatrick was developing an x-ray microscope.

There was even more good work under way. Dr. George Beadle had organized a genetics research program that later brought him a Nobel Prize. All these are merely illustrative. They do indicate that Stanford's basic research programs were alive and productive although money was extremely tight.

However, programs of applied research for industry and government were not impressive. A desire to extend this sort of activity, thereby enhancing Stanford's contributions to the economy of the area and to society, was one of the reasons why an institute idea found much appeal within the administration.

It was in this setting that I received a telephone call one day from Professor Paul Holden of the University's Business School. Dr. Gibson mentions this call and subsequent events in his history. This was how I first met Atholl McBean who told me about his interest in creating a research institute that could be helpful to western industry.

As the author of this book points out, I soon began meeting frequently with McBean and talking with him often by phone. He was a dynamic man in a hurry. I developed a high regard for him and continue to value our wonderful association. On many occasions, I have said that without McBean SRI would not exist today.

Gibson describes accurately and in detail the full sweep of McBean's role in the founding of Stanford Research Institute. Also, he gives an excellent account of some of the external influences that helped bring SRI into being. I need only mention here the importance of this background to a Stanford motivation involving the new institute. The first great need was for more income.

As is quite clear in the chapter on the Northern Troika, events moved swiftly under McBean's prodding. But, he had receptive ears at Stanford. He sensed the need and possibilities for a research institute and soon provided the necessary funds for us to invite Dr. Henry Heald, president of the Illinois Institute of Technology, to look over the situation. As Gibson indicates, I had become acquainted with Heald in Washington during World War II.

As the author explains in some detail, Heald thought we should move ahead. We quickly took the matter to the University Trustees. They agreed that a step should be taken on a separate but University-related institute. A majority of the directors for a new institute was to come from the Stanford Trustees.

The idea of Stanford's president being chairman of SRI (and its vice president being vice chairman) was not accidental or incidental. Through this organization we hoped to create a very close working relationship between the institute and the University. In essence, the two institutions were inseparable in our thoughts.

We had clearly in mind that Stanford faculty members would work within the institute on some of its research programs and thus receive a portion of their salaries from the "subsidiary" organization. This was certainly an immediate and practical motivation.

As the author says, we moved quickly in appointing the first director after receiving recommendations from two eastern research institutes. Unfortunately, early events thereafter did not move smoothly. Dr. William Talbot soon resigned, and it fell to me to seek a successor. In the meantime, Tresidder unfortunately died suddenly, and I became acting president of Stanford as well as chairman of the SRI directors. All of this happened early in 1948.

But first, as the author emphasizes, I had a major problem with the Stanford Trustees. Some of them wanted to end the whole affair. They felt that the Institute's failure to develop as they thought it should was clear evidence of a lack of real need.

I felt very keenly that the Institute was much needed and said so at a crucial early-1948 meeting in San Francisco. The discussions went on for several hours until Charles Blyth, a financier and Trustee, placed his personal guarantee on the line so to speak. Gibson's account of this key event and of those that followed is wholly correct.

In any case, the tide was turned. I was authorized to seek a new director. I knew he would have to be an imaginative and energetic soul. We needed a man who had demonstrated his ability to develop an institute such as we had in mind for Stanford.

We had already thought about Dr. J. E. Hobson of the Armour Research Foundation. Again, Dr. Gibson has fully recorded happenings of the time including Hobson's impact on SRI after arriving in March of 1948. Consequently, I need not review the situation here. He was immediately successful even though one financial problem after another arose.

But there is more to the early Stanford University involvement; it happened even before Hobson arrived. In order to accommodate the higher enrollment at the University, we set up an office in Washington, D.C., partly to seek surplus wartime housing adjacent to the University. Fortunately, a temporary hospital complex was soon obtained and quickly named Stanford Village. Some of the space was taken over by SRI in the spring of 1947. The Village was to become the Institute's permanent home even though we thought the initial move was temporary. We were still thinking about an SRI on campus more or less within the University structure.

In summary, what we at Stanford University had in mind in founding SRI can be stated simply and directly.

- Extend through research the University's service to and influence in academic, industrial, commercial and social areas

- Gain additional income that might help increase or supplement faculty salaries

- Enrich the research facilities that might be used by Stanford's faculty as well as by a nucleus staff at the Institute

- Attract to the Stanford Community additional outstanding research talent.

Clearly, as the author reveals, some of these objectives were not achieved as the Institute developed. But in terms of the overall goal — research services to business and government — SRI has been highly successful. This is indeed an understatement; the success has been far beyond even our fondest original dreams.

This overview on SRI from a Stanford vantage point at the time of its founding merely touches on a few highlights. All the details appear in this book. I find them accurate in all respects in line with my memory and papers.

Having been away from Stanford since early 1949 but in looking at SRI from a distance, I am intensely proud of the part that was my good fortune to have played in its origin. Certainly, I am most grateful for the honor Dr. Gibson accords to me in his book.

Even though our plans for close coordination and working relationships between Stanford and SRI did not materialize as originally visualized, the Institute initiative has been — and still is — a great credit to the University.

This book is confined to SRI's founding years. But as some future account will portray, the Institute soon began to serve not only the American West but the nation as a whole and countries around the world. In the meantime, it has provided substantial financial benefits to Stanford. This will continue even though the two institutions decided in the late 1960s to sever their legal ties.

As an independent organization, SRI is pursuing its mission vigorously on a worldwide basis. Its success as the years have gone by has more than met the hopes and aspirations of all who had a hand in its creation. The legacy will surely grow and flourish in the future.

One area in particular in which SRI has made a distinctive new contribution is in the social sciences. This can be attributed in great measure to Dr. Weldon B. "Hoot" Gibson who was the founder and first director of this program. Through his initiative, imagination, energy and brilliance, work in this area has achieved worldwide recognition. Many others were involved at the beginning and later, but he was the instigator.

I must admit that the direction in which this program has moved is not what I had in mind in urging that SRI be created. Being a social scientist and from my Navy experience during World War II, I was thinking principally about applied psychological research. Now, more than three decades later, I recognize that it would have been a mistake for SRI to have moved in this direction. Others were and still are meeting this need. SRI's research on economic, management and social problems has been much more fruitful and made a far greater contribution than could have been made in even the broadest field of psychology.

I am inspired to make a final note about the author in addition to what appears earlier in this book. We have known each other since SRI's beginning and even before. No person is so well qualified to write the early SRI history. In key positions through all phases of its development from the beginning to the present, he has been one of its guiding forces. Modesty has kept him from saying that he has played a major role as a steadying and dynamic force in SRI's growth.

I commend Dr. Gibson most highly and warmly for his vital part in the development of SRI and also for initiating and writing this early history. I have read with great pleasure — and indeed fascination — all the chapters covering the period when I was much involved. His prose and style are most interesting and carry the reader through a series of, at times, dramatic events in launching an organization that has since become one of the major enterprises of its kind in the world. ∎

New York, 1979   ALVIN C. EURICH, *President*
                                              Academy for Educational Development

An Exciting Time*

> *"I urge you to join; the people are interesting;*
> *the work is important; the place is exciting."*
>
> — A STAFF MEMBER - 1948

ONE OF THOSE AMONG US during the Founding Years and who is now president of a research institute in North Carolina read some of the draft chapters for this book. While finding everything in line with his recollections, George Herbert felt that somehow the text did not fully portray the interesting people and exciting times, especially during the vigorous thrust of 1948.

The same comment was made in early June 1948 by Dr. Philip Leighton, one of the Musketeers in SRI's early history. He went on to say beneath the redwood trees of the Bohemian Grove (at the same camp where some of the early SRI discussions were held) that even in 1946 and 1947 there was a certain "excitement of expectancy" surrounding the Institute. He, too, was looking for more along this line.

It is easy to characterize the Institute during its first year. A quiet and happy atmosphere pervaded the infant organization at least until the uncertain time in late 1947 when Talbot and Tresidder grew apart in their relationship. There was, of course, an undercurrent of speculation and anticipation about the future, but almost all attention was being devoted to "getting something under way" on research projects.

What's In a Name?

> *"The Stanford Research Institute? Get a new name or get off the Stanford switchboard!!"*
>
> A STANFORD PROFESSOR — 1946

Dr. J. Knight Allen, a consultant at the time from Stanford's Business School and later a senior staff member at SRI, spoke often over the years about the happy early days in our history. Personnel problems were few and far between; staff relationships were close and friendly in all respects. Perhaps, to some extent, the climate was too relaxed. Nevertheless, each person had a job to do and went about it quietly and with a smile. But there was no special sense of urgency in our endeavors.

During the autumn of 1946, immediately after SRI opened its office in the Physics Corner of the Stanford Quad, everyone assumed we would move shortly to other quarters on or close to the campus. But it soon became apparent that no suitable space was available except perhaps in nearby Stanford Village, an 80-acre World War II hospital site that had been leased by Stanford from the U.S. government for student

---

*Including a few entries in a lighter vein. See also a later section on this theme.

housing. The temporary barracks-type structures were full of students and some young faculty members, many of them married and with families.

Arrangements were made for one building to be vacated for SRI. We were promised a few more buildings when other accommodations could be found for the families. All this was supposed to be a temporary solution until more adequate space could be found or built elsewhere for SRI.

Many of the buildings were connected by narrow corridors, with children moving through them on tricycles and even bicycles. Also, the playgrounds between the buildings were teeming with children. The site included a church, commissary, power plant, school, and manager's home, along with a maze of dormitory barracks. The whole scene was an unlikely one for a research institute. Nevertheless the move was made in May of 1947. Our headquarters thus shifted from Stanford to Menlo Park.

Several graduate students and young faculty members living at the site were later to hold key positions within Stanford. The group included, for example, Kenneth Cuthbertson (later the University's vice president for finance and development); Joseph Pettit who was to be dean of engineering; Leonard Schiff, future head of the physics department; Robert North, subsequently professor of political science; and Dwight Adams, then manager of the Village but later director of business operations at Stanford. All of these people saw SRI's early activities at close hand but none had any idea that within a few short years we would occupy the entire area.

One of the narrow corridors in the Village led directly from SRI's headquarters building to the main complex of renovated apartments. It was easy and convenient for the families to go through the Institute's building to and from their temporary homes —and they did so in an endless stream. Some of the residents were fearful that SRI might be introducing something dangerous into the homelike scene, and they often raised questions with the University and with SRI people they encountered from day to day.

On the whole, however, the joint tenancy was quiet and peaceful even though SRI people occasionally fretted about a somewhat unbusinesslike atmosphere around the premises. Nevertheless, some lasting friendships arose as Institute staff members and Village residents often joined each other in a canteen area for coffee and conversation. The apartment dwellers were looking forward to moving on; SRI was anxious to occupy some of the space they would leave behind.

This early housing arrangement certainly was a good one for SRI. In effect we were able to occupy new space more or less as the need arose. Late in 1948 I wrote a few notes along this line.

> "We are lucky to be here. Otherwise, we would be in a straightjacket —
> needing space but with no capital. The longer we stay 'temporarily' the more
> certain this will be our permanent home. We cannot afford even now to
> uproot the place and move. Somehow, we must get the Village as the students
> move out."

This is just what happened, but the story of how SRI acquired the Village awaits a second book. But in the Founding Years we leased from Stanford and paid little attention to the baby carriages, playgrounds, laundry lines and assorted vehicles on the grounds. A visiting executive once glanced over the landscape and asked if we found it distracting to have our families so close at hand. But this was not a problem; SRI people did not qualify for the housing around us.

The Village was not exactly a symbol of physical security for even an embryonic research institute. There was no way to control the perimeters nor could badges be used for all those on the site. Everyone was trusted and rightly so; never was there an untoward incident as SRI gained a foothold amidst a shifting population.

Inexact Science

"Economics research in the Institute? I hope it will not feature work on the theory of the leisure class."

DEAN J. HUGH JACKSON
STANFORD GSB — 1946

Soon after Hobson arrived in the spring of 1948, he said loudly and clearly that something had to be done to improve the appearance of the entrance to the main Institute building. The result was our first capital improvement aside from a few laboratory installations; some brick steps were put into place in front of the main door. Almost immediately, the decision was controversial with the small laboratory group. Should not the money have been spent on equipment rather than on "brick and mortar?" This was by no means the last time such a question was to be raised in a capital-short institute. Incidentally, the entranceway still adorns our first building. It seems to be as permanent as the "temporary" structure still in use within the SRI complex; there is no end in sight for Building 100.

The two Bills — Talbot and Rand — and later Carsten Steffens set the tone of the Institute during its first eighteen months. Rand arrived in the autumn of 1946 and Steffens in mid-1947; both were much at the helm after Talbot's departure late in our first full year.

Talbot was a kind, courteous, soft-spoken person. He had a good sense of humor. All of us found it easy to work with him. Whether or not he was a good writer and public speaker — at least about a newly-created research institute — I cannot say. Much of the writing about SRI during the Talbot days was done by Rand and Steffens. I cannot recall ever having heard a speech by Talbot. He was, however, quite effective in interviews with the press. Certainly, Talbot was conservative in guiding the Institute's early development and well he should have been. Any other course would have quickly brought him into conflict with Tresidder. Furthermore, the stark fact is that little provision was made for working funds — let alone fixed capital — to get the organization off the ground.

Both Rand and Steffens also were easy to work with on a day-to-day basis. They were — and still are — of quite different personality. Rand always exhibited a good sense of humor and adapted quite easily to expediencies of the time. He seemed to be more at ease with administrative tasks than with various external activities that came his way. Steffens was oriented to the research operation and was much more formal in both internal and external relationships than was Rand. Although his background and experience had been in laboratory-based research, Steffens was always most helpful and cooperative in our efforts to build a social sciences program within the Institute.

Neither Rand nor Steffens found it easy to work with Hobson, not because of any differences in views on overall direction of SRI but rather as a matter of style. Hobson ushered in a highly-charged, free wheeling environment in which action was far more the keynote than was methodical planning. Rand later accepted a position with Atholl McBean in his farming and ranching operation in Southern California. Steffens decided to enter academic life at the University of New Mexico but returned to SRI on July 1, 1953, some two and a half years before Hobson's resignation.

In many respects both Rand and Steffens were well suited in temperament and background for the positions they held during the Founding Years. Both deserve far more credit for what they did — and tried to do — than has ever been accorded to them outside of a very small circle. Their tasks were not easy ones; they had little to work with. For several months they were more or less on their own during the period between Talbot and Hobson. Rand held things together administratively from November of 1947 until Hobson was in place toward the end of March 1948. Steffens did all he could to develop working relationships with Stanford and gave good counsel to the small and quite inexperienced staff.

Informality and cooperation were certainly keynotes of the working environment during our earliest days. As one staff member recalled some three decades later, the staff was a "classless" group with practically no separation between management and staff. Almost everyone was involved in setting up the research operation. All this led to a certain personal pride in being associated with the building of an organization. There was also a willingness by one and all to "put their careers on the line" (as one staff member has expressed it) in developing a new institute. Success was by no means certain. We were involved in a fascinating gamble.

No one from the formative years will ever forget the Institute's smog chamber. The reason is a simple one; all of us were part of the experimental work. One by one, we would be enticed to enter the chamber. Various amounts of known and suspected air pollutants would be fed in while the volunteer recorded his reactions. Having had enough of the experimental doses, the subject, so to speak, would signal through a window to his controller and then be released to go about his or her regular work. The value of the whole exercise was often brought into question — jokingly and otherwise — by the staff. But, we were more than willing to do whatever might be asked in advancing the cause.

High Finance

"We have spent the direct charge portion of the research project budget. Please release the overhead portion so we can start spending it and thus finish the project on time and within budget."

A STAFF MEMBER — 1947

Perhaps it is wholly understandable that there were few central services within SRI during the first year or so. Everyone pitched in to help do whatever was necessary to make the wheels turn. Staff members often did double duty taking on service tasks in addition to their full time duties. One by one, some of the usual services were added, often after some mixup in the way things were being handled.

So it was with purchasing. One day in 1947 a chemist wanted a hurry-up purchase of a rarely-used chemical. Several telephone calls soon led to an eastern company where a rush order was placed for a small bottle of the product. Nothing was asked or said about the price or other circumstances. It so happened that the chemical was no longer being produced for stock. But this did not deter the company. It simply set up production for the one order and dispatched a small bottle to the customer. A bill for $700 followed in due course. But in the meantime the experimenter had selected some other chemical. The needless expense stirred things around no end; the result was the beginning of an organized purchasing operation. Three years later the small chemical supply was discovered in stock during our first physical inventory.

Fast Track

"Getting SRI off the ground without capital is the neatest trick since the invention of money."

DR. HAROLD VAGTBORG — 1948
(Midwest)

Not everyone at SRI during the early days was exuberant about the future nor did anyone go into detail with prospective staff members about our facilities. Many people were employed without first visiting the Institute. There was no money to finance the trips. The emphasis was on selecting people known personally by one or more staff members.

Arthur Brown, one of the early chemists to join SRI, arrived in early 1948 from Canada at the invitation of Dr. J. W. McBain who was leading a project on surface chemistry. Brown had gained an impression that we had some well-equipped laboratories. What he found was something quite different — a makeshift setup in a barracks building. A few months later, he heard from one of the research directors that SRI had no future and was advised to leave sooner than later — "as I am about to do."

McBain's protege, however, had different ideas about the Institute. The surface chemistry work led in time to several million dollars worth of research projects in which Brown was much involved. He subsequently joined our Chemical Industries Center and completed thirty years' service to SRI in 1978. Never did he regret the decision to turn a deaf ear to his doubting colleague.

On the basis that we were engaged in research on an institutional basis, one of our earliest policies seemed to imply that Institute reports would not include names of the principal investigators on research projects. It is hardly surprising that a hue and cry quickly arose within the small staff at the time. It was one of the first issues that were in time to be known as "management versus staff." However, in this instance the matter was soon resolved. It was clear that results were to be institutional but project leaders must be given due credit. The "Solomon" in this case was Bill Rand. But even so, the decision came only after a full staff meeting. The democratic process worked nicely but not without some trauma.

Even from a perspective of more than three decades later — far removed from emotions of the early times — I cannot describe the atmosphere and feelings around SRI

1948 more succinctly than was done in early autumn of that year. Being in discussions with Paul J. Lovewell, a friend from Stanford days, about casting his lot with a youthful SRI, I telephoned him immediately following a weekend session of our small senior staff in Aptos, California. My clincher in persuasion was much to the point — "I urge you to join; the people are interesting; the work is important; the place is exciting."

Lovewell soon gave an affirmative response and helped build our economics programs before leaving for other pastures some eight years after arriving at SRI. But never has he questioned the basis of my early proposal. Many others responded to the same theme as the vigorous thrust of 1948 moved into the upward surge that followed.

During the last few years, while putting together the story of SRI's formative years, I invited many people who were on the staff during the first two years to share their impressions of the times. The common threads that run through their thoughts are the excitement of starting a new organization, the closeness of the staff, and expediencies in day-to-day activities. Some have called their associations "a heady experience"; others speak of "fascinating days"; still others talk about "an exciting place."

One of our early staff members, long since engaged in other pursuits, put pen to paper with these words.

> *"Perhaps most important of all was the experience of working together*
> *with complete teamwork... Through forty years of business associations, I*
> *have never found any working environment the equal of what we enjoyed*
> *(at SRI) during its formative years ..."*

He went on to say that despite a few cliff hangers and rude awakenings, the staff adjusted to the quickening pace and adopted a "can do" spirit — so much so that nothing since has seemed impossible to him. "SRI was almost an impossible dream in the founding years" but as he also suggests a dream fulfilled after thirty years of spectacular development.

There is no question about a change in the climate at SRI when Jesse Hobson took charge early in 1948. He had no intention whatsoever of letting the organization grow slowly more or less in response to individual efforts. He wanted to develop SRI quickly and insisted on doing three things — bringing in new pepple, adding facilities and promoting the institution. Within a month, he set the tone with a proposal to develop SRI on "five fronts" simultaneously. The story appears in a chapter on A Vigorous Thrust. Even with much more time, Hobson could not have better outlined his philosophy in a single sentence.

In many respects, Hobson was a complex individual. He was an enthusiastic person and had great capacity for inspiring enthusiasm and loyalty in all those around him. At the same time, he had a "short fuse" and could get terribly upset when obstacles appeared in his path or when he thought someone had doubts about the course of affairs he had set in motion.

Hobson was a master in smoothing things over by finding solutions (or what he thought were solutions) to seemingly insolvable problems that got in his way. His contributions to the Institute even during the first ten months were enormous. He completely changed its character within two or three months. His concept was wrapped up in promotion, drive, enthusiasm, energy and unity of purpose. He was growth-minded in the extreme and did not hesitate to spend money that was not yet in the till. Certainly, Hobson was an expert in explaining this spending after the fact as having been unusual and absolutely necessary in SRI's longer-term interests.

Profit and Loss

"The Institute is supposed to be a not-for-loss organization as well as a nonprofit enterprise."

CHARLES R. BLYTH — 1948

A case can easily be made — and in fact was made at the time by some of the directors — that Hobson was simply too expansion prone in his whole approach to SRI. Rapid growth under his leadership led to one financial problem after another reflected in a rising debt to Stanford. Hobson always said that the directors were fully behind his actions, but some of them simply did not grasp fully all that was happening; the pace was breathtaking by any standard at the time. Some of the directors knew fully what was transpiring and worried about it more than Hobson realized. Nevertheless, his whole thinking and approach quickly pervaded and completely dominated the Institute's operations. To say that he set SRI on a new and fruitful course is a vast understatement. This is the essence of the new excitement he instilled in the institution.

One of our senior staff members of the early-Hobson period wrote many years later about the new man at the helm. "Jesse Hobson was a unique leader, complex in his personality, brimming over with imagination and the optimism and courage to make things happen." Being a superb salesman — both internally and externally — he was susceptible, however, to the adage that a good saleman can easily be sold by another person with similar abilities. Thus, Hobson would often be "sold" on an idea advanced by others, or on a new acquaintance, and start the wheels turning before an orderly evaluation could be made by either himself or his associates. Consequently, the need often arose to sort things out carefully after a basic decision had been made. But, in many ways, this too added to the excitement of the place.

Jesse Hobson was brochure-minded to a great extent as one means of spreading the word about SRI. He insisted on promoting the Institute to one and all while letting prospective clients sell themselves on project possibilities. On the latter he was fond of saying, "The best project selling is no selling at all." Hobson was highly impatient with staff members who in his view talked too much to prospective clients rather than letting them do the talking.

Strategy

"Our long range plan? It's clear enough — meet the payroll on Friday."

GEORGE R. HERBERT — 1948

But even he fell into his own trap on occasion at least in promoting the Institute. The chairman of an eastern company visited him one day and inquired about our Associates Plan. Hobson began explaining the organization, its purposes, future and ambitions, only to be interrupted twice with questions about amounts, payment dates, etc.

Not having finished his account, Hobson continued along the path of explaining SRI. Then, in a firm voice, his visitor said, "If you will pause a minute, I'll finish what I came here to do — give you a check for $15,000." He wrote out the check and handed it to a surprised host.

An incident occurred in 1948 that illustrates in a humorous way the contrasting approaches by Carsten Steffens (from the Talbot period) and some of Hobson's early recruits. Dr. Abe Zarem, one of Hobson's friends from Cal Tech days, was attempting to build some sort of SRI operation in Los Angeles. By nature a fast-talking, enthusiastic and action-oriented individual, he sometimes found Steffens' careful reasoning to be a brake on quick decisions.

Beginning one discussion with a flat statement of fact and following it with a series of dependent plans, Zarem was only momentarily taken aback when Steffens more or less demolished the opening framework with a few carefully selected words. Zarem was not to be deterred even though he was speechless for a moment as his "house of cards" tumbled down. But his recovery came quickly — "Well, then, let's forget the opening statement and get along with the action it was intended to support."

In some respects, this was part of a new environment stemming from Hobson in a hurry. Without in any way being critical of the approach, but at least finding it different from the 1947 days, I jotted down a few words in mid-1948 — "A kind of 'act now — buttress later' sort of policy." It was all part of an institute moving into high gear. Fortunately, most of the quick actions proved to be in the right direction.

One of the early staff members who occupies a special place of honor in the annals of SRI is Dr. Thomas C. Poulter. Tom, or Doc as he was fondly known by all of us, came with Hobson from Armour Research Foundation. Almost immediately, he delved into professional work in geophysical exploration and shock wave phenomena. For thirty years he devoted his energies within SRI to a range of pursuits including oil exploration, ice cap structures and explosive materials and especially during later years to voice identification and sonar characteristics of sea mammals.

Several of us were intimately involved with Poulter later on in creating a special program that led to development of rocket fuels for U.S. space vehicles. We often had to "fly cover" for him when neighboring ranchers

"Doc" Poulter in the Field

and residents at a nearby explosives test site would bring some of Poulter's test explosions into question. His explanation that "there is no problem" did not fully satisfy startled residents in the area.

For a time in the early 1960s, Poulter was head of the Institute's physical sciences programs including the shock wave laboratories already named in his honor. Even so, he continued a personal involvement in various geophysical and biological acoustics projects, an interest that began in the 1930s while serving on the Byrd Expeditions to the Antarctic. Poulter was the man who rescued the Admiral from his lonely vigil at the South Pole. For this and other exploits, he was twice awarded a Congressional Medal of Honor.

Solution

"The Stanford Trustees are worried. We better declare a stock dividend."

PAUL L. DAVIES — 1948

Doc Poulter was often to be seen even in 1948 walking slowly around the halls of Stanford Village deep in thought on his research projects. There was no time left over to serve — as was intended — as the Institute's senior scientist and associate director. He would sometimes walk into an office and begin a discourse in the middle of his research thoughts leaving some wonderment as to what he had in mind, if anything, along other lines. Poulter was a man of few words well illustrated by a response when invited on a 25th anniversary occasion to "make a speech." His words were even less than expected, "I have just made one."

Although Tom Poulter formally retired in 1970, he continued his investigations in biological acoustics and related fields until his passing at work on June 14, 1978. Less than four months earlier he had joined the Thirty Year Group.

At no time during the founding years was SRI any sort of household name. It was quite the reverse; too few people in business and government had even heard of the organization. Time after time when contacting business executives and government officials by telephone for appointments, the reply would be "Stanford University, yes, of course." It was then necessary to launch into an explanation about SRI and its relationship with Stanford. In any event one did not need to establish credentials; the Stanford name spoke for itself. It was a great asset to SRI, especially during the early days before the organization was able to begin adding something itself to the Stanford reputation.

Even today some easterners when hearing the name "Menlo Park" will wonder if the reference is to the New Jersey site made famous by Thomas Edison. And there are some in the east who instinctively think of Stamford, Connecticut, when hearing "Stanford."

Loan Criteria

"A bank loan for a nonprofit corporation running at a loss? Maybe the bank examiner will be too busy to notice it!!"

PAUL B. McKEE — 1948

But we were far less on the map in 1947 and 1948 than today. Thomas Poulter was surprised one day to receive a telephone call from a visitor who had not arrived as expected. "I am at the Los Angeles Airport and am ready to take a cab to SRI. I have no idea where you are located. How long will it take to get there?" He also thought Stanford was in Southern California.

Fund Raising

"Spending money that doesn't exist? Better let me hear that explanation again. Looks like we'll have to get out the tin cup!!"

DONALD J. RUSSELL — 1948

In late 1947, I was involved in an amusing incident that illustrates how little SRI and its people were known on the national scene. In connection with a project for the U.S. Air Force on expansibility of the aircraft industry, I made a presentation to a group of officers in the Pentagon. Meeting the chairman for the first time, I was a bit startled in hearing him say, "My name is General Christmas; I will introduce you."

Apparently, he made more of an impression on me than I or SRI did on him. He promptly introduced me as "Dr. Gibson from Stanford" and then said something like "That's right, isn't it?" Upon sensing that it was not quite right, he changed the introduction to "Dr. Gibson of the University of California" and wondered aloud, "I hope that is correct." Upon hearing that I was not yet the holder of a doctoral degree and sensing even a further error, the third introduction came quickly, "I mean Mr. Gibson from California." My response, "Stanford Research Institute to be precise," brought forth a final comment by the general with a Yuletide name — "Well I was right in the first place — he's from Stanford University." But, by and by, he and countless others got our name straight as SRI began to make itself known by word and deed.

Some time earlier, I had the good fortune of talking with Herbert Hoover during one of his visits to the Stanford Campus. He was highly pleased that SRI was under way. Its name and purposes were not new to the former President. He recalled his early interest in the idea and remembered very well the enthusiasm my father-in-law, Dr. Eliot G. Mears, had held in 1939 for such an organization.

Capital Investment

"With the meager equipment on hand, our laboratory work may have to be half labor and half oratory!!"

DR. J. E. HOBSON — 1948

It so happened that shortly thereafter I came into contact with President Truman in connection with service on a governmental task force that was looking into the health of the nation's aircraft and aviation industries. Upon hearing the name, "Stanford Research Institute," the President said, "Oh, yes, I have heard about the Institute from Herbert Hoover." So, there was indeed someone in a high place to whom we had been announced in advance!!

These minor incidents in the experience of only one person by no means suggest that SRI was unknown even in 1947, let alone 1948. But too few had heard of SRI and fewer still knew anything about the organization. We were all involved day after day in spreading the word. At one point I dictated what seemed to be a remote hope, "Maybe, someday, we'll be well known both at home and abroad." As we were to find out, this was not wishful thinking.

With an influx of new people and projects generated by Hobson's vigorous thrust, the workload for everyone began to pile up. It mounted further because of the simple fact that the new projects tended to be larger, longer and more difficult. We did not yet have the benefits of a large bank of data and experience. Thus, more and more the working days for many years lengthened into the late hours of night. But all this was self imposed and no one objected to the extra hours.

As already implied, there were light moments in the daily regime to go along with the interesting professional life. All knew each other quite well. We were often brought into contact at staff meetings and in evening events. News about new projects — and problems as well — soon spread around the organization. Everyone seemed to be willing to help out in various ways when needs arose. New friendships were being forged and with them a certain amount of humor began to circulate. Actions and responses were sometimes taken out of context and described in a light vein. A few of them appear in the several inserts in this chapter. Again, all this was a part of the exciting time.

Bottom Line

"In the oil business, we would call this income statement a bill of particulars for a dry hole."

ATHOLL McBEAN — 1948

Late in 1948, one of Hobson's eastern friends and long-time advisers, Maurice Holland, visited SRI to take a look around for his client. After talking with a few people, Holland quickly went to Hobson and began talking about the extraordinarily high morale and spirit of the group. He was inclined to exaggerate on the basis of quick evaluations, but in this case he was on target. The morale was high; the enthusiasm was great; the dedication was enormous.

Holland went on to say that "something important is sure to develop from all this sense of excitement." He had no idea about some of the problems in the offing, but he was certainly right on the promise of the future. The Founding Years had ended; the Upward Surge was beginning. ∎

Epilogue

We have learned a lot in a short time about starting a research institute.

— CHARLES BLYTH - 1948

THE FIRST TWO YEARS of SRI's existence were not exactly easy times, especially for some of the directors. They did, in fact, ponder now and then about what their energies had wrought. The first executive director had departed. The second leader in 1948 had brought a vigorous new thrust. But, as the founding period came to an end late in the year, a financial crisis was at hand.

One of the directors, Charles Blyth, was much involved — then and later — in the Institute's affairs. But even by early December 1948, he had ample reason to reflect on the whole process of starting a research institute. This occurred at a luncheon in his Burlingame home a few miles south of San Francisco.

I was present at this small gathering but wondered then and later why he had invited me. Our host wanted to discuss the California political situation, a subject on which I was not well informed. Nevertheless, he later invited me on two similar occasions, one with Vice President Richard Nixon present. Politics aside, the 1948 luncheon began with Blyth's musings about SRI. He had reason to be concerned; our future was in doubt.

Although something had indeed been learned about creating an institute, a full perspective was not possible when Blyth brought up the subject in his home. He spoke with pride about the initiative, recounted some of the problems and then said, "We have learned a lot in a short time ..." Blyth was certainly in a good position to make the observation.

To be really successful, any public service organization must be created on a sound concept. The articulation must arise from much thought and dedication. A long-term thrust in purpose must be imparted to the institution at its very outset. Fortunately, this happened for SRI. The first source was Robert Swain. The first voice, however, was Morris Doyle. He and his associates put into words a basic concept for SRI that has served the organization long and well without any modification whatsoever. Its charter was and still is a masterpiece in legal phrasing, as well as in substance.

A sound conceptual underpinning must, of course, be followed by action. As in all organizational matters, a strong advocate is greatly needed. Someone must have the will and the clout — as well as the time — to get things done. A committee is usually involved, but it needs a leader or leaders.

SRI had two such men — Atholl McBean and Alvin Eurich. McBean was determined to get an institute under way at Stanford. Eurich felt the same way and saw to it that the pieces were put together in good fashion. Several years later, the head of an eastern institute used a more direct expression in referring to McBean's role. "Every new organization of our type — to be successful — must have a strong and persevering founder." But, it also must have an able "architect." Eurich played this role for SRI. The circumstances that brought the two men together were fortunate indeed.

Starting an institute on a completely independent basis is one thing; bringing it into being under the umbrella of a major university is another. Given a western location, there is no doubt of any sort in my mind that SRI was created under the best of all possible auspices.

I have always believed that the idea of a Stanford-SRI affiliation was sound. The reason that the relationship did not flower to the fullest possible extent over the years did not arise from concept, as will be mentioned later. In any event, the combination was a new one for research institutes. SRI gained enormously from its parentage. This is one reason why its early development was possible in so short a period of time. The Stanford name alone was a tremendous asset.

Timing and location are vitally important in the birth of any organization, especially one involved in a service. There was no better time than immediately following World War II to start a western research institute. The American West was on the verge of a peacetime economic upsurge. The mood in the West was buoyant and dynamic. Other institutes in the Midwest, Southwest and the South had similar timing advantages. But SRI had the double impetus of good timing and location in its origin.

Given a university affiliation, with all that this might imply in direction of affairs, SRI benefitted greatly towards the end of the Founding Years when wide freedom of action was delegated by Stanford. This was the way Eurich thought things should be; his predecessor had some other ideas. But Eurich was the chairman when SRI took its second step in 1948. The Institute was unleashed and this was much needed at the time.

Charles Blyth

"As a founding director, Charles Blyth was most energetic and dedicated in his support for SRI. He fully deserves the words of honor accorded to him."

Paul E. Hoover

It is quite appropriate to mention again the strength, quality and dedication of our eleven founding directors. To be successful, a research institute always needs a good governing board. But, it was abundantly clear even in 1947 and 1948 that SRI's policy-making group was second to none in the West. This was a fortuitous circumstance; the directors were soon to be put to one test after another.

The type of executive leadership needed in an organization often changes as it moves from creation through early operation and then on to other stages. Our Founding Years came to an end soon after the second executive director arrived on the scene. But in a few months Jesse Hobson brought a profound change to the institution. He set in motion a fast-moving set of events that was soon to propel the Institute towards its orbit. A great infusion of energy was evident soon after he arrived.

But this was not without a price. Rapid growth under Hobson's energetic leadership led to one financial problem after another. This was certainly the case at the end of 1948, and it was much on Blyth's mind when he thought aloud with his luncheon visitors in Burlingame. Some criticism on SRI's growth policy was already developing. More was to come. Nevertheless, Hobson launched an upward thrust that was soon to take SRI along the road to success beyond what any of the directors may have thought possible at the beginning.

Obviously, some good work in substance is necessary in a research institute even during its embryonic days. As might be expected, our track record during the first two years or so was mixed to some extent. The staff was simply not yet in a position to handle with high competence all that it was embracing in programs and projects. A shakedown was under way. But some good work was being done and more would follow. Suffice it to say that research performance was not the main problem as 1948 came to an end.

With all these features present at the beginning, one might well ask why the Institute was besieged by one problem after another during its Founding Years and why it developed later in some respects quite differently than some of the founders may have had in mind. What was left undone at the outset and what might have been done differently in both SRI's and Stanford's immediate interests?

Two or three key points stand out in this respect. They led in some ways to SRI's movement from birth through a certain vacuum in policy and structure. This is not to say that the leadership at policy and executive levels was wrong; there were simply some omissions in planning as SRI became operational. Everything turned out reasonably well in due course but not without trial and travail.

The most important of these situations resulted in part from haste in getting the Institute started. No one really came to grips with determining and obtaining the necessary initial capital. The Stanford Trustees were confident that McBean and his business friends would take care of the matter. They did this in time but initially in response to severe short-term needs, more or less after money had been spent. The result was a quick and unexpected buildup of Stanford's investment in the Institute.

It is quite understandable in retrospect — and it was evident at the time — why this "surprise financing" clouded the air around SRI. Some of the Trustees felt that a mistake had been made; others had faith that somehow everything would fall into place. The money problem was intense enough in itself, but it quickly spread to all sorts of questions about what SRI was doing and not doing.

A more fundamental problem arose within Stanford itself. It had two facets. One involved the extent to which the University, and particularly its president and SRI's chairman, was to be involved in day-to-day direction of the Institute's affairs. Tresidder had firmly in mind that he should exercise tight administration. Eurich thought in policy terms, a view that matched those of the outside founders and the operating executives.

In the absence of a widely-acceptable plan, faculty members came to their own conclusions more or less independently of each other. As a group, they were seldom consulted on the whole Institute idea. This may have been the right course, but many of them felt otherwise.

This situation produced all sorts of problems, most of which did not reach the directors in an orderly fashion. Thus, the questions went unanswered. The basic features of the Stanford-SRI operating relationships drifted in many respects. Within the faculty, a "problem image" of SRI rather than an "asset view" began to emerge. Some even resented what they called "throwing University money away" on a peripheral exercise — never expecting that future returns would be substantial.

The savior in this whole situation from SRI's viewpoint was Alvin Eurich following Tresidder's death in early 1948. But, by even this early date, the main emphasis had to be on moving SRI along a promising financial path rather than on how it could best operate within the broad Stanford system. Once a course was set, changes in the basic working relationship became increasingly difficult.

Hindsight is easy in such a situation. Nevertheless, three things might have been done to smooth the path for the future. One is to have forged a basic plan right at the beginning on division of responsibilities between Stanford officers and SRI itself. The second would have involved much more thinking during the first year or so on how Stanford and SRI might develop some joint and mutually-reinforcing research endeavors. As Stanford's later provost was to say, an early opportunity was allowed to pass. This may be an overstatement; some things were done. But, more could have been done on an organized basis.

Dr. J. E. Hobson

"The vigorous thrust at SRI in 1948 was but a quiet prelude for a further rush of events under Jesse Hobson's leadership. Much more can — and hopefully will — be said later about the man and his bold initiatives."

GEORGE R. HERBERT

The third point is the lack of a clear policy at the beginning on how SRI over time was to assist Stanford University beyond simply engaging in various research pursuits.

Resolving the first point in 1946 or 1947 would have been tedious in light of Tresidder's attitude. The fact is that only one or two people outside the University knew in advance that a problem might exist. McBean thought one was in the offing and instinctively centered his activities with Eurich.

Both the Trustees and the SRI directors could have been more helpful on intent and policy about Institute assistance to the University. The early debates on gifts could have been avoided. A clear statement on contributions — without saying when and how much — might have cleared the air.

There were other key problems at the beginning. The first executive director was sought in haste; he accepted the post with too little assessment of the situation. Also, the concept of regional emphasis on the West was too confining; it was resolved in due course by letting matters take their course in a gradual broadening of geographical horizons.

No one really anticipated that SRI might become heavily involved in government contracts and that this would bring both benefits and constraints. The absence of a sufficient financial base led early to a high emphasis on expediency in daily operations. Little thought was given to such things as buildings, growth rates and controversial projects. The board itself was not fully organized; many of the chairman's functions, in effect, gravitated to others towards the end of 1948. A closer coupling with the Stanford Trustees was needed.

One by one these and other problems were handled as time went by after the Founding Years. No one had any idea at the time that within three decades SRI would be a worldwide operation of considerable renown with well over 3,000 people, far more than a million square feet of floor space, offices elsewhere in the United States and abroad, revenues at more than $125 million per year, more than $30 million in assets, and cumulative project work well above $1.3 billion. Had Blyth known all this in December of 1948, he might have enjoyed his luncheon much more than he seemed to at the time.

As is well known, SRI and Stanford mutually agreed at the end of the 1960s to separate the legal tie between the two institutions. This involved a change in name to SRI International. But this is another story for the future. For two and a half decades SRI was legally a part of the Stanford Family, even though operated independently. The original loan by the University was repaid and a continuing financial return to Stanford was set up. In any event, SRI had become an internationally known and highly successful operation. That all this came about in so short a period of time is due in no small measure to the Stanford heritage.

One final perspective brings this Epilogue to an end. SRI is a fine example of what entrepreneurship can produce within the free enterprise system. I could never have imagined in 1948 that these final words on our Founding Years would be written in a hotel room in the Soviet Union, the citadel of state enterprise philosophy, exactly thirty years to the day after Blyth's luncheon.

In one way, this coincidence illustrates how far-flung our operations have become in a relatively short time. Much happened during the three decades following the end of the Institute's Founding Years. The story deserves to be continued in due course.

But, even in the account so far, I believe the dedication and deeds of our founders and the Stanford Trustees have been amply justified. It was an interesting and productive experience for everyone involved. ■

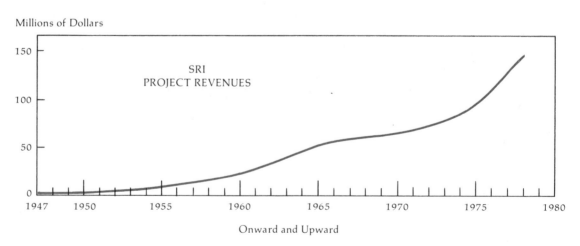

Millions of Dollars

SRI
PROJECT REVENUES

Onward and Upward

PHYSICS CORNER — STANFORD QUAD
SRI Office — 1946

BUILDING 100 — STANFORD VILLAGE
First SRI Headquarters — 1947

First Permanent Building
The New Headquarters — 1958

International Building
House of All the Lands — 1969

The International Building

From a house of all the lands comes understanding among all the people.

— From a Chinese Legend of the 3rd Century B.C.

PERHAPS THE STORY OF OUR INTERNATIONAL BUILDING does not belong in an account of SRI's formative years. After all, it was not constructed until the late 1960s. However, its origin lies in the Founding Years and involves one of our longtime directors. His name is Stephen D. Bechtel, Sr.

On several occasions during the early days when urging SRI to expand its international pursuits, Bechtel talked about the day when an International Building might be created at the Menlo Park headquarters. The idea was that the structure would be a center for our worldwide operations.

This dream was finally realized when a splendid new building was dedicated in September 1969. David Rockefeller was the principal speaker to a group of 300 senior business executives from around the world. He spoke of the building as "physical testimony" to SRI's development over the years in becoming "a significant international institution."

September 2, 1969, is a milestone day in the history of SRI. Opening of the International Building came just twenty-three years to the day after our first office — a small one indeed — was opened on the Stanford Campus.

This International Center is a symbol of our far-flung activities on the global stage. It stands in sharp contrast to an SRI of earlier days when even our name was quite unknown beyond a handful of people who had worked diligently to bring the organization into existence.

I first entered the Institute's office on the Stanford Quad in early autumn of 1946. A huge pile of architectural drawings on a side table seemed to be evidence that a building program was already under way. A few days later I helped the director move some old Stanford blueprints to the University archives. This was the closest we came to having a new building during our first decade!!

Little did anyone associated with SRI during the Founding Years visualize that we would so quickly become a national — let alone international — institution. Even after moving to Menlo Park in 1947, we had only three temporary buildings, precious little equipment, only a few staff members and no definite plans for the coming years.

International Court

However, fortune smiled on SRI and the fledgling institution soon began to grow and prosper. We were on the way to becoming a well-known research organization.

The "I Building," as it was soon called, is unique and distinctive. It is the imaginative work of one of the world's leading architectural firms. With some 62,000 sq. ft. of office and public space plus another 12,000 sq. ft. for a central court and arcade, it is one of the finest structures of its type anywhere in the world. It most certainly is an international project having been made possible by scores of individuals and companies in more than fifty countries. We have always viewed the building with a great sense of pride and gratitude.

The building is an excellent office and conference facility with a physical quality second to none. It is furnished in an international theme with objects from all the continents. It signifies a continuing commitment to research programs organized on an international scale.

The story of this building begins in the late 1940s when SRI first ventured into the international field with a project in Cuba and soon thereafter with one in Italy. Two directors, J. D. Zellerbach and S. D. Bechtel, Sr., began urging greater interest in international pursuits.

Bechtel, in particular, was most enthusiastic about opportunities on the international scene. As the years passed, he repeatedly urged management to move more energetically on a worldwide basis. There is no question about his leadership in this movement. Fortunately, his words fell on receptive ears within the councils of SRI.

In late 1955, an event occurred that was to hasten our advance in the international field. We proposed to Henry Luce that SRI and Time-Life should co-sponsor a meeting in San Francisco for 500 or more of the world's business leaders. The idea was to exchange views on various international development problems. The proposal was heartily embraced by Luce and his associates. The first International Industrial Conference (IIC) was held in 1957 just as Sputnik came on the scene. The event has since been repeated every four years under joint SRI-Conference Board sponsorship. One result has been increasing associations by SRI with major companies throughout the world.

Towards the end of 1965, the International Committee of SRI's board of directors took note of Bechtel's proposals that an international entity should be formed within the Institute and that an International Building should be created. The entity was established in mid-1966, and by mid-1967 the building idea had progressed to the first action point.

Being unable to finance the proposed structure from our limited capital, the board decided that for the first time in our history many individuals and companies in the United States and elsewhere should be invited to share in financing a major new facility. We were prepared to develop the site but not the building. The main question, then, was how to get the project under way. Could we proceed on a "build now — finance later" policy, or must we follow a more conservative "raise money first" approach?

Three directors helped answer the question when they guaranteed the architect's fee. One Saturday morning in July 1967, the plan was explained to Nathaniel Owings of Skidmore, Owings & Merrill. He listened attentively and replied — "I see the picture — a highly functional center befitting SRI's international role; we will design 'a little jewel' to meet your needs." He and his associates more than met the commitment.

By the spring of 1968, a set of plans had been prepared, and we were approaching the second action point. Whatever might have been our desires or plans for gift financing, the real question was whether or not a construction contract should be awarded. By this time we were thinking in terms of an initial $3.0 million project — but, alas, SRI had no money in hand.

Bechtel had no doubts as to what should be done, and he quickly backed up his view with resolve. The Bechtel Family and the Bechtel Corporation made substantial commitments to the project with the suggestion that many others — at home and abroad — be invited to join the endeavor.

The Kaiser Companies, the Bank of America, Standard Oil Company of California and Southern Pacific quickly pledged support. A contract was let with Williams & Burrows in the spring of 1968 — with one specific understanding. The building had to be finished in time for an Opening on September 2, 1969, and a World Dedication on September 20. There was no time to lose, and the contractor lost none.

Entering into a construction contract and being able to finance a project are two entirely different propositions. Hence, in the summer of 1968 we began to think about paying the bills even as we saw the construction under way. And to further complicate the problem, a last-minute decision was made to commit nonexistent money for a basement. At least this seemed to be a prudent course based on an earlier experience when we added a basement to a building after it had been constructed.

Having placed the project in the hands of a contractor, the financing program became more important with each passing day. Under the chairmanship of Edgar F. Kaiser, a special committee of the board began to pass the word about an exciting new International Building at SRI. I was asked to prepare a financing plan. A vacation retreat on the island of Hawaii seemed to be an ideal place for this exercise. The fact that Mauna Kea chose this moment to belch forth fire and brimstone seemed ominous at the time. Could it be that this was a warning from the Gods while work continued at home on an unfunded building contract? In any event, we soon had a financing plan and it was fully coordinated with Stanford University.

One by one, good friends joined the parade through our International Associates Plan. First there was Time, Inc., then FMC, IBM and others. We proceeded on the basis that before turning abroad we should have at least one half of the needed financial support from the United States.

The list of American benefactors began to grow — Marcona Corporation, Williams & Burrows, Tenneco, Johnson and Higgins, Industrial Indemnity, McMicking Foundation, Wells Fargo, Crocker Citizens, and several individuals including Dudley Swim, E. Finley Carter, Christian de Guigne, Marcel Palmaro and Benjamin Swig. Meanwhile, the walls of the building were rising.

The time arrived by the autumn of 1968 to bring the International Building to the attention of friends in other countries. We turned first to Japan and to Taizo Ishizaka, the dean of the Japanese business community, with whom we had enjoyed a close association since the mid-1950s. A project was soon organized within Keidanren, the leading Japanese business federation. Two other eminent executives of Japan took a personal interest in the endeavor; Kogora Uemura and Tsunao Okumura encouraged sixteen Japanese companies to join the program. The result of their generous participation is the Japan Section — a conference wing — of the building.

Major support for the new center was soon to come from the Middle East and especially from Beirut. The Triad Corporation subscribed to several units in our International Associates Plan. The Consolidated Contractors Company, also of Beirut, entered the project and so did the Behshahr Group of Companies in Iran. The Rangoonwala Trust of Pakistan and Birla Brothers, Ltd. of India added South Asia to the program.

Foreign participation in the building soon spread to several other countries. To the list were added Marcus Wallenberg and Axel Johnson, two longtime SRI friends in Sweden, along with Fiat and Olivetti of Italy, Barclays Bank of the United Kingdom, Dr. Lawrence Kadoorie and the Hotung Group in Hong Kong, Broken Hill of Australia, Philips' of Holland, and eleven German companies.

This display of support from outside the United States — and there are many more names on the Recognition List — was followed by even more American support. The International Associates List was growing — Pacific Car and Foundry, the Estate of Lucie Stern, Union Oil, Castle & Cooke, Utah Construction, and Skidmore, Owings & Merrill.

Beginning early in 1969, the roster of Associates began to expand, particularly as a program of regional meetings for Associate Companies emerged on the international scene. This operation led — within a few months — to Sydney, Djakarta, Singapore, Seville, Vienna, Lima, Tokyo and Manila.

The financing story could go on and on. Suffice it to say that the building was erected within budget and that the financing program was successful. The money received would not have been available for any other purpose. Friends around the world joined the project because of their interest in matters international at SRI.

In many respects, the most interesting facet of the building lies in the many gifts in kind received from individuals and companies throughout the world. Here are a few examples.

- An Aubusson tapestry (18th century) from twelve French companies
- A 27 cubic foot marble dedication stone from Taiwan
- Fifty specially designed wicker chairs from the Philippines
- A bronze replica of "The Little Mermaid" from Denmark
- 1,500 sq. yards of handwoven Tai Ping carpeting from Hong Kong
- Pure white marble from Italy and the Middle East
- A large wrought iron Spanish gate from Seville
- Persian rugs and antique furniture from Iran and Lebanon
- Audio equipment from the Netherlands
- An electronic time system from Switzerland
- A Val-St. Lambert crystal vase from Belgium
- A pre-Colombian Chancay tapestry from Peru
- Twenty gold artifacts from the Gold Museum of Colombia
- Three ancient Korans from the Middle East
- Orrefors glass from Sweden and Salviati glass from Italy.

There are also areas of the Building with designs and furnishings provided by companies in various countries, e.g., Philippines, Australia, Germany and New Zealand.

The list goes on — and more names are added each year. There is Delft Blue China from Holland, Rosenthal from Germany, Noritake from Japan, and Royal Danish Sterling. Hundreds of bulbs from Holland burst into bloom each spring. And one sees the skill of Sunset Magazine experts in the Central Court plantings.

It is obvious, of course, that these and other gifts from around the world did not increase SRI's capacity for research. But, they did — and still do — enhance the quality as well as the international theme of our fine building. Thus, they are important in the grand design for an International Center.

This building provided facilities long needed within SRI. The ground floor is a first-class conference center with an auditorium, meeting rooms, reception halls and dining areas. The building is the setting for conferences, seminars and symposia — many of them organized on an international scale. We are able to receive hundreds of executives, research leaders and government officials who visit SRI each year from scores of countries.

The International Building is an SRI-wide facility and is available to one and all as needs arise. The International Dining Room is the scene of daily luncheons and special evening events. The International Auditorium is heavily booked for research presentations and other SRI-sponsored events. And, the central court and arcade are locales for many relaxed discussions with visitors and among staff members.

The interior design of the building features a basic black-and-white pattern. This sets the stage for color to be added through the selection of carpeting, exhibits, art objects and other decorations. This design plan fits well into a building that emphasizes strong clean lines in a rectangular, painted concrete structure.

Both the exterior and interior designs of this International Center will surely stand the test of time. Furthermore, the interior may never be completed. The plan can and will be changed as new art objects and furnishings become available.

We should now turn our attention away from the physical aspects of the building and to the intellectual pursuits it helps support. One of our charter objectives is "to establish a center for the accumulation of information useful to scientific and industrial research." Another is "to foster the exchange of scientific and technical information with other research and educational institutions." Still further, we are expected to contribute to improvements in "the general standard of living and the peace and prosperity of mankind." These goals are especially pertinent to our international interests.

A new building does not guarantee that these or other research objectives will be met. Nor does a physical structure insure that one can maintain excellence in a research organization. However, the International Building is a symbol of deep commitment to the lofty ideals for which SRI was organized; these ideals are certainly not constrained by geographical boundaries. The building signifies a dedication to high quality research aimed at enhancing economic and social progress around the world.

In service to business and industry and in its efforts to benefit the public at large — wherever this may lead among the continents — SRI has a great future. And, nowhere does it have a greater future than in the international field. Many problems confront peoples and nations in their relationships with each other and in their efforts to increase national productivity and the exchange of goods, services, capital and technology on a multinational basis. These are problems on which SRI can be helpful. There are many others.

The international movement that has long characterized SRI as a whole is in keeping with the times. And, it is my belief that the "I Building" expresses to one and all — both within SRI and among our friends at home and abroad — that we shall always strive for excellence in intellectual pursuits matching the physical quality of our International Center.

This building is not an insignificant factor in SRI's efforts to enhance international understanding and cooperation. Being made possible by so many people in so many lands — with decor from so many distant places — the structure seems to give current meaning to a Chinese expression from the 3rd Century B.C. "From a House of All the Lands Comes Understanding Among all the People."

A special word of appreciation is most appropriate to all who helped bring our International Building into existence. Without solid research accomplishments from the professional staff over the years, development of the center in any form would not have been feasible. To all who provided financial and other support for the project, a salute drawn from the early 19th Century seems appropriate — "Hail, Glorious Edifice, Stupendous Work!"

On September 20, 1969, SRI expressed its great appreciation to the Bechtel Family for helping in a major way in bringing the building into being. This took the form of a message inscribed on a central court wall near the main entrance.

S. D. BECHTEL, SR.
LAURA P. BECHTEL

With grateful appreciation for his energetic leadership and their generous support in making SRI a significant international institution.

Steve and Laura Bechtel were present on the occasion. They seemed greatly pleased, but suggested that the credit should go to others. The record shows otherwise; their names will always remain in high honor at the very center of SRI's House of All the Lands.

Steve Bechtel has always been proud of the International Building and well he should be. It will probably last far beyond any other SRI structure built during his tenure as a director. It may have been over-designed and over-built in strength and ground preparations. Bechtel saw it one day under construction and later remarked — "One thing is sure, it will never fall down; it will last a long, long time." So will the Bechtel name.

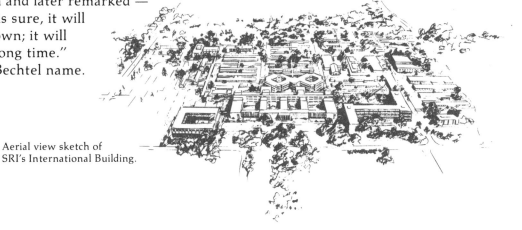

Aerial view sketch of SRI's International Building.

A Grand Design

One thing is for sure; you have an excellent set of Articles.

— CLYDE WILLIAMS - 1948

AS EMPHASIZED IN THE CHAPTER on The Founding Charter, the purposes of Stanford Research Institute were written in mid-1946 under the guidance of Morris M. Doyle, a San Francisco attorney and counsel to Stanford University. The statement is a masterpiece in legal phraseology, but more importantly it was and remains an inspiration for the institution it serves. Battelle's chief executive was right in 1948 in giving high praise to SRI's Articles.

"To promote the educational purposes of the Leland Stanford Junior University by encouraging, fostering and conducting scientific investigations and pure and applied research in the physical, biological and social sciences, engineering and the mechanic arts, and to extend scientific knowledge in the several pursuits and professions of life; and to devote its resources to the advancement of scientific investigation and research and to the assistance of the Leland Stanford Junior University in the promotion and extension of learning and knowledge;

"To provide, equip and maintain laboratories, experimental and other facilities for general and specific scientific and industrial research and to make such facilities available to the Leland Stanford Junior University and other institutions and organizations, public or private, for the conduct of research and investigation;

"To engage, maintain and develop a staff of qualified educators, scientists and research experts to carry on the investigations and research projects of the corporation; to provide for the development and improvement of research techniques; and otherwise to aid in the advancement of scientific investigation and of pure and applied research;

"To establish a center for the accumulation of information useful to scientific and industrial research; to foster the exchange of scientific and technical information with other research and educational institutions and to publish and disseminate such of its findings as may be deemed of general public interest;

"To promote and foster the application of science in the development of commerce, trade and industry, the discovery and development of methods for the beneficial utilization of natural resources, the industrialization of the western United States of America, and the improvement of the general standard of living and the peace and prosperity of mankind;

"To apply for, obtain, register, purchase, lease or otherwise to acquire and to hold, own, use, develop, operate and introduce, and to sell, assign, and grant licenses or territorial rights in respect of, or otherwise to turn to account or dispose of, own, introduce, assign, lease, mortgage, or pledge, any copyrights, trademarks, trade-names, brands, labels, inventions, devices, formulae, processes, and all improvements or modifications thereof, patent rights or letters patent of the United States of America, or any other country or government, whether used in connection with or secured under letters patent or otherwise;

"To make and receive gifts upon such terms and conditions as the Board of Directors may determine;

"To make and enter into contracts of every sort and kind permitted by law with any individual, firm, association and private, public or municipal corporation or body politic or any agency or department thereof;

"To property by devise or bequest, subject to the laws regulating the transfer of property by will, and to otherwise acquire and hold all property, real or personal, including shares of stock, bonds, and securities of other corporations;

"To act as trustee under any trust incidental to the principal objects to the corporation, and to receive, hold, administer, and expend funds and property subject to such trust;

"To convey, exchange, lease or encumber, transfer upon trust, or otherwise dispose of all property, real or personal; to borrow money, contract debts, and issue bonds, notes and debentures and secure the same;

"To do all other acts necessary or expedient for the administration of the affairs and attainment of the purposes of the corporation."

Morris Doyle has always taken great care to point out that he was not the sole author of this grand design in substance for SRI. But, he was certainly the leader of the exercise and the credit is rightly placed at his doorstep. ∎

FOREVER TO THEIR CREDIT

Leadership

Dr. William F. Talbot — 1946-47

Opened Our Doors

Dr. J. E. Hobson — 1948-55

Opened the Horizons

The Fortunate Few

Forget the temporary idea; think long term;
the Institute has great potentials.

— PAUL E. HOLDEN - 1946

UPON HEARING IN EARLY AUTUMN OF 1946 that a research institute was at last being created at Stanford and that one of his former students was joining it "temporarily," Paul Holden of the University's Business School had some good advice. He counselled me to forget the temporary idea and look to the longer-term future. Having been involved with the principals of the Stanford initiative, Holden thought the new organization would grow and prosper. I heard what he said and stored the thought in the back of my mind.

At the end of 1978, thirty-two years and four months after SRI's first employee arrived on the scene, the staff included 3,210 people. In the meantime, more than 17,000 persons had joined the organization for varying periods of time. The difference between the two numbers, of course, is turnover.

The staff count at the end of 1948 was about 200 people. They had come from a variety of places to join the young institute located in Stanford Village "across the tracks and up the road a bit" from Stanford. This is how our Menlo Park location was once described by Bill Talbot, the first executive director. In any event, it was in "close proximity" to the University as The Three Musketeers had suggested.

Only thirteen persons who began their affiliation with SRI prior to the end of 1948 were still on the full-time staff at the end of 1978. Dr. Thomas Poulter completed thirty years during the year but died in mid-June.

This long-service contingent includes a group of people I choose to call The Fortunate Few. We have indeed had the great pleasure and satisfaction of a long and interesting professional association. I could hardly have imagined in 1946 — even with Holden's advice — that by the 1970s my name would be first in chronological order among the veterans of the formative days.

Although each member of the first Thirty Year Club — especially the other thirteen — has made a contribution to SRI's remarkable development over the years, the major upward thrust was made possible by the thousands who followed the early group. This growing staff helped insure a wonderful professional life for those who emerged from the opening gates.

Thus, the credit goes to those dedicated men and women who have joined SRI since January 1, 1949, the end of The Founding Years. Perhaps all whose names appear below would subscribe in full measure to the sense of a paraphrase from Churchill's famous words — "never have so few owed so much to so many."

The men and women whose names follow the first entry have dedicated themselves over and over again to SRI's welfare. To them and to others who have since entered the Thirty Year Club, I have often spoken along these lines.

*"The Institute's development over the years since 1946 has been
remarkable by any measure. You are responsible for a proportionate
share of this development; your contribution will remain for all
to see so long as SRI continues — perhaps in perpetuity.
I urge you to take great personal satisfaction in all that your
efforts have wrought."*

I intend to continue the refrain as more and more people join the long-service group. To myself, I merely repeat now and then what I said to my wife at the very beginning — "A marvelous opportunity has come our way." ∎

THIRTY YEAR GROUP

(at SRI as of December 31, 1978)

Weldon B. Gibson	06/23/47
Constance W. Gould	11/01/47
Arthur G. Brown	01/26/48
Arnold Mitchell	05/03/48
V. Lorraine Pratt	07/01/48
Robert W. Smith	07/01/48
Milton B. Adams	09/01/48
Lucien G. Clarke	09/01/48
Betty P. Bain	09/15/48
Robert O. Shreve	10/18/48
Shirley B. Radding	11/15/48
Mary F. Armstrong	11/17/48
Jane Goelet	12/01/48

Debits and Credits

FROM A VANTAGE POINT in the late 1970s, one might expect that financial statements of some sort on SRI's operations would have been issued at the end of 1946. Receipts and outlays were being handled by Stanford's business office. There was an informal statement; it consisted of a telephone call from the University. The information came to William Rand who shared it with Talbot and two or three others on the staff. The data also went directly to the Stanford Trustees who raised a question or two about the deficit. But in the main the year-end results went unnoticed.

As the months of 1947 moved along, both Rand and Talbot began receiving monthly notices from Stanford on its financial advances to SRI. Tresidder had a few questions along the way but for the most part all was quiet on debits and credits, at least until the autumn. But in the interim between Talbot's departure late in the year and Tresidder's death early in 1948, more than a few questions on money were raised by Stanford and its Trustees.

Two things happened on finances during the spring of 1948 following Hobson's arrival at SRI. The monthly deficits began to mount and the income and expense statements moved to center stage. Then, as the months passed by and Stanford became increasingly concerned about the "red ink" at SRI, anxiety began to engulf the young Institute. A money crisis was resolved temporarily in early 1949 but not without extensive soul searching by all hands on the financial front. In retrospect, the numbers at the end of 1948 seem minor indeed — but this was not the case as The Founding Years came to a close.

INCOME AND EXPENSE — 1948

$231,806.08	—	Project Revenue
180,128.07	—	Project Costs
$ 51,678.01	—	Gross Income
94,525.31	—	Overhead Costs
$ (42,847.30)	—	Operating Deficit
53.66	—	Other Income
$ (42,793.64)	—	Net Deficit

CONDENSED BALANCE SHEET

December 31, 1948

Assets

$ 1,300.00	—	Cash
8,560.42	—	Accounts Receivable - Stanford
208,508.10	—	Accounts Receivable - Projects
10,526.75	—	Inventories
54,130.78	—	Deferred Charges
150,788.82	—	Fixed Assets (Net)
$433,814.87	—	Total Assets

Liabilities and Net Worth

$ 705.62	—	Accounts Payable
541,798.61	—	Payable to Stanford
18,068.18	—	Accrued Liabilities
$560,572.41	—	Total Liabilities
84,000.00	—	Contributions
(210,757.54)	—	Cumulative Deficit
$433,814.87	—	Total Liabilities and Net Worth

When SRI's financial statements became available shortly after the end of 1948, someone asked if there were any accompanying footnotes. None was needed. The debits and credits were in balance, but all eyes were fixed on the minus numbers.

SRI Staff

December 31, 1947

Research

Auernheimer, A. H.	Chemistry	Porro, E. D.	Chemical Engineering
*Brady, A. P.	Chemistry	*McIsaac, D. N.	Economics
*Crawford, J. R.	Economics	Richards, L. M.	Chemistry
Cutler, L. W.	Library	*Rolston, M. V.	Chemistry
**Dolan, I. L.	Home Economics	*Rosston, J. W.	Library
Farmer, M. A.	Secretarial	*Schulten, A. J.	Economics
**Finley, W. L.	Meteorology	**Sparrow, J. K.	Food Technology
Gibson, W. B.	Economics	*Stewart, W. M.	Economics
*Green, F. C.	Chemistry	*Thompson, J. E.	Economics
*Henniker, J. C.	Chemistry	Thorson, E. D.	Meteorology
*Holly, F. F.	Secretariat	*Thuman, W. C.	Chemistry
*Huff, H.	Chemistry	Tornbom, F. L.	Chemistry
Magill, P. L.	Chemical Engineering	*Ullman, P.	Dietetics
**Marsden, S. S.	Chemistry	Whittington, V. M.	Psychology
McCormic, M. L.	Physics	*Wilkinson, L. A.	Economics
**McGee, C.	Chemistry	Willard, C. M.	Chemistry
*Mosher, C.	Chemistry	**Yankie, J.	Economics
*Niemi, T. H.	Civil Engineering		

Research — Part-Time Consulting from University

Allen, J. K.	Economics	Holden, P. E.	Economics
Crook, W. J.	Photomicrography	Hutton, C. O.	Petrography
Eastman, R. H.	Chemistry	McBain, J. W.	Chemistry
		Taylor, D. W.	Psychology

Administration

Ashworth, E. T.	Secretariat	Rand, W. E.	Acting Executive Director
**Garbell, M. A.	Meteorology and Aerophysics	Ray, M. D.	Secretariat
Hagendorn, G. S.	Secretariat	Steffens, C. C.	Acting Research Director
Lloyd, P. R.	Food		

Office and General Clerical

Barry, L. N.	Stenographic	Sebern, R. E.	Office Manager
Bator, E.	Accountant	Snyder, R. J.	Messenger
**Berg, R. W.	Clerical	Thomas, R. W.	Clerical

Service and Maintenance

Dellenbaugh, M.	Library	Peterson, W. A.	Custodial
MacLeod, J. A.	Chemical Engineering	**Synan, J.	Custodial

---

*Temporary, full-time.
**Part-Time or Consulting.

A Lighter Vein

Autumn 1946

"Please join when you can ... after we incorporate ... it's a temporary job ... bring your own project."

DR. WILLIAM F. TALBOT — 1946

A Thin Line

"We will study upper surface layers between liquids and the atmosphere; we might learn something."

DR. J. W. McBAIN — 1947

A Crucial Question

"We must make a decision on laboratory notebooks for the economics staff. Do you want horizontal lines or cross hatch?"

DR. CARSTEN STEFFENS — 1947

Basic or Applied?

"He wants to study possible collapse of gravitational fields — but I don't think it will sell!!!"

DR. J. E. HOBSON — 1948

Without a Computer?

"I wonder about (John Doe). How long would it take him to write the equations of motion for ten variable-weight steel balls bouncing on a bed of weakening springs?"

DR. ABE ZAREM — 1948

Restraining Growth

"I was asked to 'watch the growth' of the Institute and have done so. It has been fascinating!!!"

RALPH A. KRAUSE — 1948

Man of Few Words

"I want to do some explosive work!!!"

DR. THOMAS C. POULTER — 1948

Calendar of Key Events

1925	—	Research institute idea arises in Stanford University
1927	—	Stanford president suggests plan be developed
1929	—	Faculty proposal appears in Stanford's annual report
1930	—	Institute idea set aside as Great Depression spreads
1939	—	Stanford committee meets at Bohemian Grove
1941	—	Plans tabled as U.S. enters World War II
1944	—	Research foundation idea emerges in Los Angeles
1945	—	Stanford committee meets with University president at Bohemian Grove
August 6, 1945	—	Research foundation plan presented to Governor Earl Warren
August 23, 1945	—	Pacific Research Foundation (PRF) formed in Los Angeles
November 6, 1945	—	Atholl McBean of San Francisco and Ernest Blackof PRF meet with Dr. Alvin Eurich at Stanford
November 14, 1945	—	McBean-Black develop concept for an institute
December 21, 1945	—	Stanford committee presents proposal for a research institute
January 24, 1946	—	Dr. Henry Heald presents results of brief study on western needs for a research institute
February 21, 1946	—	Stanford Trustees approve research institute proposal in principle
March 11, 1946	—	San Francisco attorneys submit comments on proposed research institute
September 1, 1946	—	First SRI executive director arrives at Stanford
September 27, 1946	—	Stanford president announces creation of Stanford Research Institute
October 24, 1946	—	SRI Articles of Incorporation executed in San Francisco
November 6, 1946	—	Articles filed with State of California
November 15, 1946	—	Incorporating directors meet for first time in San Francisco
December 13, 1946	—	Stanford University Trustees elect eleven SRI directors
January 8, 1947	—	Founding directors meet on Stanford Campus
May 21, 1947	—	Staff moves from Stanford to Menlo Park, California
December 16, 1947	—	Resignation of first executive director accepted by directors
January 20, 1948	—	Directors decide on possible successor to first executive director
March 1, 1948	—	Second executive director begins service
April 6, 1948	—	Vigorous development program approved by the directors
September 24-26, 1948	—	Senior staff meeting at Aptos, California
December 31, 1948	—	Founding years end with severe cash problem at hand.

The Chapters*

An Early Vision   1920s-1930s

Origin and gradual development of an idea within Stanford University for a research institute in the biological sciences.

> Genesis in the chemistry department — a University committee proposal — initiative set aside by the Great Depression — continued promotion of the concept — inspiration from earlier days — widening circles in the Stanford community — honor to the man with a vision.

Some early advocates — Robert E. Swain, Herbert Hoover, Ray Lyman Wilbur and Eliot G. Mears.

The Three Musketeers   1939 & 1945-1946

A movement within Stanford University leading to a specific proposal for creation of an industrial research institute within the Stanford family of institutions.

> Renewal of the institute initiative — a meeting at the Bohemian Grove — World War II delays action — another session in the redwoods — a Stanford committee surveys the eastern institutes — recommendations for a Stanford Research Institute by the Musketeers.

Some leading lights — Robert E. Swain, Philip A. Leighton, H. Dudley Swim, Donald B. Tresidder and Alvin C. Eurich.

The Southern Trio   1944-1946

An initiative in Southern California leading to creation and promotion of the Pacific Research Foundation including discussions with Stanford University.

> An idea within Lockheed in mid-1944 — a committee of three is formed — organization of a foundation-institute to serve western industry — a potential relationship with Stanford University — exploration of possible ties with Stanford — impetus shifts to Northern California — gradual decline of the southern initiative.

Some key figures — Maurice Nelles, Earnest L. Black, Morlan A. Visel, Fred B. Ortman, Atholl McBean and Alvin C. Eurich.

---

*See Table of Contents page iii.

The Northern Troika   1945-1946

A driving force from San Francisco toward Stanford University that led to the formation of Stanford Research Institute.

> An approach on the Pacific Research Foundation idea — a western survey by a mid-western educator — an energetic team of three on the institute idea — advice from eastern institutes — specific proposals to Stanford — emergence of the founder — a good idea at the right time.

Some principal people — Paul Holden, Alvin C. Eurich, Donald B. Tresidder, Earl P. Stevenson, Clyde Williams, Henry T. Heald, Harold Vagtborg and Atholl McBean.

The Right Time   1946-1947

The buoyant and expansive environment and a drive for industrialization in the American West during the immediate post-World War II period.

> Wartime economic gains in the western states — a certain euphoria on the Pacific Coast about the future — a rapidly rising population — the need for an industrial research institute — a golden time for action.

Some key spokesmen — Paul Montgomery, Robert E. Wood, Harry S. Truman, Herbert Hoover, Nelson Rockefeller and Eliot G. Mears.

The Founding Charter   1946

Drafting and adoption of a charter for a Stanford-affiliated industrial research institute.

> Implementing the Stanford Grant — questions of control and taxation — alternative approaches in organization — the tie with Stanford University — purposes of the institute — final steps in late 1946 — a perfect founding document — some early debates.

Leaders of the movement — Morris M. Doyle (and associates), Alvin C. Eurich and Donald B. Tresidder.

The First Year   1946-1947

Beginnings of the Institute and its first year of operations through the summer of 1947.

> Opening the doors prior to incorporation — the first executive director arrives — offices at Stanford University — the guayule project for government — the first directors meet at Stanford — a move to Stanford Village in Menlo Park — research programs in chemistry and economics — a proposed fund-raising plan — a special working environment.

Principal executives — Donald B. Tresidder, William F. Talbot, William E. Rand and Carsten C. Steffens.

The Gathering Clouds   1947

Growing problems in management and development policy between the senior executives of SRI and Stanford University.

> Questions about centers of responsibility and authority — two aborted proposals — the need for capital — a strain in personal relationships — the executive director resigns — an uncertain future for the Institute — development plans held in abeyance.

Two central figures — Donald B. Tresidder and William F. Talbot.

The Quiet Transition   1947-1948

A quiet period between two administrations of the Institute as basic decisions are made by the Stanford Trustees and SRI's founding directors.

> Some proposals to bring SRI to an end — seeking a new executive director — the first SRI brochure — problems in organization and development — exploring western research potentials — the first annual report — a backward glance — articulating the needs of the institution — an atmosphere of uncertainty — death of the chairman.

The main caretakers — Donald B. Tresidder, Alvin C. Eurich, Atholl McBean, William E. Rand and Carsten C. Steffens.

A Vigorous Thrust   1948

The swift rise of SRI during the last ten months of 1948 under the leadership of a man of great energy, enthusiasm and courage.

> The second executive director takes immediate charge — a development program launched on five fronts — a new SRI brochure published — beginnings of a new organization — a strong emphasis on growth — new research programs put in place — a developing financial problem.

Some principal people — J. E. Hobson, Thomas C. Poulter, Ralph A. Krause, Carsten C. Steffens, William E. Rand, George R. Herbert, Alvin C. Eurich and Atholl McBean.

The Policymakers   1946-1948

The founding directors and their dedicated service to a fledgling institute striving to become a significant institution in the West, then for the nation and later on a worldwide basis.

> The first eleven directors plus one — a magnificient group of leaders — role of the founder — relationships with the Stanford Trustees — changing role of the chairman — key decisions for SRI's future.

Leaders of the cause — Charles R. Blyth, John E. Cushing, Paul L. Davies, Alvin C. Eurich, W. P. Fuller, Jr., Atholl McBean, Paul B. McKee, Donald J. Russell, William L. Stewart, Jr., Donald B. Tresidder, James D. Zellerbach and Stephen D. Bechtel, Sr.

One of a Kind

1945 Onward

A man of energy and perseverance in a founder's role dedicated to the utmost in creating and developing an industrial research institute at Stanford University.

> A strong personality — a man of action in a hurry — insistence on financial performance — an executive chairman — instigator of standards for executive action — faith in the SRI concept — high dedication to the American West — humor in high places — honor to the founder.

The father of SRI — Atholl McBean.

A Stanford Motivation

1945-1946

The circumstances and basic motivation within Stanford University leading to the creation of Stanford Research Institute.

> A conference at Yosemite in late 1941 — World War II intervenes — building the University in the early post-war years — the need for money — potentials of an institute — other reasons for its creation — later developments at SRI.

The architect of SRI — Alvin C. Eurich.

An Exciting Time

1946-1948

An underlying sense of enthusiasm and expectancy during the earliest days in building an institute followed by a wave of high energy and excitement in a vigorous thrust of 1948.

> The quiet but interesting days of 1946 and 1947 — the new environment of 1948 — the physical setting — building staff and programs — some interesting personalities — circumstances surrounding an embryonic institute — some humor from the early days.

The key people — All who helped launch and build SRI through its Founding Years.

CHARTER   1946

STANFORD UNIVERSITY   1945-46

FOUNDING BOARD   1946